TURBULENCE

A New Perspective For Pilots

By Peter F. Lester

JEPPESEN®
Sanderson Training Systems

Library of Congress Cataloging-in-Publication Data

Lester, Peter F., 1937-
   Turbulence: a new perspective for pilots/by Peter F. Lester.
      p. cm.
   Includes index.
   ISBN 0-88487-141-X
   1. Atmospheric turbulence.   2. Airplanes--Piloting--Safety measures.
   I. Title.
TL557.A5L47 1993
629.132'4--dc20

                                                            93-13133
                                                            CIP

JS319006A

Acknowledgements

I gratefully acknowledge San Jose State University for granting me a sabbatical leave to accomplish a major portion of this project. I thank the faculty, staff, students, and alumni of the Department of Meteorology; you all helped in many ways. I extend my thanks to the administration, faculty, staff, and students of Whitman College for providing me with a productive intellectual environment to accomplish the bulk of this work. The important help of the library staff at Whitman is acknowledged, particularly that of Marilyn Sparks. Rodney Wingrove and Ralph Bach of NASA-Ames Research Center are recognized for rekindling my interest in aviation turbulence by involving me in their research. I thank the many pilots, aviation meteorologists, and researchers who have shared their ideas and experiences with me. The advice and explanations of Mark Burton and Roy Endlich, in particular, got me through some rough spots. Several important photographs and figures were contributed by Art Rangno, Carl Melquist, Dick Mamini, Hal Klieforth, United Airlines, Northwest Airlines, Milton Van Dyke of Parabolic Press, and John Monteverdi. Thank you. Senior Editor Richard Snyder of Jeppesen Sanderson is applauded for his consistent efforts to make the manuscript better. The graphic talents of Rich Hahn and his staff significantly enhanced some of my very rough drawings to produce clear and instructive figures.

Sidney M. Serebreny and Robert T. Lamson critically read the first draft of the manuscript. I thank them both for their experience, interest, questions, useful suggestions, and constructive criticisms.

This work could not have been accomplished without the inspiration of my family: Daphne Hogan Lester, my partner through thick and thin for 27 years; Rachael and Heather and Bret, who never doubted that I could do it; my mother, Marie Burns Lester; my sisters and brothers and their families; and the rest of my relatives . . . always interested, always encouraging, thank you all for your faith in me.

This book is dedicated to the memory of my father, Frank William Lester; and my brother, Michael Kent Lester.

Preface

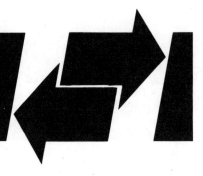

Although our knowledge of the causes and characteristics of atmospheric turbulence has grown substantially in the last three decades, turbulence continues to be an important problem for aviation. Part of the reason for this is that the dimensions of turbulence are so small that it is poorly measured and not forecast with any detail. So a pilot's ability to minimize turbulence effects still depends strongly on his/her basic understanding of turbulence and the correct interpretation of current and forecast weather conditions.

Unfortunately, the basic training of many general aviation pilots in the area of turbulence is minimal. An examination of most ground school training programs conducted for general aviation will show that the subject of turbulence is a relatively small part of the curriculum. This situation also prevails in most aviation meteorology courses at universities. Students who successfully complete these courses usually have a grasp of the basic concepts of meteorology, but they do not have an adequate understanding of turbulence. This problem is partly due to the extensive material that must be covered in a short time in introductory meteorology courses and it is aggravated by the brief and disconnected discussions of turbulence in aviation meteorology texts.

Among experienced pilots, there usually is a better understanding of the relationship between turbulence and meteorological phenomena such as jet streams, thunderstorms, and mountain waves. However, even that understanding is often incomplete.

General aviation pilots usually suffer more from these training inadequacies than military and airline pilots. The latter group is more likely to be exposed to better initial training and to follow-on-training to help them refresh and update information.

The objective of this book is to give pilots the knowledge to recognize conditions favorable for turbulence so that its effects can be avoided or minimized. An effort has been made to bring information on all types of aviation turbulence together in a single text, providing explanations and examples. The book will provide answers to questions such as:

What is turbulence?
What does it "look" like?
What are its typical dimensions and intensities?
How long does it last?
What causes it?
Where is it found?
What are its indicators?

These topics are addressed with a minimum of mathematics and a maximum of practical information.

In order to get the most out of the book, the reader should have at least some training in elementary meteorology as it applies to aviation. Although topics that are key to particular discussions of turbulence will be reviewed at various points in the text, a basic understanding of meteorological terms and concepts is assumed. A list of terminology and texts for review is given in the **Appendix**.

This book is aimed at pilots who usually operate at altitudes below 25,000 feet. However, for the sake of completeness, turbulence which occurs more often above that level will also be considered. This includes turbulence near the tops of thunderstorms, clear air turbulence near the jet stream, and high-level mountain wave turbulence. Therefore, the material covered here should be useful to pilots who operate anywhere between the ground and the lower stratosphere. The chapter topics are broken down as follows:

BACKGROUND
The introductory chapter lays important groundwork upon which the succeeding chapters are built. This includes the impact of turbulence on flight, the definition and general description of aviation turbulence, some useful turbulence models, measures of turbulence intensity, a summary of the basic causes of turbulence, and aviation turbulence classifications.

LOW-LEVEL TURBULENCE
Turbulence is commonly encountered during critical flight operations in the atmospheric layer closest to the ground. The causes and consequences of turbulence and wind shear in that region are examined. Examples of the effects of low-level turbulence encounters are given with several useful guidelines for the recognition and assessment of turbulence conditions.

TURBULENCE IN AND NEAR THUNDERSTORMS
Thunderstorms are one of the most common causes of turbulence accidents. Thunderstorm turbulence is described in all of its forms ranging from turbulence within the thunderstorm to turbulence below, over, and around the storm. Useful models of airflow near thunderstorms are presented and helpful rules for the avoidance of thunderstorm turbulence are reviewed.

CLEAR AIR TURBULENCE

Turbulence in clear air, well away from both the earth's surface and visible convective activity, offers special problems to the pilot because of the frequent lack of visual indicators. In addition to an explanation of the causes and nature of clear air turbulence, techniques are given to recognize potential turbulence regions with the use of ordinary weather maps and satellite images.

MOUNTAIN WAVE TURBULENCE

Airflow over mountains may create waves and turbulent conditions at many levels between the ground and the stratosphere. Generating processes and preferred locations of these disturbances relative to topographic features are discussed. Methods are presented to help anticipate mountain wave turbulence conditions along your flight track both prior to and after takeoff.

TURBULENCE AND FLIGHT PLANNING

The chapter considers the practicalities of dealing with potential turbulence hazards during flight planning. Procedures are presented for the systematic assessment of current and future turbulent conditions with special attention given to the sources and acquisition of related meteorological information.

THE FUTURE

Finally, research directed toward the solution of the turbulence problem is described. Pending improvements in turbulence detection, reporting, and prediction are described.

For convenience, a **Glossary** of turbulence-related terms is found in the appendix at the back of the text. Also included in the appendix are **References and Recommended Readings** and a section for decoding **PIREPs.**

As you begin your study of turbulence, it is well to keep in mind the old saying, "know your enemy." Here is an excerpt from an airline pilot report that emphasizes what that "enemy" is capable of . . .

". . . we encountered the most violent jolt I have ever experienced in over 20,000 hours of flying.

"I felt as though an extremely severe positive, upward acceleration had triggered off a buffeting, not a pitch, that increased in frequency and magnitude as one might expect to encounter sitting on the end of a huge tuning fork that had been struck violently.

"Not an instrument on any panel was readable to their full scale but appeared as white blurs against their dark background.

"From that point on, it could have been 10, 20, 60 or 100 seconds, we had no idea of attitude, altitude, airspeed or heading. We were now on instruments with no visual reference and continued with severe to violent buffeting, ripping, tearing, rending, crashing sounds. Briefcases, manuals, ashtrays, suitcases, pencils, cigarettes, flashlights flying about like unguided missiles. It sounded and felt as if pods were leaving and the structure disintegrating.

"The objects that were thrashing around the cockpit seemed to momentarily settle on the ceiling which made it impossible to trust one's senses, although I had a feeling that we were inverted as my seatbelt was tight and had stretched considerably. As my briefcase was on the ceiling, I looked up and through the overhead (eyebrow) window and felt that I was looking down on the top of a cloud deck. (The First Officer) later said he had the same impression at the same instant as we acted in unison applying as much force as we could gather to roll aileron control to the left. The horizon bar at this time started to stabilize and showed us coming back through 90° vertical to a level altitude laterally. At this time, I had my first airspeed reading decaying through 250 knots. The air smoothed out and we gently leveled off at between 1,400 and 1,500 feet . . ."

(Davies, 1973)

Table of Contents

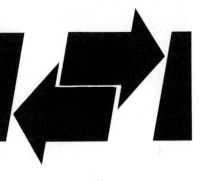

BACKGROUND

INTRODUCTION

Before attacking the details of the various aviation turbulence types in Chapters 2 through 5, we must establish some necessary background to help us with our task. We begin by examining the impact of turbulence on aviation. Subsequently, you will learn the important difference between the scientist's definition of "classical turbulence" and the pilot's definition of "aviation turbulence." Simple conceptual models are used to help you visualize the shape and dimensions of turbulent disturbances critical to aviation. The broad range of atmospheric circulations that generate those disturbances is then examined. Various measures of turbulence intensities are reviewed together with the basic causes of turbulence and, finally, the traditional aviation turbulence classifications are specified.

TURBULENCE DESCRIBED
THE IMPORTANCE OF TURBULENCE

Turbulence is a property of most fluids (liquids and gases) encountered in nature. Perhaps the best examples of turbulent flow are found in the atmosphere where those who fly may experience turbulence at its worst.

Fortunately, flight is smooth much more frequently than it is turbulent. In fact, the chance that an aircraft flying anywhere in the troposphere or lower stratosphere will encounter noticeable turbulence is only about one in twenty. The risk can be significantly greater or less depending on geographical location, altitude, season, local weather conditions, and time of day, but even in regions with high frequencies, most turbulence intensities are light. For greater intensities, the chances become very small. The odds of a random encounter with severe turbulence is one in several hundred or less. In fact, in 2,775 weather-related U.S. Civil Aviation accidents between 1982 and 1984, only 222 (8%) were caused by turbulence (McLean, 1986).

We must be careful when interpreting these statistics because they do not reflect the total impact of turbulence on flight. For example, lower turbulence intensities can affect passenger comfort and cause pilot fatigue. Also, turbulence often occurs in situations where low ceilings, poor visibilities, heavy precipitation, and icing are present. In these cases, lower intensities may contribute significantly to serious flight problems. For example, in 739 weather-related accidents in Canada during the period 1977 to 1983, turbulence was a contributing factor in 281 (38%) of the cases (Shaw, 1991).

It also is important to keep in mind that, although the probability of encountering the worst turbulence is small, it is not zero. Severe or extreme turbulence encounters do occur, often unexpectedly and, occasionally, catastrophically. The following are some examples from actual accident reports.

> A Cessna flying in the downwind of a mountain range crosses an isolated line of clouds paralleling the mountains; the pilot loses control and crashes.
> Cause: Flight through a rotor in mountain wave conditions.

> Radio communications from a business jet in normal cruise at 43,000 feet are being monitored by Air Traffic Control (ATC). Suddenly, strange sounds are heard followed by a report from the pilot that he is spinning out of control. Less than a minute later contact is lost. The aircraft crashes.
> Cause: Clear air turbulence.

> A commuter airliner takes off as a thunderstorm moves over the runway. A wing makes contact with the ground just after the aircraft enters the rainshaft of the storm. The aircraft cartwheels, crashes, and burns.
> Cause: Severe downdraft (downburst) and wind shear associated with the thunderstorm.

It should be clear at the outset of this study of turbulence that your efforts will be devoted not only to unraveling the causes and characteristics of extreme turbulence, but also to the understanding of the more frequent and less intense occurrences. As you will see, the understanding of one will enhance the understanding of the other. We begin by making some important definitions.

TURBULENCE DEFINED

In the study of fluid motions, **classical turbulence** is defined in terms of the "state of the fluid."

> The velocity is chaotic and apparently random.

In contrast, the term **aviation turbulence** is commonly defined in terms of the "response of the flight vehicle" which encounters the turbulence. Simply put, it is

> bumpiness in flight.

The distinction between these two definitions is very important. Since aviation turbulence is defined according to aircraft reaction, it can be generated by a wider variety of disturbances than classical turbulence. Therefore, it results from not only disorganized atmospheric motions, but also from certain organized atmospheric motions that are strong enough and of the right size to influence aircraft in flight.

It must also be understood that because of its broader definition, aviation turbulence (henceforth referred to simply as turbulence) will occasionally be masked by maneuvering. This is the introduction of accelerations by pilot input rather than by atmospheric motions.

VISUALIZING TURBULENCE

You usually are not able to see the small scale turbulence that affects your aircraft, but only to feel it and to react accordingly. For this reason, we will develop a few conceptual models to help us visualize turbulence in further discussions and descriptions.

SIMPLE TURBULENCE MODELS

What does turbulence look like? Figure 1-1 shows the generation of turbulence in a laboratory experiment by flow through holes in a vertical plate. The flow is from left to right. Smooth flow, indicated by the laminar streams of smoke to the left of the grid becomes turbulent on the right due to shears created when the flow is forced through the holes. Because turbulence is often so chaotic, it is difficult to draw an average picture of the phenomenon. However, with atmospheric turbulence, there are some useful simplifications.

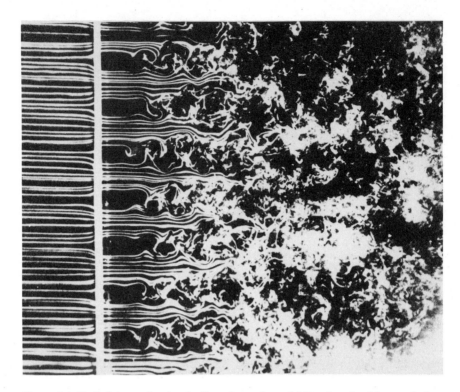

Figure 1-1. Turbulent production by flow through a grid. Reprinted, with permission, from Milton Van Dyke, *An Album of Fluid Motion*, fig. 152.

WIND GUSTS

Those who study atmospheric turbulence find it convenient to deal with the horizontal wind averaged over a period of a few minutes to an hour. This wind is usually referred to as the **average** or **sustained wind**. The deviation of the instantaneous wind from the average wind is identified as a **gust**, which is commonly taken as a characteristic of turbulence.

An example of gustiness is illustrated in the airport wind speed records shown in figure 1-2. The left hand diagram in figure 1-2 is a wind speed record for nearly nonturbulent conditions. The record of instantaneous winds is given by the thin line and the average wind speed for the period of record is indicated by the thick horizontal line. There is little deviation of the instantaneous wind speed from the sustained value. In other words, small gusts, weak turbulence. In contrast, on the right, large turbulent gusts are clearly evident as significant deviations from the average speed.

Conventional surface weather reports give one minute sustained winds with gusts equal to the maximum speed recorded during that minute. There is also the technical requirement that in order to report a surface gust, the wind speed variations must be at least 10 knots between peaks (maximum speeds) and lulls (minimum speeds).

TURBULENT EDDIES

Turbulence can also be described as having an eddy structure. An **eddy** is an individual turbulent vortex embedded in the general airflow. The eddy

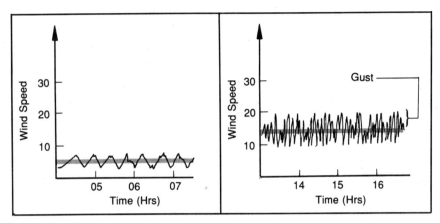

Figure 1-2. Airport wind speed record

twists, turns, and stretches with a wide variety of orientations and shapes until it finally dissipates because of friction. One useful simplification of this structure is shown in figure 1-3. The eddy, indicated by the dark arrows, takes the form of a circulation about an axis directed into the page. The axis can be chosen to be either vertical or horizontal. For the purposes of discussion, we have chosen a horizontal axis.

The average wind field in which the eddy is embedded is shown with broad horizontal arrows. The increase in the length of those arrows from the bottom to the top of the diagram indicates an increase in the average wind speed with height. Increases or decreases of the sustained wind with height are common where turbulent eddies occur. This model allows us to define the diameter (D) of the eddy as a rough measure of the size of the turbulent circulation. As will be seen, this dimension is critical in determining the response of an aircraft as it passes through a turbulent eddy.

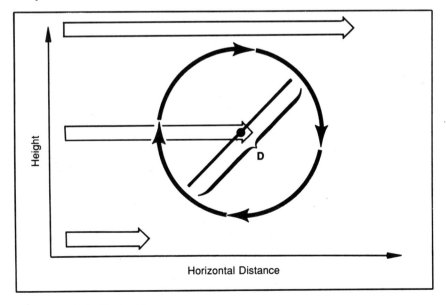

Figure 1-3. Simplified eddy structure

As a first approximation of the eddy behavior, we can assume that the eddy maintains its shape and circulation as it is swept along by the average wind. Figure 1-3 shows that as the eddy is blown along the surface, its circulation will carry faster horizontal winds downward ahead of the eddy (on the right) and carry slower horizontal winds upward behind the eddy (on the left). Thus as the eddy moves past a fixed point, or as an aircraft passes through an eddy, the turbulent circulation creates alternating strong winds and weak winds. Near the ground this effect is manifested in gusty winds, such as those shown on the right of figure 1-2. This process of creating gustiness is not limited to the earth's surface. It happens anywhere there is a similar eddy and a change in the wind with height.

In addition to causing gustiness in the horizontal winds, the simple turbulent eddy also produces vertical wind gusts. Figure 1-3 shows vertical gusts that are downward ahead of the eddy and upward behind it. Except near the ground, vertical gusts are often more important in contributing to turbulence than horizontal gusts because they change the angle of attack of the aircraft's wings which affects the lift.

In Figure 1-4, an aircraft is shown penetrating three different patterns of vertical motions caused by different eddy sizes and configurations. In all of these examples, as is often the case in the real atmosphere, the aircraft is moving through the eddies much more rapidly than the eddies are moving downwind.

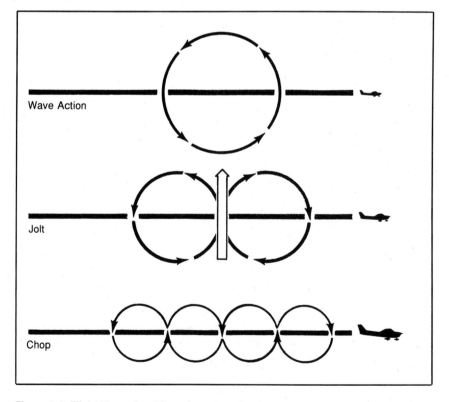

Wave Action

Jolt

Chop

Figure 1-4. Flight through eddies of varying sizes

In the first diagram, the eddy is a few miles in diameter and a pilot attempting to fly straight and level might report "wave action." In contrast, a single "jolt" might be reported if two vortices occur in succession and are very intense in the updraft area (middle diagram). A pilot might report "chop" if there are several small vortices in succession (bottom diagram).

Two important turbulence properties are illustrated in figure 1-4. First, the character of the turbulence experienced by the pilot is influenced by the size of the eddies and the speed of the aircraft. Second, turbulence can also be described in terms of wave motions.

WAVE MOTIONS

Wave-like disturbances, which in many ways resemble waves in water, occur often in the atmosphere. The concept of a simple two-dimensional wave form will prove useful in the explanation of a variety of related turbulence mechanisms. As shown in the top panel of figure 1-5, the critical dimensions of the wave are its wavelength (L) and its amplitude (A).

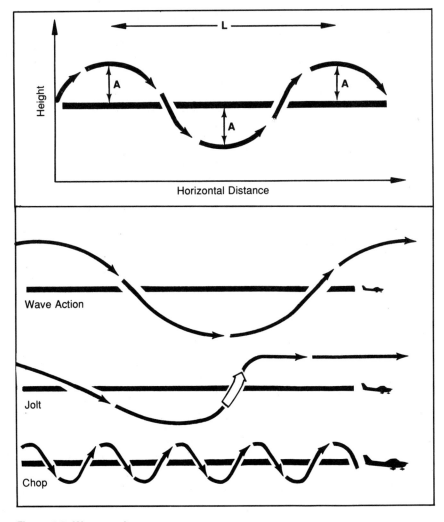

Figure 1-5. Wave motions

The direction of airflow through the waves in figure 1-5 is shown by the arrows on the wave-shaped flow lines; that is, from left to right. Vertical motions are indicated where the flow line deviates from horizontal. The magnitudes of the maximum upward and downward motions in the wave depend on the wind relative to the wave and the ratio of the wave amplitude to the wavelength (A/L). Thus, for a given wave configuration (A/L fixed), as the relative wind increases, the vertical gusts associated with the waves increase.

In the bottom panel of figure 1-5, an aircraft is shown penetrating three different patterns of vertical motions caused by different wave configurations. Note that pilot reports of the encounters can be identical to those discussed in figure 1-4. In this case, if the wave in the top diagram has a length of a few miles or more, the report would be "wave action." In the center diagram, the wave is asymmetrical; that is, it has a single high amplitude updraft area. The result is a "jolt." Finally, in the last diagram, a series of very short waves yields a report of "chop."

The choice of the eddy or wave model is somewhat ambiguous at this point because these models are mainly geometric in nature. That is, they don't tell us anything about the physics of the turbulence. Their applications will become clear as we use them to describe turbulence mechanisms and interpret turbulence observations later in the text.

In subsequent chapters, the models (gust, eddy, and wave) will be expanded slightly to cover a few more complex turbulence circulations. However, keep in mind that more realistic models require rigorous theoretical or statistical approaches which are beyond the scope of this text. The models used here are only rough first approximations of actual turbulence structures.

THE DIMENSIONS OF ATMOSPHERIC MOTIONS

Turbulent eddies are embedded in larger scale atmospheric circulations that both create the turbulence and are modified by the turbulence. The application of the models is more meaningful if we place turbulence in perspective with the types and sizes of those other circulations.

Figure 1-6 shows the approximate space scales (horizontal dimensions) and time scales (life times) for a selection of familiar meteorological phenomena associated with well-defined circulations. On the right hand side of the diagram, are the words **microscale**, **mesoscale**, and **macroscale**. These are common meteorological terms which are defined in the figure. We will use them frequently throughout the text.

As shown in figure 1-6, the space and time scales of atmospheric circulations are directly proportional. The smaller the horizontal dimension of the phenomena, the shorter its life span. This fact has important negative effects on our ability to observe and predict small scale phenomena such as turbulence. These effects will become obvious in the succeeding chapters.

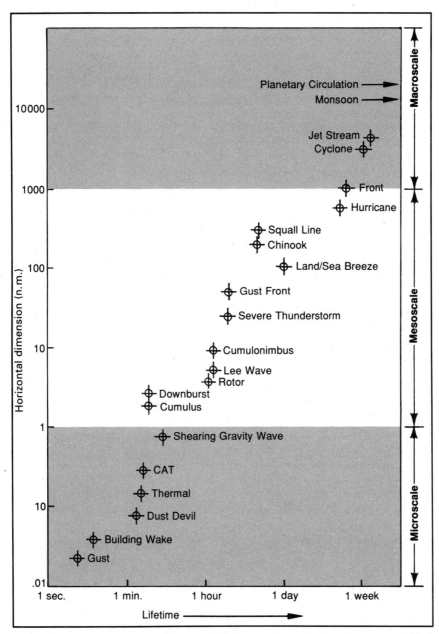

Figure 1-6. Horizontal dimensions and lifetimes of a selection of meteorological disturbances

Figure 1-6 indicates that turbulence can occur in the presence of larger scale and longer lived circulations such as jet streams and fronts. Chapters 2 through 5 will show how those larger scale disturbances provide a favorable environment for the production of turbulence.

RESPONSE TO TURBULENCE

Aircraft in flight are affected by atmospheric motions on all scales. Macroscale motions translate primarily into navigational problems through variations in wind directions and speeds over large distances. Most mesoscale motions also allow the pilot time to make control adjustments to compensate for horizontal and vertical wind variations. It is primarily when the dimensions of the motions fall into the microscale that "bumpiness in flight" becomes a concern. Within the microscale, there is a small range of sizes of circulations that is important as turbulence. That **critical range** depends primarily on aircraft design, speed, and on the effect of the motions on the pilot.

If the eddies are smaller than the critical range, the aircraft passes through them before they can significantly affect the lift. If they are too large, there is sufficient time during flight through the eddy to allow pitch changes and vertical movements to alleviate the impact of the gust. Within the critical range of eddy sizes, sensitivity to turbulence decreases with wing loading and increases with altitude and airspeed. Therefore, turbulent eddies of the same size and strength may have different effects on different aircraft. In a later section, we will see how this influences the interpretation of pilot reports (PIREPs).

Pilot performance is negatively affected by turbulence, depending on the strength of the bump, the rapidity of onset of the turbulence, and the frequency of the turbulence. There are two particular ranges of "bumpiness" frequencies which affect pilot comfort. They peak at approximately 0.25 Hz (one cycle per four seconds), and 4.5 Hz (4.5 cycles per second). The former is related to rigid aircraft motion. It promotes motion sickness. The peak at 4.5 Hz is due to airframe vibration and is extremely uncomfortable. It can affect visual acuity among other things (Money, 1970, Guingnard and McCauley, 1990). It should also be mentioned that continuous flight through turbulence promotes pilot fatigue, even at lower intensities and at frequencies intermediate to those given above.

The critical ranges of turbulent eddies for most aircraft flying today fall between about 50 feet and 1,500 feet. Exceptions are found with very fast aircraft and when larger eddies have sharp boundaries creating extreme changes in horizontal wind and/or vertical speed in short distances. An example of such an eddy is a thunderstorm downburst. This topic is discussed in more detail in later chapters.

MEASURES OF TURBULENCE INTENSITY

The occurrence of turbulence is common, but it is not very intense in the vast majority of cases. However, in a small but significant number, turbulence intensity is so great that it can produce unwanted effects ranging from passenger discomfort to loss of control of the aircraft. Therefore, as a first step in an effort to separate the "bad stuff" from the "not-so-bad stuff," we will review the yardsticks used to measure the intensity of turbulence. With regard to the gust and eddy models, "intensity" is proportional to the magnitudes of the horizontal and vertical gusts generated by the eddy. In terms of the wave model, the intensity is also proportional to the wave amplitude.

QUALITATIVE MEASURES

The most common turbulence intensity scale is the one that you were introduced to in your first aviation meteorology course. (Figure 1-7) An advantage of this scheme is that it is simple to use, because it provides

TURBULENCE REPORTING CRITERIA TABLE			
Intensity	**Aircraft Reaction**	**Reaction Inside Aircraft**	**Reporting Term-Definition**
Light ∧	Turbulence that momentarily causes slight, erratic changes in altitude and/or attitude (pitch, roll, yaw). Report as Light Turbulence;* or Turbulence that causes slight, rapid and somewhat rhythmic bumpiness without appreciable changes in altitude or attitude. Report as Light Chop.	Occupants may feel a slight strain against seat belts or shoulder straps. Unsecured objects may be displaced slightly. Food service may be conducted and little or no difficulty is encountered in walking.	Occasional-Less than 1/3 of the time. Intermittent-1/3 to 2/3. Continuous-More than 2/3.
Moderate ⋀	Turbulence that is similar to Light Turbulence but of greater intensity. Changes in altitude and/or attitude occur but the aircraft remains in positive control at all times. It usually causes variations in indicated airspeed. Report as Moderate Turbulence;* or Turbulence that is similar to Light Chop but of greater intensity. It causes rapid bumps or jolts without appreciable changes in aircraft altitude or attitude. Report as Moderate Chop.	Occupants feel definite strains against seat belts or shoulder straps. Unsecured objects are dislodged. Food service and walking are difficult.	NOTE: 1. Pilots should report location(s), time (UTC), intensity, whether in or near clouds, altitude, type of aircraft and, when applicable, duration of turbulence. 2. Duration may be based on time between two locations or over a single location. All locations should be readily identifiable.
Severe ⋀̲	Turbulence that causes large abrupt changes in altitude and/or attitude. It usually causes large variations in indicated airspeed. Aircraft may be momentarily out of control. Report as Severe Turbulence.*	Occupants are forced violently against seat belts or shoulder straps. Unsecured objects are tossed about. Food service and walking are impossible.	EXAMPLES: a. Over Omaha, 1232Z, Moderate Turbulence, in cloud, Flight Level 310, B707. b. From 50 miles south of Albuquerque to 30 miles north of Phoenix, 1210Z to 1250Z, occasional Moderate Chop, Flight Level 330, DC8.
Extreme	Turbulence in which the aircraft is violently tossed about and is practically impossible to control. It may cause structural damage. Report as Extreme Turbulence.*		
* High level turbulence (normally above 15,000 feet ASL) not associated with cumuliform cloudiness, including thunderstorms, should be reported as CAT (Clear Air Turbulence) preceded by the appropriate intensity, or light or moderate chop.			

Figure 1-7. Turbulence intensity scale. Standard turbulence symbols are shown on the left side of the figure.

some very obvious clues to turbulence intensity. For example, if the coffee cup flies off the tray, the turbulence is at least severe.

This system also has some disadvantages. The turbulence reporting criteria are qualitative and quite subjective. For example, the reported turbulence level will often depend on pilot experience. Even knowledgeable pilots will sometimes report an intensity exaggerated by some "surprise factor" when the turbulence occurs unexpectedly.

Another problem with the turbulence reporting criteria in figure 1-7 is they do not take into account aircraft type or speed. In other words, one aircraft's severe turbulence may be another aircraft's moderate turbulence.

The sensitivity of different aircraft to turbulence is important in your interpretation of pilot reports (PIREPs). For example, if a pilot of a DC-10 reports "moderate, occasionally severe turbulence," how would you interpret that report as a pilot of a Cessna 182 approaching the same location? As noted in the last section, the sensitivity of a particular aircraft to turbulence depends on the aircraft design and speed. High wing and power loadings allow large aircraft to operate safely in turbulence intensities that would be dangerous for light aircraft (Turner, 1985).

A comprehensive treatment of turbulence sensitivity classifications for the conversion of turbulence reports between aircraft types is beyond the scope of this text. The best practice is to assume that the turbulence experienced by a small aircraft will be greater than that reported by a large aircraft. The degree of difference usually will be one half to one turbulence category. An example of a half category is "light, occasionally moderate." In the example given above, the Cessna would expect severe turbulence. The conversion going the other way (from small to large aircraft) is similar except for severe and extreme turbulence reports. Those must be treated with great caution and a conservative interpretation is best (U.S. Air Force, 1982).

Exceptions to the rough conversion procedure outlined above are found with certain helicopters and fixed wing aircraft that are extremely sensitive to turbulence. In those cases, the difference between the turbulence reported by a large aircraft and a small aircraft may be one and one-half turbulence categories or more.

QUANTITATIVE MEASURES

More objective and quantitative turbulence intensity measures do exist. Two of the most common are **airspeed fluctuation** and the incremental change of **vertical acceleration**. Airspeed fluctuation is simply the maximum variation from the sustained airspeed. The vertical acceleration change commonly is expressed as a peak deviation from normal acceleration (1.0g) measured at the center of gravity of the aircraft.

Rate of climb also is used as a crude indication of vertical gust intensity, however, it depends strongly on aircraft design, speed, and altitude. A more accurate estimate is the **derived gust velocity**, a theoretically determined, nearly aircraft-independent estimate of the vertical gust velocity. It has been used for many years to compare turbulence intensities measured by different aircraft. The ranges of airspeed fluctuation, vertical acceleration, and gust velocity are listed in figure 1-8 for the same turbulence intensity categories found in figure 1-7.

	Airspeed Fluctuation (kts.)	Vertical Acceleration (g)	Derived Gust (f.p.m.)
Light	5 - 14.9	0.20 - 0.49	300 - 1199
Moderate	15 - 24.9	0.50 - 0.99	1200 - 2099
Severe	≤25	1.0 - 1.99	2100 - 2999
Extreme	-	≤2.00	≤3000

Figure 1-8. Quantitative measurements of turbulence intensity

Although the quantitative measures are an improvement over the subjective measures, they still do not completely separate the effect of aircraft design and/or pilot input from the atmospheric gusts. Other, more sophisticated aircraft- and pilot-independent measurements of turbulence intensity include actual vertical and horizontal wind gusts and their kinetic energy. Measurements of these require instrumentation such as inertial or satellite-based navigation systems, devices for the precise determination of angle of attack, and/or on-board computers. Currently, these measurements are not made on most general aviation aircraft.

Automated aircraft- and pilot-independent turbulence measurement systems will be placed on airliners in the near future. These systems will be capable of overcoming most of the problems inherent in current turbulence measurement and reporting systems including subjectivity and timeliness in reporting. More on this topic will be discussed in Chapter 7.

For general aviation aircraft, turbulence reports will continue to depend on the criteria in figure 1-7 to specify turbulence intensity for the near future. Despite the problems inherent in the use of those subjective descriptions, they remain an important source of turbulence information for pilots and forecasters.

Section B

CAUSES OF TURBULENCE

An overview of the basic causes of turbulence is necessary at this point to set the stage for the classification of turbulence types. In addition, we will review some important physical concepts and establish some useful vocabulary.

THE ROLE OF STABILITY

A key to understanding the various modes of turbulence production is knowledge of atmospheric stability. Therefore, we will begin this discussion with a brief review of that topic.

Atmospheric flow tends to be mainly horizontal. When air does move vertically, turbulence may be experienced, especially when vertical speeds are large. **Atmospheric stability** is a measure of the resistance of the atmosphere to vertical motions. In a **stable layer**, air that is forced upward is more dense (colder) than its surroundings and tends to return to its initial level when the forcing is removed. In an **unstable layer**, air that is forced upward is less dense (warmer) than its surroundings and accelerates upward with no further forcing. Unstable air is usually associated with larger vertical velocities than stable air; although, as we will see, there are some important exceptions. Familiar stratus clouds form in stable air, while cumulus clouds indicate unstable air.

Stability is commonly evaluated by examining vertical soundings. A sounding gives us the observed distribution of temperature with height at some location and time. The stability of a layer is determined simply by comparing the observed change of temperature with height to the change of temperature that a dry parcel of air would have if it was displaced vertically in the same layer. This process essentially determines if air displaced upward in the layer will be colder or warmer than its surroundings; that is, stable or unstable.

The observed temperature variation with height is known as the **lapse rate (LR)**. Note that the lapse rate is positive when the temperature decreases with height. The standard atmosphere is the average lapse rate in the troposphere and is equal to a change of temperature of 3.5 Fahrenheit degrees (2.0 Celsius degrees) per thousand feet.

The variation of temperature that a dry (unsaturated) parcel of air would have if it were displaced vertically is the **dry adiabatic lapse rate (DALR)**. While the actual lapse rate depends on the conditions at the time of the sounding, the dry adiabatic lapse rate is a constant equal to a change in temperature of 5.4 Fahrenheit degrees (3.0 Celsius degrees) per thousand feet.

If the displaced parcel is saturated, its decrease in temperature with height will be less than the dry adiabatic lapse rate due to the release of latent heat in the cloud-forming process. The change in parcel temperature with height in this case is called the **moist adiabatic lapse rate (MALR)**. Whereas the value of the dry adiabatic lapse rate is a constant, the moist adiabatic lapse rate varies depending on the temperature. For example, at -40°F, it will be nearly equal to the 5.4 Fahrenheit degrees per thousand feet, while at 68°F, it is less than half that value.

The evaluation of the sounding stability is now reduced to the application of one of two sets of stability criteria; depending on whether conditions are dry or saturated, as shown in figure 1-9.

STABILITY CRITERIA		
Dry	**Saturated**	**Stability**
LR>DALR	LR>MALR	unstable
LR=DALR	LR=MALR	neutral
LR<DALR	LR<MALR	stable
LR: Lapse Rate DALR: Dry Adiabatic Lapse Rate MALR: Moist Adiabatic Lapse Rate		

Figure 1-9. The stability criteria are used as follows: if, for example, a layer is dry and the observed lapse rate is less than the dry adiabatic lapse rate, then the layer is stable. If the layer is saturated and the actual lapse rate exceeds the moist adiabatic rate, the layer is unstable.

The stability criteria in figure 1-9 are usually applied layer by layer to a sounding such as that shown in figure 1-10. The observed temperature sounding is indicated by the solid line labeled "LR." Lines representing dry adiabatic and moist adiabatic processes are also shown and labeled "DALR" and "MALR," respectively. Note that each "lapse rate" label refers to the slope of the particular line.

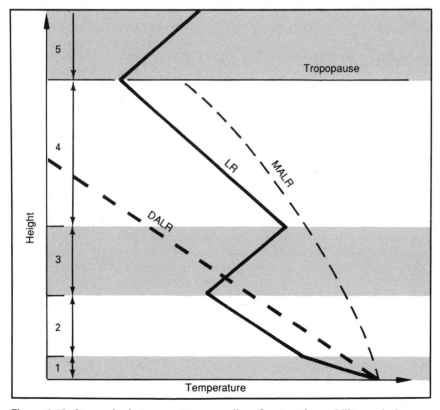

Figure 1-10. Atmospheric temperature sounding. See text for stability analysis.

There are five distinct layers in the temperature sounding. They are numbered 1 to 5 on the left hand side of the diagram. Applying the stability criteria of figure 1-9 to the sounding in figure 1-10, it should be clear that layer 1 of the sounding is absolutely unstable whether it is dry or saturated. This is because the observed lapse rate in layer 1 is greater than the dry adiabatic lapse rate. Such a layer is often referred to as a **superadiabatic layer**.

If layer 2 is dry, then its stability is neutral, because the observed lapse rate is equal to the dry adiabatic lapse rate. In this case, the layer is called an **adiabatic layer**. If the layer is saturated, it is absolutely unstable because the observed lapse rate is greater than the moist adiabatic lapse rate.

Layer 3 is absolutely stable, whether it is dry or saturated. This is because the observed lapse rate is negative (temperature increases with height) and both the dry and the moist adiabatic lapse rates are always positive. Layer 5 above the tropopause is also absolutely stable for the same reasons. Any layer where the temperature increases with height is known as an **inversion layer** or simply an inversion. Another absolutely stable layer is an **isothermal layer**, that is, a layer where the lapse rate is zero (the temperature remains constant with height).

The stability of layer 4 is not obvious because the observed lapse rate falls between the dry and the moist adiabatic lapse rates. In order to make a judgement, the moisture conditions must be known. If the layer is dry, it is stable; if it is saturated, it is unstable. This state is known as **conditionally unstable**.

TURBULENCE PRODUCTION

What creates turbulence? How do turbulent eddies and waves form? What role does stability play? There are four basic turbulence causes: convection, surface roughness, gravity waves, and wind shear.

CONVECTION

In the convection process, unstable air rises freely because it is warmer (less dense) than the air around it. As shown in figure 1-11, the warmer air rises in bubble-like eddies. Depending on the eddy size and strength, it can be an important source of turbulence for any aircraft that encounters it. The presence of moisture strengthens convection, often leading to cloudiness and, occasionally, to thunderstorm development. Some aviation texts and manuals refer to the turbulence caused by the convection process as thermal turbulence.

SURFACE ROUGHNESS

Any pilot who has ever landed on a windy day has experienced increasing turbulence during the descent. Within a few thousand feet of the ground, eddies form due to the surface friction or roughness. (Figure 1-12) The shape, size, and strength of the eddies depends on wind speed, stability, and complexity of the surface. This process of turbulent eddy development is often called "mechanical mixing," and the associated turbulence is referred to as **mechanical turbulence**.

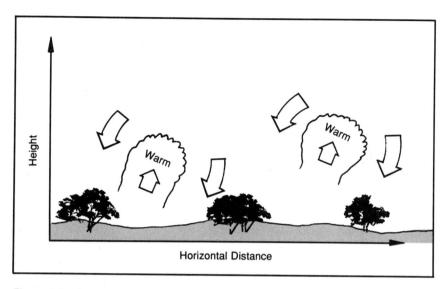

Figure 1-11. Convective turbulence

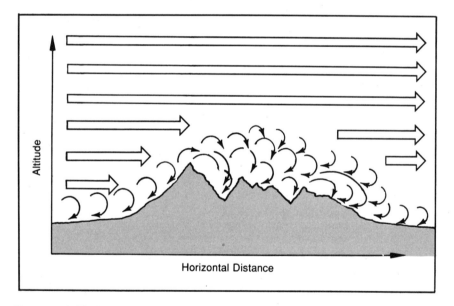

Figure 1-12. Mechanical turbulence

ATMOSPHERIC GRAVITY WAVES

Turbulence is often caused by periodic motions which result when stable air is displaced upward or downward. Because the displacement is in the vertical, gravity plays a major role in restoring the displaced air to its original location. The resulting wave-like oscillations which propagate away from the original point of disturbance are known as **atmospheric gravity waves**. These waves occur over a wide range of scales from a few hundred feet to a few hundred miles. Wave properties (length, amplitude, movement) are determined by their meteorological environment and how they are forced. Gravity wave phenomena of primary interest as turbulence producers are those forced by mountains (mountain waves), by convection (thermal waves or convection waves), and those caused by strong vertical shear in thin stable layers (shearing-gravity waves).

Gravity waves may contribute to turbulence in at least three ways. First, the existence of a gravity wave implies the presence of upward and downward motions — vertical gusts. The flow in the waves is often smooth, but if the wavelength is short enough and/or the wave amplitude is large enough, then the vertical motions associated with the wave may be perceived as turbulence. This process was illustrated in figure 1-5.

Second, turbulence is produced when gravity waves amplify and "break" producing truly chaotic flow. These waves are often of the shearing-gravity wave type; that is, the result of strong changes in wind speed and/or direction with height. (Figure 1-13)

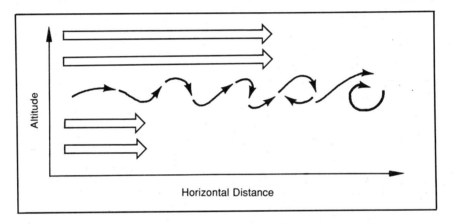

Figure 1-13. Breakdown of shearing-gravity waves. Thin horizontal arrows indicate rapid change of wind across the layer where the waves appear.

Third, longer gravity waves can cause turbulence indirectly due to flow curvature and when their amplitudes vary with height as shown in figure 1-14. Note the circled areas. In these locations the wind velocity changes more rapidly with height and the production of shorter shearing-gravity waves is favored.

WIND SHEAR

A wind shear or "wind gradient" is the change of wind speed and/or direction over a distance. Wind shear of interest to pilots is the change in the wind along the flight path. It is made up of two components, **horizontal wind shear**, the change in wind over a horizontal distance, and **vertical wind shear**, the change in wind over a vertical distance. Both types are commonly encountered in the atmosphere.

It is important to note that the wind is a vector. It has both speed and direction. Therefore, wind shear refers to differences in both speed and direction. If the wind directions are the same at two points, then the wind shear (magnitude) between those points is simply the difference between the two speeds. However, if there is a wind direction difference between

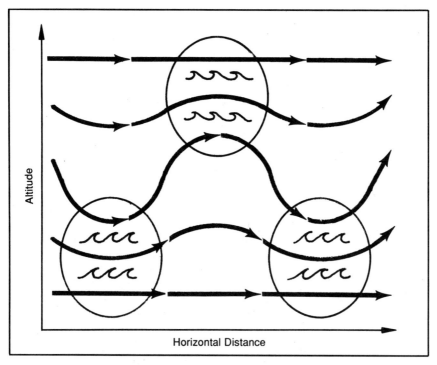

Figure 1-14. The production of shearing-gravity waves within longer gravity waves. The sawtooth pattern within the circled regions indicate the shorter, breaking waves.

points, then the shear magnitude could be as large as the sum of the two speeds (if the directions were 180° apart). The important point is that the "speed shear" does not necessarily tell the whole story. The "vector shear" does. Figure 1-15 shows two examples of vector wind shear determinations.

A simple map showing the flight track between points A and B is shown in the upper left panel of figure 1-15. The general method of vector wind shear computation is outlined in the upper right hand panel. The winds at points A and B are plotted as vectors; that is, the length of the arrow is proportional to the wind speed and the orientation represents direction. The shear vector is then given by the heavy arrow drawn from the arrowhead of the A vector to the arrowhead of the B vector. The vector wind shear magnitude is the length of the shear vector divided by the distance between points A and B. If the flight path is horizontal, then the computation has determined the horizontal wind shear.

In the lower panel of figure 1-15, a vertical wind shear computation is shown. The method is identical to that previously discussed, except that point B is located directly over point A. The plot of the upper and lower winds and the vector shear is shown at an intermediate level in the figure.

It is important to note that the wind shears are significant in both examples given in figure 1-15. If we had based our shear calculations on wind speeds alone, it would be extremely misleading since the speed shears are zero!

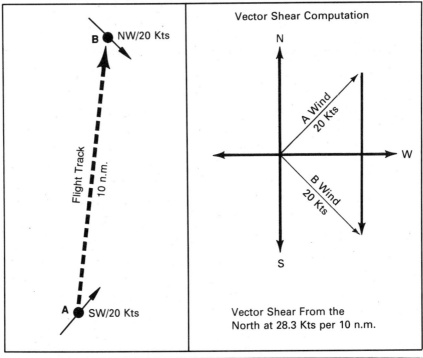

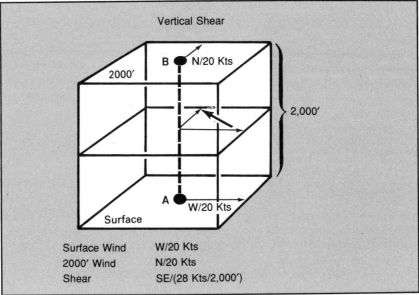

Figure 1-15. Examples of horizontal wind shear (top) and vertical wind shear (bottom)

Vertical wind shear occurs near the surface of the earth due to frictional effects and elsewhere in the atmosphere in the vicinity of certain stable layers. Horizontal wind shear near the ground is caused by the interaction of the wind with surface roughness elements (buildings, hills, mountains, etc.). Away from the earth's surface, it is caused by fronts, jet streams, and strong convection.

When strong wind shear is present, turbulence can be created by two main processes. Turbulent eddies are produced mechanically in wind shear near the surface with strong winds. Also, turbulence is created when vertical wind shear across a stable layer causes gravity waves to amplify and break. This process was also mentioned when we discussed gravity waves in figure 1-13.

In addition to causing turbulence, wind shear may cause serious control problems in the absence of turbulence. For example, strong wind shear can lead to large airspeed fluctuations.

This rather brief summary of turbulence causes (convection, roughness, gravity waves, and wind shear) has been presented as background to help us classify aviation turbulence types. The turbulence causes and their interactions, which account for each of the types, will be discussed in detail in Chapters 2 through 5.

AVIATION TURBULENCE CLASSIFICATIONS

The aviation community has applied a number of different classifications to aviation turbulence. These have evolved rather unevenly from research and operational experience. They are related to a variety of causes, locations, and descriptions of the turbulence.

It would seem that a better approach to a systematic turbulence classification scheme would be to apply the specific causes of turbulence described in the last section. Unfortunately, that is not as simple as it sounds, because the causes of turbulence often overlap. For example, convection can set off gravity waves and simultaneously produce strong shears.

In the approach to be taken here, the familiar aviation classification system will be used with a few minor modifications to eliminate ambiguities and to integrate them with the basic causes previously discussed. The turbulence types discussed in the next four chapters are listed below and illustrated in figure 1-16.

Low-level turbulence (LLT): Turbulence in the layer within a few thousand feet of the ground where surface influences are significant. Phenomena include dry convection, mechanical turbulence, wind shear, and turbulence associated with low-level frontal zones.

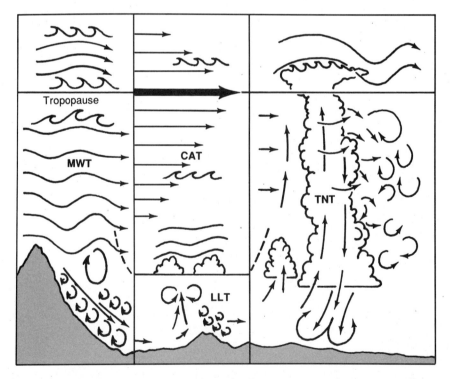

Figure 1-16. Aviation turbulence classifications. This figure is a pictorial summary of the turbulence-producing phenomena that may occur in each turbulence classification.

Turbulence in and near thunderstorms (TNT): Turbulence and wind shear within thunderstorms, the vicinity of thunderstorm tops and wakes, downbursts, and gust fronts. Turbulence and wind shear associated with less well-developed cumulus clouds are also included.

Clear air turbulence (CAT): Turbulence which occurs in the free atmosphere away from visible convective activity. CAT includes high-level frontal and jet stream turbulence and strong vertical wind shears.

Mountain wave turbulence (MWT): Turbulence produced in connection with mountain lee waves. It includes high amplitude mountain waves, rotors, turbulence in highly sheared layers near the tropopause and near the surface, three dimensional wakes behind isolated mountain peaks, and downslope windstorms.

KEY TERMS

Average Wind
Aviation Turbulence
Classical Turbulence
Clear Air Turbulence (CAT)
Critical Range
Dimensions of Turbulence
Dry Adiabatic Lapse Rate
Gravity Waves
Gust
Horizontal Wind Shear
Lapse Rate
Low-Level Turbulence (LLT)
Measures of Turbulence Intensity
Mechanical Turbulence
Microscale
Moist Adiabatic Lapse Rate
Mountain Wave Turbulence (MWT)
Speed Shear
Stability Criteria
Thermal Turbulence
Turbulence Causes
Turbulence In and Near Thunderstorms (TNT)
Turbulence Intensity Scale
Turbulence Response
Vector Wind Shear
Vertical Wind Shear
Wind Shear

CHAPTER QUESTIONS

1. At first glance, one might suppose that turbulence is a minor aviation problem. After all, the probability of encountering severe or extreme turbulence in flight is very small, and light turbulence is often only a minor annoyance. Discuss.

2. Aviation Turbulence includes a wider range of atmospheric motions than classical turbulence. Discuss.

3. Make sketches explaining the three simple models of turbulence developed in this chapter. Label the important features of each model indicating the critical dimension(s).

4. Obtain a surface weather map, a 300 mb chart, a radar chart and, if possible, a satellite image. At your instructor's direction, identify atmospheric circulations of different sizes on each chart (e.g., cyclones, fronts, thunderstorms, etc.). Measure the horizontal dimension of each circulation. Prepare a table listing the name of the circulation, the horizontal dimension, and the classification as micro-, meso-, or macroscale.

5. In question 4, how long would it take you to cross each circulation in a Cessna 182? In a B-767? Add the answers to the table that you developed in question 4.

6. Write a brief documentation of the worst turbulence you've ever experienced. Include aircraft type, location, and altitude. Describe turbulence intensity (use figures 1-7 and 1-8). Describe the general meteorological conditions. What type of turbulence was it? (LLT, TNT, CAT, TNT)

7. Why are so many turbulence reports subjective?

8. Obtain a plotted temperature sounding from your instructor. Classify the stability of each layer. Identify all inversions, isothermal layers, and adiabatic layers.

9. (True, False) Temperature can decrease with height in an absolutely stable layer. Discuss.

10. The surface wind is 270° at 14 knots. The wind at 1,000 feet AGL is 090° at 14 knots. Determine the vertical wind shear including the speed shear and the vector wind shear (magnitude and direction).

LOW-LEVEL TURBULENCE (LLT)

INTRODUCTION

Concern over the causes and consequences of turbulence in the lowest layers of the atmosphere are as old as flying. In 1896, Otto Lilienthal, one of the pioneers in flight was killed when his glider pitched up and stalled in gusty winds (Lieurance, 1969).

As early as 1915, a study of turbulence was conducted over Point Loma near San Diego, California. Pilots had reported significant vertical gusts at altitudes up to 4,000 feet over the narrow peninsula. A scientific observer aboard the military biplane sent to investigate reported the following:

> ". . . The pilot drove the machine straight toward Point Loma and those unseen aerial breakers. Suddenly there were two distinct 'wallops' and I felt the fuselage beneath me respond as if struck by a stuffed club. There was evidently first a surge than a drop . . ."

> (Lieurance, 1969).

THE BOUNDARY LAYER

Aircraft and turbulence measurements have improved radically in the last 75 years. We have a much better understanding of turbulence now than in the earliest days of flight. However, the occurrence and potential danger of turbulence at low levels has not changed. In fact, of all the turbulence types discussed in this text, that which occurs nearest the ground is probably the most important. The reasons are simple: the frequency of flight in the lowest few thousand feet of the atmosphere is high and there is less room to maneuver.

In this chapter we examine the causes and characteristics of **low-level turbulence (LLT)**. It is described as turbulence in the layer within a few thousand feet of the ground where surface influences are significant.

The focus of this chapter is on mechanical turbulence and on turbulence produced by dry convection, gravity waves, wind shear, and low-level fronts. Attention is also given to mesoscale circulations which may contribute to turbulence and wind shears. Mesoscale topics include land and sea breezes, sea breeze fronts, shear lines, and mountain and valley breezes.

It should be pointed out that, for operational forecasting purposes, LLT is defined simply as turbulence below 15,000 feet MSL. There should be no conflict with the definition used in this chapter, since most of the circulations discussed here occur within a few thousand feet of the earth's surface, or have their greatest influence within that layer. Those that do extend to greater heights, including macroscale fronts, convection over desert areas, and some atmospheric gravity wave activity, will be discussed in later chapters.

For organizational purposes, turbulence which occurs near the ground in thunderstorms and in other moist convection will be included in the chapter on turbulence in, and near, thunderstorms (TNT). Turbulence which occurs near the ground in mountain wave conditions will be dealt with in the chapter on mountain wave turbulence (MWT).

Upon completing this chapter, you will not only gain a better understanding of low-level turbulence and its causes, but you will also take away a practical list of rules of thumb useful for the diagnosis of the presence and intensity of LLT.

BOUNDARY LAYER

Any time a fluid moves over a surface, a layer of transition, or boundary layer, develops because of friction between the fluid and the surface. For example, air moving over a wing develops a thin boundary layer where important frictional processes occur due to the relative motion between the wing and the air. Aerodynamacists spend much time studying this layer in their search for an optimum wing design.

On a much larger scale, an atmospheric boundary layer develops where the atmosphere and the earth's surface are in contact. Most LLT is produced here. For convenience, we will refer to this layer simply as the **boundary layer**.

In your elementary aviation meteorology course, you learned that the effects of surface friction on the wind become very small above an altitude of about 2,000 feet AGL. Above that altitude, wind direction and speed are more closely related to the orientation and spacing of the isobars as shown in the upper part of figure 2-1. Surface friction has little influence at that level, so the wind (in the Northern Hemisphere) blows parallel to the isobars with the low pressure on the left. Furthermore, the wind speed increases as the spacing between the isobars decreases. So at point A in figure 2-1, winds are westerly and stronger than the southwesterly winds at B.

In the lower part of the figure 2-1, the effects of surface friction at the bottom of the boundary layer are illustrated. Note in this example that the spacing and orientation of the isobars are the same at the surface as they are at the top of the boundary layer. However, because of friction, the winds near the surface have lower speeds than the winds aloft, and they blow at an angle across the isobars toward lower pressure. That angle is typically 30° but ranges from 10° to 90°.

In order to understand LLT, we must look a little closer at the vertical structure of the lower atmosphere. An important detail in the boundary layer is that the change of wind direction with height does not usually start at the surface. In the first 100 to 500 feet above the ground, the sustained wind direction tends to remain constant, although wind speeds increase with height as friction decreases. Above that altitude, the wind direction usually changes about 30° in a clockwise direction to the top of the boundary layer. This change in direction with height can be seen in figure 2-1. These "typical" vertical wind shears are occasionally masked in the presence of fronts and mesoscale circulations. More on these topics will be covered in later sections.

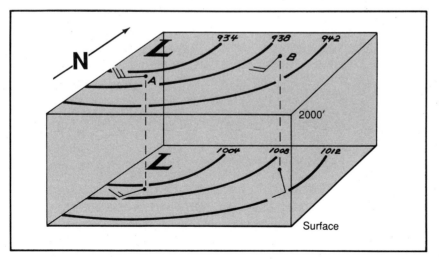

Figure 2-1. The effects of surface friction on wind speed and direction within the boundary layer.

Another important detail that should be added to your elementary view of the boundary layer is that 2,000 feet is only a very rough estimate of its depth. The maximum height reached by surface effects can vary over thousands of feet depending on the environment. The following are a few guidelines to help in the estimation of the boundary layer depth:

1. The top of the boundary layer is higher over rough terrain than flat terrain.

2. The boundary layer is relatively shallow under the influence of an anticyclone (high pressure area) and deeper when influenced by a cyclone (low pressure area).

3. The boundary layer is deeper in unstable conditions than in stable conditions.

4. Over land, the boundary layer "swells" in the daytime and "shrinks" at night.

5. The layer is deeper in summer and shallower in winter.

These variations in boundary layer depth reflect variations in wind, stability, and surface roughness which, in turn, produce a variety of mesoscale and microscale circulations. In the following sections, we examine the most important of those phenomena which are either turbulent or are capable of producing turbulence and/or shear.

MECHANICAL TURBULENCE

Section

B

We start our discussion by examining the most obvious form of LLT, **mechanical turbulence**, which is caused by friction between the wind and the earth's surface. We are interested in the intensity of the turbulence, the height to which it extends, and the effects of varying surface roughness.

INTENSITY

The structure of mechanical turbulence is best described as a collection of eddies which produce vertical and horizontal wind gusts. An example of one of these eddies was presented in the previous chapter. (Figure 1-3)

The intensity of the wind gusts produced by the turbulent eddies and the depth of the turbulent layer are both related to wind speed and stability. On cloudy, windy nights or anytime the sustained wind exceeds 20 knots, the lowest levels of the atmosphere tend to be well mixed. In this case, stability is neutral which neither helps nor hinders the vertical movement of air. (Figure 1-9) The result is purely mechanical turbulence. A simple rule of thumb for mostly flat terrain is when surface winds exceed 30 knots, the mechanically produced LLT will be moderate or greater. Care must be exercised in applying this rule over rough terrain. Also, lighter turbulence associated with winds less than 30 knots is not necessarily insignificant, especially in flight at low altitudes. The following excerpt from an accident report is a good example.

> PA-25. No injuries. Aircraft destroyed. Gust rolled aircraft close to inverted during a turn close to the ground. Flat terrain. Winds 15 knots gusting to 25 knots.

Sometimes you are only given the sustained wind and gusts must be estimated. When the winds are strong, the maximum gust is approximately 1.4 times the sustained wind. The value 1.4 is called the **gust factor**. For example, with a 20 knot sustained wind, the maximum gust is about 28 knots. This is for flat terrain. The gust factor increases with lighter winds. More importantly, it increases for all wind speeds as the terrain becomes more rugged. There is no simple rule here, except that gust factors of 2.0 or more are common in mountainous areas.

DEPTH

In general, the boundary layer deepens as the turbulence intensity increases. Since the strength of the turbulence depends on the wind speed, we can use the surface wind to make some rough estimates of the boundary layer depth. For example, if the sustained wind speed doubles, the depth of the turbulent layer approximately doubles. For very strong winds, the depth may reach a few thousand feet AGL. The intensity of mechanical turbulence is not constant through the layer. It reaches its maximum near the surface, and decreases to the top of the boundary layer. The following table gives estimated turbulent layer depths based on surface wind gusts over flat ground. The heights to which significant turbulence extends may be greater for very light aircraft (USAF, 1982).

GUSTS (knots)	TURBULENT LAYER (feet AGL)
30-39	surface to 2,000
40-49	surface to 2,000-3,000
>49	surface to 3,000-5,000

WIND SHEAR

When surface winds are strong, the vertical wind shear close to the ground is also strong. This shear hazard is compounded by the presence of the mechanical turbulence. The gustiness produced by the turbulent eddies will cause the shear to fluctuate significantly. Particularly large variations in vertical shear can be expected with strong winds in rough terrain.

Vertical shear and its variations can produce significant airspeed fluctuations during takeoff or landing. A simple rule of thumb is when the sustained surface wind speed exceeds 20 knots, the chances are good that airspeed fluctuations of 10-20 knots will occur on approach. We will see later that when the boundary layer is stable and surface winds are light, mechanical turbulence will not exist, but vertical wind shear and related airspeed fluctuations may actually be worse.

OBSTRUCTIONS

The intensity and the height to which mechanical turbulence extends above the surface also depends on the roughness of the surface. Even apparently small changes in the nature of the surface can cause distinct changes in LLT. For example, in moderate winds, an aircraft on a landing approach over water will often experience an increase in turbulence near the approach end of the runway simply because of the difference in roughness between the water and land surface.

In the vicinity of an airport, turbulent eddies are generated by obstacles to the wind such as fences, buildings, and trees. The effects of these barriers depend on their size, shape, location, and their direction from the runway relative to the wind direction. Serious takeoff and landing problems may be caused by small, isolated obstacles if they are in critical locations. (Figure 2-2)

Figure 2-2. Both natural and man-made obstacles produce turbulent eddies downwind.

With light winds, eddies tend to occur in the immediate vicinity of obstacles. However, with strong winds, eddies of significant sizes and intensities are swept downwind in turbulent wakes.

It is nearly impossible to give specific rules for the effects of all obstacles. However, there are some general guidelines for simple obstacle shapes. For example, a long line of dense trees perpendicular to the wind (a windbreak) does more than reduce the windspeed downwind of the trees. The airflow is disturbed just upwind of the trees as it flows over the tree line. The wind immediately over the trees is accelerated, and the vertical shear is strengthened above a turbulent wake downwind of the windbreak. (Figure 2-3)

The downwind influence of a line of trees or a similar barrier increases with the length, height, and density of obstruction. For a long, dense windbreak, significant reductions in surface wind speeds occur on the lee side of the trees over a distance equal to at least 10 times the tree height. For example, a windbreak 50 feet tall would produce wind speed decreases of 50% or more at least 500 feet downwind. A critical aspect of such blocking by long lines of trees, tall hedges, or walls is that a reversal of the flow may occur in their wake, enhancing wind shear and turbulence hazards. The following is an example of such a hazard:

> Aeronca 7AC. No injuries. Substantial damage. Encountered wind shear just above a stand of trees after takeoff. Twenty knot crosswind with gusts to 40 knots. Crashed in the trees.

When the wind is perpendicular to one side of a block-shaped obstacle, such as a building, flow patterns are produced similar to the one shown in

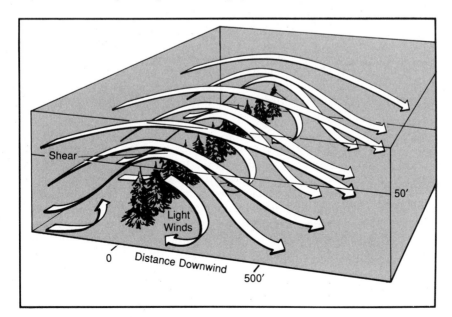

Figure 2-3. LLT created by a tree line (windbreak).

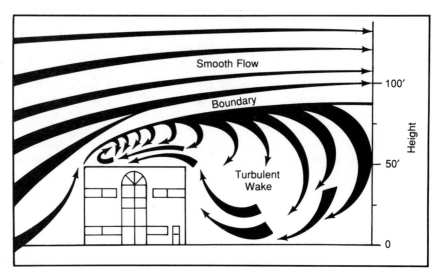

Figure 2-4. Flow patterns over a block-shaped obstacle.

Figure 2-4. Accelerated flow over the structure separates from the roof forming a turbulent wake on the lee side of the building. Sometimes this effect can be seen in the smoke pattern from a chimney on the building roof.

The boundary between the smooth and turbulent flow reaches approximately 1.5 to 2.0 times the height of the building. Potential flight problems occur when the flight path intersects the boundary of the turbulent wake. Also, there will generally be a zone of stronger winds near the top of the wake and around the sides of the building.

If a low building has a slanted roof, eddies similar to wingtip vortices (discussed later in this chapter) may be generated at the edges of the roof. The wake typically extends several building widths downwind. The potential danger of these eddies was illustrated a number of years ago during the testing of an automatic landing system. A long hangar with a double apex roof oriented at approximately 45° to the wind evidently produced a longitudinal vortex which "resulted in a landing impact close to the structural limits of the aircraft." (McManus, 1973).

The relatively simple eddy patterns described here should provide some general guidance in helping you determine the nature of wakes downwind of obstacles in moderate or stronger winds. However, such generalizations are not possible when the obstacles have more complicated shapes, are angled to the wind, and/or are combined in clusters with other obstacles of different sizes, shapes, spacings, and orientations. In these cases, a local study will often reveal that the turbulence patterns are repeatable for given wind conditions.

TERRAIN

The depth of the turbulent boundary layer and the size of turbulent eddies increase in the presence of hills and mountains. The increase depends on the slope, height and orientation of the terrain, the wind speed and direction, and atmospheric stability. In this chapter, you have already been given some guidelines for estimating LLT over "flat" terrain. It is not possible to give similar rules for every type of "rough" terrain you will encounter. However, there are some gross measures of terrain roughness as well as some models of air flow over simple topographic shapes to help you understand the basic effects of topography.

When you look at an aeronautical chart for flight planning purposes, you commonly judge the ruggedness of the terrain on the basis of its maximum heights along the flight track. This is a fairly easy task because the heights of the major peaks are marked on the map. But for turbulence diagnosis, this procedure can be misleading. A better indication of the terrain roughness is the height of each peak above the surrounding terrain. For some forecasting purposes, the U.S. Air Force identifies terrain as **rough** when topographic features extend more than 1,000 feet above their surroundings (USAF, 1982).

For large areas, say 200 n.m. or so on a side, this measure of roughness is quite helpful for general flight planning. For example, a useful rule for so-called rough terrain is that moderate or greater LLT can be expected when winds exceed 25-30 knots, and severe turbulence can be expected with winds of 40 knots or more (Mathews, 1988). However, when you consider a particular location, these thresholds must be applied very carefully. Pilot experience and scientific studies in a variety of mountainous areas have shown that exact locations of turbulence are usually related to specific local terrain features and certain wind speeds and directions. Therefore, severe turbulence may occur with wind speeds less than 25 knots around a steep mountain peak, while some nearby areas may have only light turbulence. These variations are illustrated in the following observations of pilots experienced in low-level flight in rough terrain (Smith, 1983; Lester and Burton, 1988).

> A rule of thumb used by helicopter pilots familiar with Guadalupe Pass in southwestern Texas is "never cross the pass if the winds at the remote observation site exceed 15 knots."

> During an approach to a 6,000-foot pinnacle near Fort Irwin, California, a helicopter was caught in a severe downdraft then updraft, causing shoulder harnesses to lock. Estimated wind velocity (only) 20-30 knots.

> While flying near a canyon (also near Fort Irwin) with winds from the west, a helicopter experienced heavy turbulence when no turbulence was reported anywhere else in the area.

The following three excerpts are from reports of aircraft accidents related to mechanical turbulence. These serve to emphasize wind speeds are only approximate measures of the LLT hazard, especially in rough terrain.

> ERCC 415-C. Serious injury. Substantial damage. Pilot hit tree attempting to turn around. Wind 25 gusting to 35 knots.

PA-22. Serious injuries. Aircraft destroyed. Pilot entered canyon at too low an altitude to clear rapidly rising terrain. Downdrafts and updrafts. Wind 25 gusting to 30 knots.

PA-18. No injuries. Substantial damage. Aircraft took off from a gravel strip in a river bed. Encountered turbulence from bluffs at approximately 50 feet AGL. Wind 20 knots and gusty.

AIRFLOW OVER HILLS

If topographical shapes are simple, then particular eddy patterns will recur with similar flow conditions. For example, when the wind blows perpendicular to a long, gently sloping ridge or plateau, the airflow tends to be smooth. (Figure 2-5) With steeper slopes (20° to 45°) and winds of at least 20 knots, air ascending at a few hundred f.p.m. may be felt up to 1,500 feet above the upwind slope (assuming no convection). Similar downward motions are often found over a smooth slope on the lee side of the hill.

The intensity of LLT increases with wind speed and slope of the terrain. We have already seen an example of this in the Point Loma turbulence investigation described in the introduction to this chapter. Point Loma rises sharply from sea level to 500 feet, presenting a substantial barrier to the frequent low-level northwesterly winds.

The sharp edges of cliffs may cause the airflow to separate from the slope. This will often result in a reversal of the flow in an area where it is not expected. If the windward slope is steep, a large eddy may form at the base of the cliff. (Figure 2-6) Similarly, separation may occur at the sharp up- and downwind edges of the cliff. The lee side eddy in figure 2-6 may be periodically detached and blown downwind, only to reform again in its original location. Such changes lead to very unsteady and unpredictable motions over the lee slope. Low-level turbulence related to these flow patterns can be intensified by convection, especially on sun-facing slopes, or by lee waves. Convection will be discussed in detail later in this chapter, and lee waves are considered with mountain wave turbulence in Chapter 5.

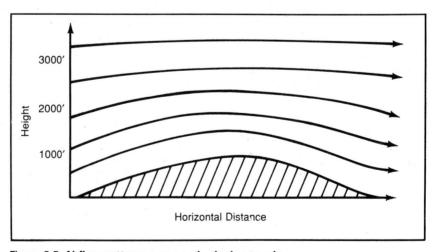

Figure 2-5. Airflow patterns over gently sloping terrain.

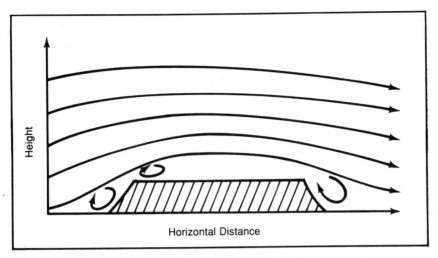

Figure 2-6. Turbulent eddy formation in airflow over hills with steep slopes.

Winds over rough terrain will be accelerated near peaks and ridges similar to the effects of the smaller obstacles that were discussed earlier. This is a very important consideration when attempting to fly across terrain at low levels as illustrated in the following excerpt from an accident report. This problem is aggravated with mountain top cloudiness and with mountain waves.

> PA-28. Three fatalities. Aircraft destroyed. Pilot encountered high velocity downdrafts during low altitude flight in mountain pass. Wind speed 40 knots.

When terrain is very complicated, the size, configuration, and orientation of the turbulent eddies becomes equally complicated. For example, when air flows across a ridge, eddies that rotate about nearly vertical axes can be produced. A dramatic illustration of this effect is found just downwind of a snow-covered, "sawtooth" ridge where strong winds interact with the terrain to produce mechanically driven whirlwinds, known as "snow devils." (Figure 2-7)

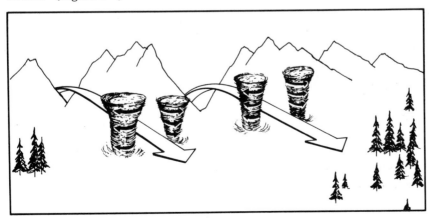

Figure 2-7. Turbulent eddies generated by flow across a "sawtooth" ridge.

The models and rules of thumb given above will be useful for understanding mechanical turbulence and estimating its intensity. However, attempts to explain all details of low-level turbulence in the vicinity of rough terrain with a few simple, conceptual models will be marginally successful at best and may even be dangerous. In addition, the impact of terrain-induced turbulence is often worsened in the presence of generally poor weather and wind shear. The following example and figure 2-8 illustrate a lethal combination of IFR conditions and topographically modified airflow.

A few years ago, an aircraft crashed during an IFR approach to an airport located on the shore of a reservoir. Ceilings and visibilities were low in rain and fog. The approach was made in strong crosswinds. Winds varied from about 60 knots at 1,600 feet AGL to 20 knots with gusts at the surface. Moderate to severe turbulence was reported at low levels. The last minute and a half of flight took the aircraft past a series of inlets and peninsulas with hills reaching a few hundred feet above the level of the reservoir. A detailed investigation of the incident provided strong evidence that the drift of the aircraft from the centerline of the approach course was partially due to the pilot's efforts to adjust to significant wind shear and turbulence along the flight path. Wind variations were caused by the alternating influences of smooth

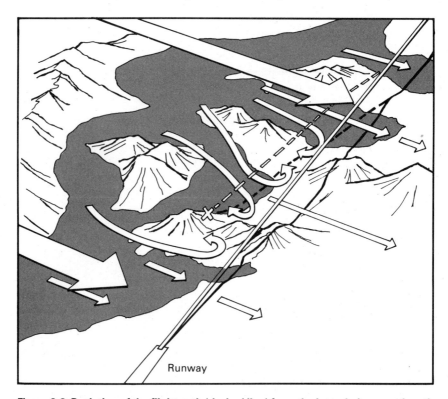

Figure 2-8. Deviation of the flight path (dashed line) from the intended approach path. Shear and turbulence produced by strong crosswinds over rough terrain. Crash site is indicated by "X." Winds at the surface are shown with thin arrows. Stronger winds aloft are indicated by broad arrows.

water surfaces and low hills upwind of the flight track. The final descent was made into the sheltering effect of a hill, most likely resulting in a sharp decrease in airspeed.

(Frost, et al, 1985).

WAKE TURBULENCE

As most pilots know, turbulent wakes are generated by aircraft in flight. This is also a form of mechanical turbulence. In this case, rather than the air blowing past the obstacle, the obstacle (the aircraft) is moving through the air. The result is still the same, a turbulent wake is produced behind the obstacle. The term **wake turbulence** is applied to the turbulence that forms behind an aircraft in flight.

Wake turbulence occurs at all flight levels. A discussion in this chapter with other LLT hazards is relevant because encounters with wake turbulence near the ground are often critical, especially during landing and takeoff operations. We will also consider wake turbulence at higher altitudes with the discussion of clear air turbulence (CAT) in Chapter 4.

In contrast to other types of mechanical turbulence, wake turbulence is somewhat more predictable because aircraft have the same basic shape. The turbulent eddies they produce tend to be similar. Wake turbulence produces two counter-rotating vortices that form at the wingtips and trail behind aircraft in flight. (Figure 2-9) Vortex generation begins at liftoff and ends at touchdown. Each vortex provides downwash inboard of the wingtips and upward flow outboard. The sizes, rotational speeds, and persistence of the vortices depend on aircraft weight, speed, and wing characteristics. Aircraft that are heavy, slow, and have aerodynamically smooth wings produce the biggest, strongest, and the longest-lasting eddies.

When fully formed at a distance of about two wingspans behind the aircraft, the vortices are typically 25 to 50 feet in diameter; their actual size depends on the wing dimensions. They tend to remain about three quarters of the wing span apart. The two vortices descend 800 to 900 feet below the aircraft within about two minutes and remain at that level until they

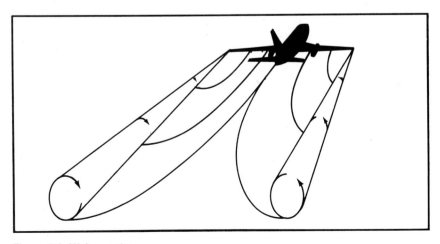

Figure 2-9. Wake vortices.

dissipate. They weaken with time and distance from the generating aircraft. Atmospheric turbulence will hasten their dissipation.

If the vortices reach the ground, they will move outward from the aircraft at about two to three knots in calm wind conditions. If there is an ambient wind, then the net movement of the eddies will be the sum of the ambient wind velocity and the "no-wind" motion of each vortex. Thus a light cross wind could cause one vortex to remain nearly stationary over the runway.

The flight hazard of wake turbulence is obvious. A small aircraft departing or arriving too close to a large aircraft may be subjected to vertical and horizontal gusts which cannot be compensated for by any flight maneuver. This is especially true when a trailing aircraft enters directly into a vortex. The maximum gusts in the wake of the aircraft occur in the cores of the vortices. Gusts of more than 10,000 f.p.m. have been reported. Flight into the downwash region between vortices will also cause serious difficulties when the trailing aircraft is taking off or landing. The other possible conflict occurs when an aircraft intersects the wake at a large angle. Significant turbulence can be encountered as the aircraft passes through the vortex, the downwash, and then another vortex in close succession.

Wake turbulence is not restricted to fixed wing or "heavy" aircraft. Helicopters and light, fixed wing aircraft can cause significant wake turbulence. For example, there are many cases where an aircraft involved in aerial spraying, flying near stall speed, has crashed after intersecting its own wake from a previous spraying swath. Some descriptions of other wake turbulence accidents are given below.

Cessna 310H. No injuries. Aircraft destroyed. Parallel runways in use. Runway 28R used by jet aircraft. Cessna encountered severe turbulence over threshold of runway 28L. Winds 070/04.

PA-28 Minor injuries. Substantial damage. Aircraft cleared to land runway 24R. Flew into vortex turbulence of DC-9 landing 24L. Wind 160/06.

Beech B-50. No injuries. Substantial damage. Pilot initiated runway 09 takeoff at intersection of runway 03 while B-727 departing runway 09 was in takeoff climb.

Piper Navaho. Three fatalities. Navaho pilot turned on final approach 250 feet below the glide path of a B-727 that had passed that point 52 seconds previously. Shortly after B-727 landed, Navaho was seen to roll from side to side, pitch up, roll inverted to the left and fly into the ground nose first.

Bell 47H-1. No injuries. Substantial damage. Pilot flew into vortex of a second helicopter during formation take off.

Specific flight procedures have been developed to avoid the effects of wake turbulence. The details of these have been published widely in manuals, circulars, and other training media. (FAA, 1975, 1991, Jeppesen, 1993).

DRY CONVECTION

Section

C

In general physics, convection refers to the transfer of heat through mass motions within a fluid. In meteorology, the term **convection** is commonly used to describe heat transfer by atmospheric motions in the vertical direction, while **advection** refers to mass transfer in the horizontal direction.

There are two basic types of atmospheric convection processes: forced and free. In **forced convection**, the air must be mechanically pushed upward or downward, such as by a front or a mountain. In **free convection**, air moves upward or downward without any external help. You should recognize that forced convection involves neutral or stable air, whereas free convection requires unstable air. In this text, as in most aviation meteorology books and manuals, the term **convection** implies free convection.

Although the topic in the present section is dry (cloudless) convection in the boundary layer, a brief examination of the behavior of cumulus clouds is a good place to start. The cumuli shown in figure 2-10 are known as "fair weather cumuli" because they don't show much vertical development and are not associated with showers and thunderstorms. In fact, the individual small cumuli only have lifetimes of a few minutes. If their behavior is captured with time lapse photography, the film record will show rapidly forming and dissipating clouds which give the impression that the clouds are at the upper surface of a boiling liquid. Of course, what is actually being seen is the top of a convectively active boundary layer.

Figure 2-10. Fair weather cumulus clouds. Photo courtesy of A. Rangno, Seattle, WA.

The cumuli shown in figure 2-10 are actually the tops of "bubbles" of warm air that have risen from the ground and have passed through the condensation level. The bubbles are more frequently called **thermals**. They are the cloudless "roots" of the cumuli, and are a major source of LLT in the boundary layer. Their moist counterparts are covered in Chapter 3.

CONVECTIVE BOUNDARY LAYER

Over land the development of instability and dry convection under fair weather conditions is a daytime occurrence. Solar radiation heats the ground generating convection at the bottom of the boundary layer. During the morning and early afternoon, the convection intensifies and deepens. Convective activity reaches a maximum in the afternoon, then gradually dies out as the earth's surface cools.

An example of the late afternoon decrease in turbulence in the convective boundary layer is illustrated in figure 2-11 with a series of PIREPs for a hot July day near Las Vegas, Nevada. Skies were reported clear in each PIREP. The deep, dry convective layer indicated by the reports is typical for the deserts and mountains of the Western U.S.

Time (LST)	Flight Level (feet)	Turbulence
1453	11,500	MDT
1541	11,500	CONT LGT-MDT
1618	10,500	CONT LGT CHOP
1742	9,000	OCNL LGT DURGC
1748	9,500	OCNL VRY LGT DURGC
1902	7,500	SMTH

Figure 2-11. Pilot Report excerpts showing the late afternoon weakening of turbulence due to dry convection. A PIREP code breakdown is given in the Appendix.

Figure 2-12 shows a diagram of the boundary layer environment with well-developed dry convection. There are three primary layers, a lower **superadiabatic layer** where thermals are generated, an **adiabatic layer** where the thermals rise and grow, and the **capping stable layer** where the thermals die. The lower two layers are sometimes called the **mixed layer**.

SUPERADIABATIC LAYER

In the superadiabatic layer, heat input from the surface produces a lapse rate which exceeds the dry adiabatic lapse rate. It is here that thermals and their rotating counterparts, dust devils, take form.

Ideal conditions for the development of a superadiabatic layer are clear skies and light winds. At sunrise, a stable layer (often an inversion) is present at the ground. A shallow superadiabatic layer begins to develop after sunrise. At the time of maximum convective activity (afternoon), the superadiabatic layer typically deepens to about 300 feet AGL.

Large variations in the depth of the superadiabatic layer are possible. It can extend to a few thousand feet over desert regions in the summer, or be

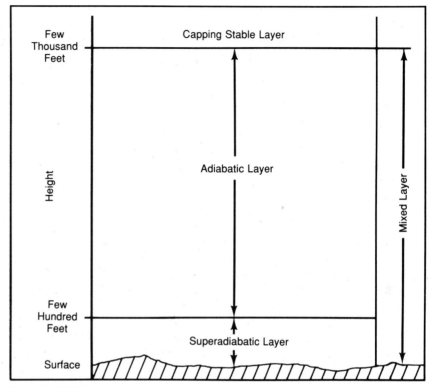

Figure 2-12. The three layer structure of the convective boundary layer.

non-existent with heavy cloud cover or snow cover. The superadiabatic layer does not usually exist at night over land, except over isolated natural or man-made heat sources. It can be present any time day or night over warm water surfaces, depending on the difference between the water and air temperatures.

THERMALS

Daytime sources of thermals are those surfaces that heat up more rapidly than surrounding areas. Favorable surfaces include dry fields, paved roads, parking lots, and runways. Occasionally, large power plants generate very warm thermal plumes which can be the source of moderate or stronger turbulence within a few hundred feet of the ground. Unfavorable thermal sources are forested areas, cool bodies of water, irrigated fields, and ground dampened by rain.

Elevated terrain is also an efficient producer of thermals. High, bare hills generate thermals earlier in the day and for a longer period than nearby valleys. In addition, sun-facing slopes produce stronger and narrower thermals than flat land. The following PIREP documents turbulent conditions on an afternoon flight from Bakersfield (BFL) in the San Joaquin Valley of California to a nearby mountainous area.

BFL UA /TM 2314/FL095/TP 172/SK CLR/TA 20
/TB DURGC BFL SMTH, INTMT LGT-MDT O/MTNS
(NOTE: TM 1514 LST)

If surface air is blown too quickly across warm surfaces, heating is less intense and thermals are weaker than those that are stationary or drift slowly over a relatively warm area. In windy conditions, glider pilots often find lift in thermals generated in **wind shadows** on the downwind side of obstructions, such as trees or low hills. In those areas, stronger "shadow thermals" will develop because the lighter winds allow the thermals to remain close to a favorable heat source for a longer time.

Thermals in the superadiabatic layer are plume-like structures of warm air rising over their sources. Under weak wind conditions, the plumes may extend several hundred feet in the crosswind direction and only 100 feet or so along the wind. This irregular shape has led some to describe thermals in the superadiabatic layer as narrow "curtains" of rising air.

With stronger winds, the long axis of the thermal plume is aligned along the wind as shown in figure 2-13. The main region of rising air is along the upwind edge of the plume (shaded). This edge has a well-defined boundary or **microfront** across which the temperature rises 1°C or so. In contrast, the downwind edge is diffuse. Developing thermals are blown along the surface with the average wind in the superadiabatic layer. The vertical axis of a thermal plume may tilt downwind as much as 45° when winds increase with height.

Thermal plumes have many indicators. These include birds soaring over flat surfaces; looping smoke plumes; variable wind directions under light wind conditions; "cats paws" patterns on water surfaces; undulations on fields of long grass; and small, but noticeable, temperature fluctuations over periods of a minute or less as thermals blow past a surface observer. The best indicator of a lack of dry convective activity is reduced visibility in smoke or haze.

The thermal structure shown in figure 2-13 is idealized. Because of the instability in the superadiabatic layer, both updrafts and downdrafts undergo accelerations which result in the distortion and merging of thermals.

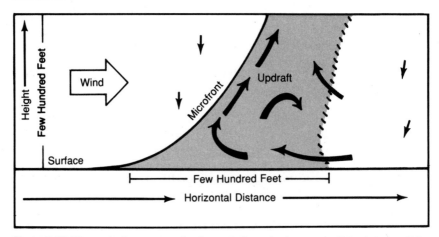

Figure 2-13. The typical structure of a thermal plume in the superadiabatic layer. (After Kaimal and Businger, 1970)

If surface winds are too strong (greater than 20 knots), the superadiabatic layer is best described as "chaotic." Individual thermals are difficult to identify, although LLT can be significant due to combined mechanical and thermal effects.

The strength of thermals depends on how much warmer they are than their surroundings. The temperature excess depends on the depth of the superadiabatic layer and how much the actual lapse rate (LR) exceeds the dry adiabatic lapse rate (DALR). This is illustrated in figure 2-14.

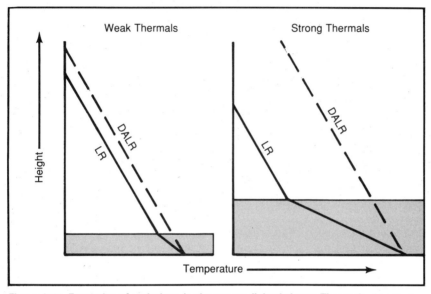

Figure 2-14. Examples of variations in the superadiabatic layer. Thermals are stronger for conditions on the right.

The two soundings represent conditions from the ground through the lower part of the adiabatic layer. The dashed line labeled DALR represents the decrease in temperature a parcel of air rising from the surface would have. The solid line represents the observed variation of temperature with height as determined from a sounding. In both cases the rising parcels are warmer than their surroundings; but on the right, the superadiabatic layer (shaded) is deeper and the observed lapse rate is much greater than the adiabatic lapse rate. Therefore, a rising parcel on the right is significantly warmer than is the rising parcel of air on the left. Deep superadiabatic layers with steep lapse rates and strong thermals are commonly found on hot days over arid regions.

DUST DEVILS
Some of the most dramatic products of thermal development in the superadiabatic layer are vortices known as whirlwinds or **dust devils**, not to be confused with more violent tornadoes or waterspouts. (Figure 2-15)

Dust devils are only about one tenth as frequent as ordinary thermals, because of the more extreme environmental conditions required for their development. They are formed under light wind conditions over very hot surfaces. Favored areas are dry, barren regions that experience cloudless

Figure 2-15. Dust devils in the superadiabatic layer are flight hazards, especially during takeoff and landing operations.

skies and high sun angles for maximum heating. These conditions are most frequently found over desert areas in summer.

Dust devils occur most often in early afternoon, at the time of maximum ground temperature and just prior to the time of maximum air temperature. Surface air is subjected to rotation, usually caused by airflow around some sort of surface obstruction. If this occurs with a developing thermal, the thermal will stretch the vortex as it rises, causing an increase in rotation rate. There is no preferred direction of rotation.

In light winds, dust devils tend to move either along terrain contours or uphill. They may become stationary over a small rise in the ground where there is a good supply of warm air. In stronger winds, vortex behavior is similar to that of thermal plumes. They move with the speed and in the direction of the average wind and are often tilted downwind.

Dust devils are typically 5 to 100 feet in diameter with life times of four minutes or less. Dust lifted by the vortex commonly reaches heights of 100 to 300 feet, although aircraft studies have shown that the circulations often extend above the top of the dust. Flying over a visible dust devil at low altitudes is certainly not a good idea. Over desert areas in the summer, dust devils will occasionally extend to several thousand feet. Generally, the taller the vortex, the longer it lasts; extreme lifetimes of several hours have been reported.

Wind gusts ranging up to 20 knots and vertical gusts of a few hundred feet per minute are common with dust devils. Extremes of more than 50 knots and 2,000 f.p.m. have been reported. Horizontal and vertical gusts caused by dust devils can be a danger to aircraft, especially near the ground. Aircraft with very low wing loading (such as gliders) are particularly vulnerable. Some examples of problems that dust devils can cause are given in the following excerpts from accident reports.

B-A75. No injuries. Aircraft destroyed. During takeoff, aircraft encountered a local whirlwind and crashed into a shed and haystack. Reported surface wind speed was 3 knots.

Blanik. No injuries. Substantial damage. Parked Sailplane lifted by dust devil and collided with Libelle.

B-A75. Minor injury. Substantial damage. During aerial spraying operation, aircraft encountered a dust devil, struck 40-foot trees. Surface winds 180° at 10 knots.

Beech 35. No injuries. Substantial damage. Aircraft encountered a local whirlwind on touchdown. Ground looped. Winds were variable and gusty.

Fortunately, dust devils are often made visible by dust and debris swept upward by the circulations. However, on some occasions, they are not so obvious, except perhaps by motions in the ground cover. Close attention to these clues is required in dust devil-prone regions (Cooley, 1971; Stull, 1988).

ADIABATIC LAYER

In the afternoon, when convective activity is most intense, the adiabatic layer is dominated by thermals. In the adiabatic layer, the chaos of the superadiabatic layer is left behind. Well-defined circulations develop within thermals. Glider pilots have long taken advantage of the upward motions in these circulations to gain altitude and for cross-country flights. However, these sources of lift for slow-moving gliders are often sources of LLT for powered aircraft. Examples of PIREPs from an area where glider pilots reported an excellent day for thermal lift are shown below.

WJF UA/OV PMD 330020/TM 2118/FL116/TP C172/SK CLR/TB LGT-MDT, UDDF 500-1000FPM (NOTE: TM 1318 LST)

DAG UA/OV PMD-DAG/TM 2351/FLO95/TP MO20/SK CLR/TB CONT LGT-MDT, STG UDDF (NOTE: TM 1551 LST)

THERMALS

Some investigators (and many aviation meteorology manuals) describe the circulation in thermals as a **vortex ring**. Similar to the shape of a donut, the vortex ring circulation has a relatively narrow core of upward motions surrounded by a broad region of weaker sinking motions. A smoke ring is an example. However, most observations of thermals characterize the circulation as more elongated than a true vortex ring. It appears to be more like a tube or a column that extends through much of the depth of the mixed layer.

The upward and downward motions shown in figure 2-16 are superimposed on the overall rising motion of the warm thermal. Because of this, a sailplane entering a thermal from below can sometimes move to the top in the core of stronger upward motions as the entire thermal circulation rises.

The characteristics of thermals over level terrain are fairly well known. When the mixed layer is shallow early in the day, thermals are small and weak, perhaps only a few hundred feet in diameter. As the depth of the mixed layer grows, the sizes of the thermals also grow. Later in the afternoon, diameters of several thousand feet are possible.

The core of more intense rising motions is much smaller than the overall size of the thermal. The average diameter of the updraft area of a thermal is about one quarter of its height above the ground; that is, an updraft encountered at 2,000 feet AGL will be about 500 feet wide. At usual airspeeds a light aircraft would pass through a typical thermal core in only a few seconds. Thermals over hills and over the western deserts of the U.S. tend to be taller and narrower.

In contrast, the distance between updrafts is usually much larger than their diameters. That separation increases as the mixed layer deepens. Updrafts are typically 1.5 times the depth of the mixed layer apart. If, for example, thermals are reaching a maximum height of 2,800 feet AGL, they will be about 4,200 feet apart (a little over 20 seconds at an airspeed of 120 knots).

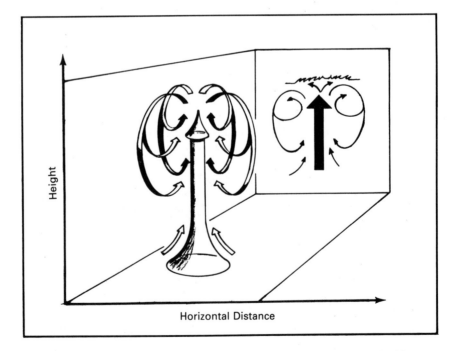

Figure 2-16. Perspective diagram of an idealized thermal in the foreground with a two-dimensional cross section in the background. Wind shear will tilt and distort the pattern.

Although the updraft is the dominant feature, a real thermal twists and distorts as it rises due to internal temperature differences and external influences. Wind shear can tilt the thermal as we saw in the superadiabatic layer. Also, as the thermal rises, it grows in volume as outside air is mixed or **entrained** into the circulation. Entrainment, together with a tendency for thermals to merge, accounts for larger thermals (3,000-6,000 feet in diameter) at the top of the adiabatic layer.

In general, turbulence intensities in the adiabatic layer range from "light" to "light-to-moderate" turbulence. These correspond with typical vertical gusts in thermals of 200 to 400 f.p.m. and extremes of 1,000 to 2,000 f.p.m. The latter occur more frequently in deep mixed layers found over desert areas and bare hills, and with clearing skies behind cold fronts.

THERMAL PATTERNS

Thermal activity may be arranged into regular, larger scale patterns by certain combinations of wind, wind shear, stability, and surface characteristics. For example, after a cool airmass moves across a relatively flat surface, a characteristic "honey comb" pattern of convection will develop with winds of about 10 knots or less. The pattern is often made visible by cumulus clouds which form at the top the thermals. (Figure 2-17) If hills are present, stronger convective activity and cumulus clouds will persist over the hills.

If winds in the mixed layer are 20 knots or more and the wind direction shows little change with height, the thermals are often organized into lines

Figure 2-17. Cumulus clouds at the top of the mixed layer. Clouds have formed as merging thermals have passed through the condensation level. The pattern of shadows cast by the clouds indicates the distribution of thermals.

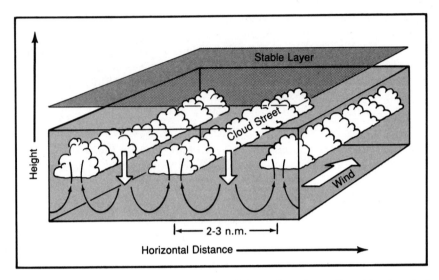

Figure 2-18. Cloud streets form at the tops of thermals and are aligned by the winds in the mixed layer.

nearly parallel to the wind. (Figure 2-18) This behavior is favored when the mixed layer is about 6,000 feet deep and capped by a well-defined inversion. Lines of clouds known as "cloud streets" often form in the updrafts. The lines of updrafts are typically separated by a distance of two or three nautical miles.

CAPPING STABLE LAYER

The **capping stable layer** is where the thermals end their vertical rise, because they are no longer warmer than their surroundings. When the stability of the capping layer is strong, as with an inversion, the base of that layer is often easy to see. Dust and pollutants carried by thermals from the surface form a distinctive haze layer that ends abruptly at the top of the mixed layer.

As an aircraft climbs through the capping stable layer and above any small cumulus that may be present, the turbulence characteristic of the mixed layer disappears. Perhaps more dramatic than the marked decrease in turbulence during ascent is the rapid onset of turbulence during descent through the capping stable layer. As described by Robert N. Buck in his book *Weather Flying* (© 1988), the abrupt transition to the turbulent mixed layer during descent is a "special time" that demands that the pilot be "concerned, slowed down, and alert to use best turbulence-flying technique." Passage into turbulence of unknown intensity must be approached with caution to avoid excessive loads on the aircraft.

Even though thermals are cooler than the air in the capping stable layer, they will continue to penetrate (overshoot) some distance vertically into the warmer air. The extent of penetration depends on the upward speed of the thermals as they leave the adiabatic layer and on the stability of the capping layer. For example, if the thermals are weak and the capping layer is an inversion (strongly stable), penetration will be minimal.

The capping stable layer is a transition zone between the unstable daytime boundary layer where LLT due to dry convection is a maximum, and the free atmosphere where turbulence is minimal. Within the transition zone, some convective turbulence associated with dying thermals may occur together with turbulence associated with atmospheric gravity waves and shear.

If winds are very light, penetrating thermals may set off gravity waves which move outward from the thermal along the stable layer. These oscillations are like waves on a water surface which move away from a spot where a stone has been dropped into the water. Turbulence produced by this mechanism is not known to be significant in the capping stable layer. However, when thunderstorms interact with stable layers, such waves may be strong enough to affect aircraft. This process is discussed in a later chapter.

If the vertical wind shear across the capping stable layer is great enough, another type of wave disturbance known as a **shearing-gravity wave** can develop in that layer. Described briefly in Chapter 1, these waves often appear similar to ocean waves breaking on a beach, although the mechanism that produces them is different. The shear causes the wave crests to overtake the wave troughs so that the wave overturns. In contrast to rapidly breaking water waves, this atmospheric wave-breaking takes a few minutes. This process generates patchy (intermittent) turbulence in the capping stable layer. The turbulence is usually light.

Sometimes, the vertical shear is not quite strong enough to cause shearing-gravity waves to overturn until a thermal carries mixed-layer air with lighter winds into the capping stable layer. (Figure 2-19) Any shear already present in the stable layer (shaded) will be strengthened by the thermal, causing the shearing-gravity waves to develop in that part of the layer. The horizontal dimension of the breaking waves is short compared to the

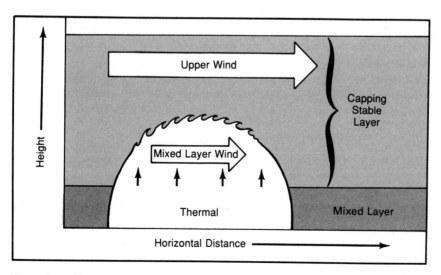

Figure 2-19. Shearing-gravity waves at the top of a thermal in a capping stable layer.

diameter of the thermal, and several waves may be visible as hook-shaped filaments on the tops of cumulus clouds penetrating the stable layer.

Another type of atmospheric gravity wave occurs in the stable air when there is strong wind shear between the mixed layer and airflow aloft. Strong mixed layer convection acts as a block to the upper flow, creating waves similar to the mountain waves discussed in Chapter 5. As shown in figure 2-20, this effect is especially noticeable when thermal activity is in lines parallel to mixed layer winds (cloud streets are often present) and the wind shift is 90°.

Discovered by glider pilots, these phenomena are known as **thermal waves** or "convection waves." Thermal waves have lengths of a few miles and, on occasion, their effects can extend to the tropopause. Their known impact on flight above the capping layer is wave action with up- and downdrafts of 200 to 600 feet per minute (Jaeckisch, 1968; Kuettner et al, 1987).

As we leave the discussion of dry convection, it is important to qualify our description of the convective boundary layer. There are several important variations from the idealized structures we have just described. For example, over some desert areas, dry convection can exceed 18,000 feet, much deeper than the typical mixed layer depths previously described.

Another more common variation from the ideal picture is suppression of the daily cycle of convection in the boundary layer. This occurs over wet or snow-covered surfaces and with cloud cover. Also, the daily convection cycle can be sharply modified when airmasses of different temperatures move through the area (advection). In the spring, for example, stronger-than-normal thermal activity is common for about two days after a cold

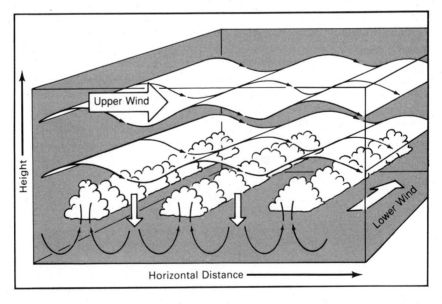

Figure 2-20. Thermal waves created by the flow of stable air over lines of thermals in the convective boundary layer.

front passes. LLT and wind shear specifically associated with fronts will be discussed in detail in the next section.

Finally, it should be noted that when instability is very large, moist convection and thunderstorms are often the result. The boundary layer is greatly modified under these conditions and it is often difficult to separate turbulence due to boundary layer processes from turbulence due to thunderstorms. These topics are combined in the next chapter.

STABLE LAYERS

Up to this point, we have concentrated on the neutral and unstable boundary layer related to mechanical turbulence and dry convection. Stable conditions were only noted where they directly influenced the turbulence produced by convection (for example, the capping stable layer). In this section, our concentration shifts to stable conditions. We will address the development of wind shear and turbulence in several different types of stable layers in the lower part of the atmosphere, in and above the boundary layer. These include nighttime ground-based inversions, macroscale fronts, and other elevated stable layers.

IMPACT OF WIND SHEAR ON FLIGHT

Wind shear in the boundary layer has two important impacts on flight. The first is that it may cause the outbreak of sporadic turbulence. If vertical wind shear in a stable layer becomes large enough, turbulence will occur in the form of amplifying and breaking shearing-gravity waves. You have already been exposed to these phenomena in our brief discussion of the capping stable layer. In the stable boundary layer, these waves are typically a few hundred feet in length. The wave-breaking does not ordinarily occur simultaneously everywhere in the stable layer, rather the turbulence tends to occur in local "bursts" or patches.

An example of the wave breaking in a stable layer is shown in figure 2-21. In the photo, the clouds simply act as tracers of the airflow. They are not necessary for the formation of the waves.

The greater the stability in the atmosphere, the more difficult is it for the shear to cause shearing-gravity waves to break. Put another way, the

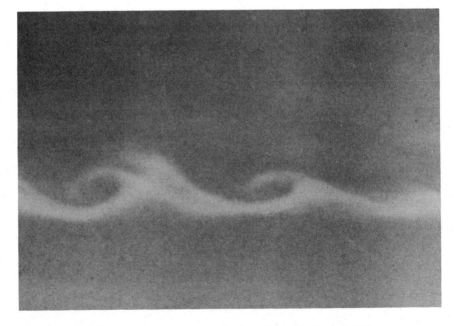

Figure 2-21. Breaking shearing-gravity waves made visible by a cloud layer.

vertical shear required to produce turbulence through the wave-breaking process becomes larger as the stability increases. For example, shear in a strong inversion near the ground would have to be 5-10 knots or more per hundred feet for wave breaking to be possible. In cases with stronger stability, the vertical shear can be even larger but wave breaking and turbulence will not necessarily occur.

The other, and probably more important, impact of wind shear in the boundary layer is its effect on takeoffs and landings. The critical wind shear for flight operations is always the shear along the aircraft path. Wind shear below 2,000 feet AGL along the final approach path or along the takeoff and initial climbout path is known as **low-level wind shear (LLWS)**. It is important to realize that anytime an aircraft is descending or climbing, the observed wind shear may be due to vertical wind shear or horizontal wind shear, or both.

The influences of wind shear on aircraft performance during landing and takeoff are well-known. If the pilot of an aircraft encounters wind shear on approach and fails to adjust for a rapidly decreasing headwind (or increasing tailwind), the airspeed will decrease and the aircraft will undershoot the landing. Similarly, a rapidly increasing headwind (or decreasing tailwind) can cause an overshoot.

When wind shear is encountered on takeoff and the headwind decreases (or tailwind increases), the climbout will be slower. In critical situations, obstacles near the airport may not be cleared. During both takeoff and landing, a strong wind shear with a crosswind component may cause the aircraft to deviate from the centerline of the runway. Close to the ground, clearance of nearby obstacles may become difficult.

Low-level wind shear is often described in terms of the vertical wind shear over a 100-foot layer. Critical values are given in figure 2-22.

In flight, the severity of low-level wind shear is reflected in the magnitude of airspeed fluctuations. A shear is considered significant when airspeed fluctuations are 15 to 20 knots or more. This is equivalent to the effect of moderate or greater turbulence.

LOW-LEVEL WIND SHEAR	
Severity	Magnitude (kts/100 ft)
Light	less than 4.0
Moderate	4.0 to 7.9
Strong	8.0 to 11.9
Severe	12 or greater

Figure 2-22. Critical values of low-level wind shear.

WIND SHEAR CAUSES

A stable layer provides a favorable environment for the development of vertical wind shear because it resists vertical mixing. One stable layer often characterized by strong vertical shear is the stable boundary layer. This fact has led many pilots to describe it as potentially one of the more dangerous meteorological conditions for landings and takeoffs. It should be well understood.

AIRMASS WIND SHEAR

The boundary layer stabilizes when the ground becomes cooler than the overlying airmass. Over land this is a common result of nighttime radiational cooling of the earth's surface. On clear, cold nights, a ground-based inversion is often found in the boundary layer. This is also referred to as the **nocturnal inversion**.

An important effect of the extreme stability of the nocturnal inversion is the general tendency for vertical wind shear to increase. This happens because vertical mixing associated with convective activity is no longer possible. Therefore, effects of surface friction are no longer "felt" at levels as low as few hundred feet above the surface. Winds at those levels accelerate. In addition to this increase in winds aloft, after sunset there is also a general tendency for surface winds to decrease. The result of these two effects is that vertical wind shear increases at night. After sunrise, mixing by convection reestablishes the connection between surface friction and the flow aloft and the vertical shear weakens as vertical mixing takes over. (Figure 2-23)

The process of vertical wind shear production described above leads to what is called **airmass wind shear**; that is, vertical shear which occurs at night under fair weather conditions in the absence of strong fronts and/or strong surface pressure gradients. In these circumstances, the strongest airmass wind shear occurs near the top of the nocturnal inversion.

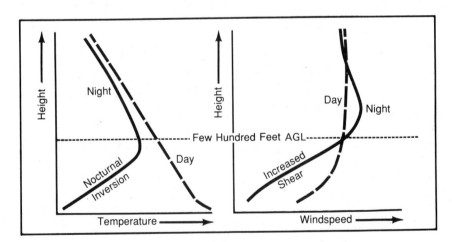

Figure 2-23. Nighttime (solid lines) and daytime (dashed lines) boundary layer soundings are compared. Note that wind shear is greater at night when the nocturnal inversion is present.

Strong ground based inversions with the potential for airmass wind shear (both day and night) occur in very cold airmasses over snow and ice surfaces. These conditions are common in winter at high latitudes.

FRONTS

In addition to airmass wind shear, **frontal wind shear** also occurs in the boundary layer. Sources are both macroscale and mesoscale fronts, which are common in, and above, the boundary layer. A brief review of the critical properties of fronts is in order.

Technically, a **front** is the boundary between two airmasses of differing densities. In most cases, "densities" can be equated to "temperatures." An **airmass** can then be defined as a body of air that has a uniform horizontal distribution of temperature. As shown in figure 2-24, where two different airmasses lay next to each other, the colder airmass wedges under the warmer airmass so that the frontal surface between the two slopes upward over the colder airmass.

A detail that should be noted in figure 2-24, is that the vertical coordinate of the figure is exaggerated. This distortion is necessary, because the horizontal scale of the front is much larger than the vertical scale. Put another way, the front is actually very flat. Consequently, it is often necessary to stretch the height scale of vertical cross sections to show the detailed structure of fronts (and many other circulations). This convention is used throughout most aviation meteorology texts, although it is rarely mentioned. In order to develop accurate conceptual models of the atmospheric circulations, this vertical exaggeration must be kept in mind.

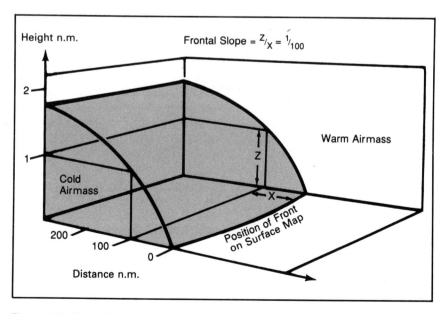

Figure 2-24. Frontal boundary between two airmasses. The slope of the front is the ratio of the height (Z) of the frontal surface to distance (X) from the surface position of the cold front. The slope of this front is 1:100 since X = 100 n.m., Z = 1 n.m.

Macroscale fronts are those associated with large scale mid-latitude cyclones that appear on daily weather maps. In contrast, **mesoscale fronts** are produced by a number of small scale circulations including sea breezes (sea breeze fronts) and thunderstorms (gust fronts). Sea breeze fronts will be discussed later in this chapter and gust fronts will be covered in a later chapter.

The identification of individual macroscale fronts differs depending on the behavior of the front. As seen in figure 2-25, the front on the east side of the cyclone is identified as a warm front because warm air is replacing cold air. On the west side, a cold front is found where cold air is displacing warm air. If a front shows little or no movement, it is identified as a stationary front. An example is shown at the southwest end of the cold front in figure 2-25.

The slope of the advancing cold front is usually greater than that of the warm front. Typical slopes for cold and warm fronts are 1:50 and 1:200, respectively. There are wide variations.

A cyclone involved with fronts often goes through a life cycle lasting a few days. On the left side of figure 2-26 is a developing wave cyclone. Over a period of several hours, the central pressure falls rapidly and winds around the low increase significantly. After a half day or so, the faster-moving cold front begins to overtake the warm front as the cyclone occludes. The resulting frontal structure, shown on the right of figure 2-26, is known as an occluded front. The cyclone reaches its greatest intensity (lowest pressure) within 24 hours after occlusion. It gradually dissipates over a few days.

When a cold front is strong and fast moving, it will often produce LLT. Part of the reason for this is that cold fronts in the boundary layer are often

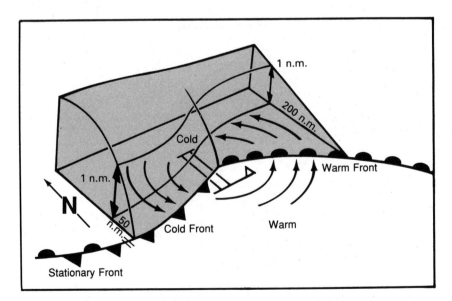

Figure 2-25. Three types of macroscale fronts: warm, cold, and stationary.

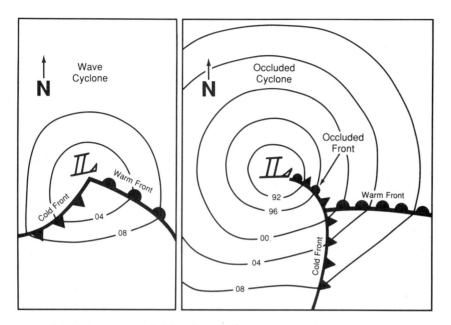

Figure 2-26. Wave cyclone (left) and occluded cyclone (right).

stronger and have steeper slopes than at higher levels. Slopes of 1:10 or less in the lowest 1,500 feet of the boundary layer have been observed. A cross section through such a front is shown in figure 2-27. In this case, a narrow updraft region is found just ahead of the steep portion of the front. Vertical gusts in this zone can reach 1,000 f.p.m. or more.

In practice, we do not measure the airflow around fronts in enough detail to resolve the vertical gusts. However, on the basis of experience, we are

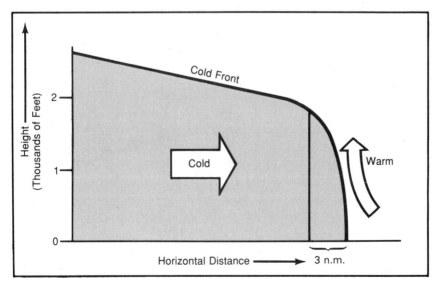

Figure 2-27. Cross section through a fast-moving cold front.

able to estimate LLT from the larger scale behavior of the front. Three related rules of thumb are the following:

1. A front moving at 30 knots or more will have moderate or greater LLT.

2. A front moving across rough terrain will generate moderate or greater LLT.

3. A front associated with a horizontal temperature change of at least 10°F per 50 n.m. will have moderate or greater LLT.

As illustrated in figure 2-28, the LLT pattern associated with a cold front moving over flat terrain extends from about 200 n.m. behind the front through the region of strong southerly surface winds ahead of the front (indicated by the broad arrow and closely packed isobars). This simple "model" recognizes not only the LLT caused by the front, but also mechanical turbulence on both sides of the front. This pattern may be significantly different when thunderstorms are present.

It should be clear that the frontal models and definitions that you learned in your elementary aviation meteorology course are useful in the interpretation of macroscale fronts that can produce LLT. However, when dealing with wind shear, we must expand our view of fronts.

FRONTAL ZONES

As illustrated by the expanded view of a cold front in figure 2-29, the front is actually a zone of transition between the two airmasses it separates. In the frontal zone, strong temperature gradients and horizontal wind shear are common. Depending on the frontal type and altitude, the width of a frontal zone may be 0.5 n.m. to more than 100 n.m. wide. In general, all frontal zones tend to be narrower near the ground than aloft, and warm frontal zones are usually wider than cold frontal zones.

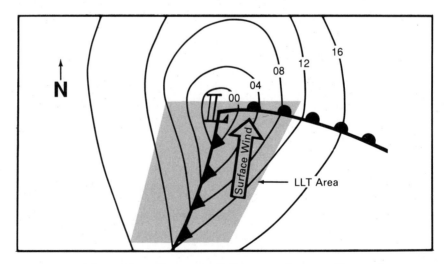

Figure 2-28. LLT area (shaded) near a typical wave cyclone over flat terrain.

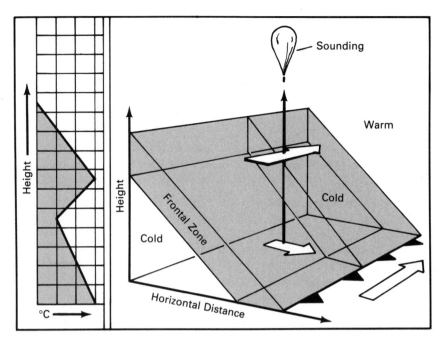

Figure 2-29. The characteristics of the transition zone in a typical front.

The frontal zone is always on the cold side of the line that represents the surface position of the front. The zone slopes upward over the cold air (regardless of the type of front). This configuration means that a sounding taken in the cold air would penetrate the frontal zone. A plot of temperature versus height from such a sounding is shown on the left side of figure 2-29. Note that the lower part of the sounding reflects the cold airmass while the upper part is representative of the warm airmass. The frontal zone appears as a stable layer (in this case, an inversion) between the airmasses. This is an important property of all frontal zones. They are not only zones of strong horizontal temperature changes, but also of strong vertical changes. So, wherever you find a frontal zone, you will also find a stable layer.

When a front develops, both horizontal and vertical wind shear develop across the sloping stable layer. This is shown as a shift in direction of the wind arrows across the cold front in figure 2-29. An important rule here is the stronger the horizontal temperature change across the front, the stronger the vertical wind shear in the frontal zone.

Having identified a frontal zone as a stable layer and the source of both vertical and horizontal wind shear, an important question is, "when will a front produce a LLWS hazard for a particular location?" The answer is a matter of geometry. That is, we must estimate where the lower part of the frontal zone is (or will be) relative to the airport of interest. As illustrated in figure 2-29, the cold frontal zone is moving in the direction of the low-level winds in the cold air. The associated LLWS will arrive over an area after the passage of the cold front. Since the cold frontal passage is usually well defined by a temperature fall and wind shift, the subsequent arrival of the frontal zone and LLWS can be accurately estimated.

The location of a LLWS region with a warm front is more of a problem. In contrast to a cold front, the warm frontal zone precedes the surface position of the warm front. Therefore, the precursors of LLWS (wind shift, temperature rise, etc.) are not present as they are with the cold front.

The critical period for a low-level wind shear hazard will be longer for a warm front for two reasons. The slope of a warm front is less than that of a cold front and the warm front is slower. Typical critical periods for LLWS are one to three hours after a cold frontal passage and up to six hours before the passage of a warm front.

SHALLOW CYCLONES

Low-level turbulence and wind shear in frontal zones is favored in shallow cyclones during the cooler part of the year. In contrast to deep, occluded cyclones, those cyclones that are in their initial stages of development may not extend 10,000 feet above the surface. Although these structures occur anywhere, they are particularly hazardous along the east coast of the U.S. (Chandler, 1986). An example is shown in figure 2-30. Surface winds (thin arrows) are northeasterly in the shallow cold airmass north of the warm front, and northwesterly in the cold air to the west of the cold front. In the overrunning warm air aloft, winds are strong southwesterly (broad arrow). Strong LLWS and moderate to severe turbulence are often found aloft and near the surface along frontal zones.

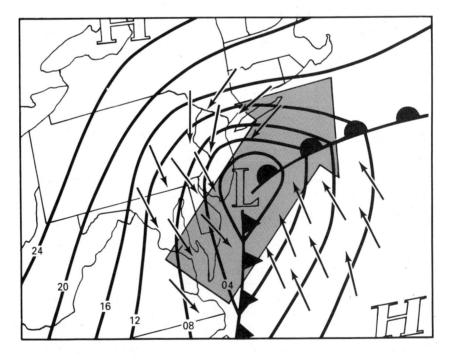

Figure 2-30. Wind shear in a shallow cyclone. Broad arrow represents flow above the cyclone while thin arrows show flow around the low near the surface. Critical LLWS and turbulence occur across frontal zones, especially in areas where surface and upper airflow are opposed.

An example of the shear problem caused by this type of situation is illustrated in the following report.

> During a two hour period in the early evening of January 4, 1971, there were nine missed approaches to runway 04R at JFK. Several other aircraft reported difficulties on takeoff. During the same period, an accident occurred at La Guardia Airport where one of the probable causes was stated as "The failure of the pilot to recognize the wind shear problem and compensate for it." The cause of the wind shear was an approaching warm front associated with northeasterly winds at the surface changing to south southwesterly winds within 1,000 feet of the ground. IFR conditions prevailed with low ceilings, poor visibilities, and rain or drizzle.
> (Kraus, 1972; Chambers, 1973).

Flight conditions in strong wind shear are aggravated when LLT is also present. The coexistence of turbulence and wind shear in frontal zones is related to the speed of movement of the front and the frontal strength, measured as the temperature difference across the frontal zone. These characteristics have been summarized quantitatively in a nomogram developed by Northwest Airlines. (Figure 2-31) For example, the nomogram indicates that if the frontal speed is 20 knots and the temperature difference across the front is 20°F, then both wind shear and turbulence are expected in the frontal zone. However, if the speed is only 10 knots, and the temperature difference is 15°F, only wind shear is expected.

ELEVATED STABLE LAYERS

Besides macroscale frontal zones, stable layers associated with other macroscale circulations are often found above the ground in, or just above, the boundary layer. These layers are generally called **elevated stable layers**. Many are horizontal, not strongly sheared, and smooth. However, there are situations when ascent or descent through elevated stable layers will expose you to unexpected wind shear and turbulence. The effects are more often brief and of minor consequence, but they occasionally contribute to serious flight problems.

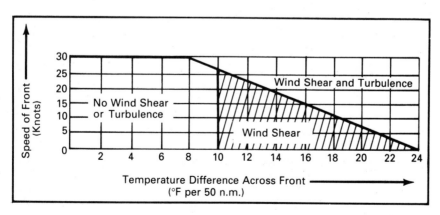

Figure 2-31. Nomogram for the estimation of wind shear and turbulence in a front. Reprinted, with permission, from Northwest Airlines.

Many, non-frontal, elevated stable layers are found in or near high pressure regions. One example we have already seen is the capping stable layer atop the convective boundary layer. Usually a high pressure system is responsible for the accompanying fair weather conditions.

Another situation is found along the west coasts of continents in mid-latitudes where high pressure dominates during the warmer months of the year. For example, along the California coast, a very strong and persistent elevated inversion is found at altitudes of 500 to 1,500 feet MSL, especially in summer. Figure 2-32 shows a temperature sounding through this so called "marine inversion." The inversion caps fog and low stratus clouds in the cool maritime air in the boundary layer. Near the coast and over coastal waters the lower few hundred feet of the inversion are characterized by vertical wind shear. Over the coastal waters of Northern California, the shear effect in the elevated inversion is often aggravated by the presence of a layer of strong northerly winds just above the inversion base. This and other similar low-level jets are discussed further in the next section.

Elevated stable layers extending over thousands of square miles are also found over shallow cold airmasses which occupy high pressure regions north of the macroscale cyclone track. When one of these cold airmasses moves out of a mountainous area, cold air will often remain trapped in the valleys as warmer air moves in aloft. A strong, elevated inversion typically will be found just below the mountain peaks. (Figure 2-33) If strong winds are present at and above the mountain peaks, large vertical wind shears will exist in the inversion between the weak, cold airflow in the valleys and warmer air flowing across the mountains.

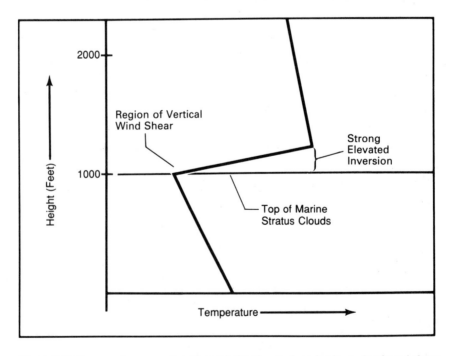

Figure 2-32. Temperature sounding through the elevated marine inversion found along the California coast in the warmer months of the year.

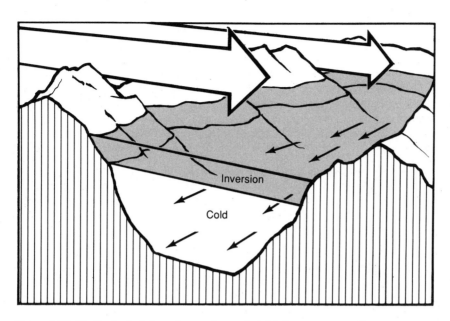

Figure 2-33. Vertical wind shear in an elevated stable layer over a valley.

MESOSCALE CIRCULATIONS

In this section, we will consider the production of LLT and wind shear by mesoscale circulations. Mesoscale circulations refer to organized patterns or systems of airflow that are of relatively small dimensions (less than 1,000 n.m.). As used here, these circulation systems affect mainly the boundary layer. Discussions of low-level effects of thunderstorm and mountain wave effects are reserved for later chapters.

Many of the turbulence and wind shear hazards experienced with the mesoscale circulations discussed here will not be important by themselves. However, flight hazards may increase significantly when those circulations occur in potentially dangerous combinations with mountainous terrain and/or low ceilings and visibilities.

Another potential flight problem with mesoscale circulations is the unexpected mesoscale-induced bump or shear that complicates your flying. These occurrences are often a surprise because weather reports are so widely separated. A glance at a few pieces of weather data or at a weather map will not provide very detailed information about the presence or intensity of a mesoscale system, much less the microscale turbulence and wind shear it produces. Therefore, a better knowledge of the causes, typical structures, and behavior of mesoscale circulations is needed to fill in the gaps in the observational system.

LOW-LEVEL JETS

Low-level jet streams are narrow, horizontal bands of relatively strong winds located 500 to 5,000 feet above the surface. Speeds range from 20 knots to about 80 knots. Low-level jets are typically several hundred miles long and a few hundred miles wide. They are an elevated source of wind shear and often occur in a stable boundary layer.

NOCTURNAL JETS

Many low-level jet streams that occur over land are nighttime phenomena. A well known nocturnal jet is found in the warmer part of the year over the west Texas, Oklahoma, and Kansas region. An example is shown on the left of figure 2-34. In that figure, the broad arrow indicates the jet axis. Thin lines are surface isobars.

The jet is produced by nighttime cooling of the higher terrain to the west. This strengthens the east-west pressure difference at the top of the boundary layer with lower pressures in the west. This effect is combined with the general tendency for vertical shear to increase in a nocturnal inversion. The result is a southerly low-level jet in the region.

Before sunrise, the jet attains maximum speeds of 25 to 40 knots at heights between 650 and 1,500 feet AGL. At the time of peak development of the low-level jet, significant vertical shear is common at levels just below and just above the level of the maximum wind.

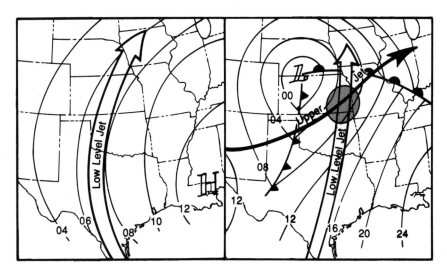

Figure 2-34. Two low-level jet stream situations over Texas and the southern plains. The pattern on the left corresponds with the common nocturnal, low-level jet. The pattern on the right is associated with severe convective weather in the shaded area.

After sunrise, radiational heating and convection destroy the low-level jet. Early morning and afternoon soundings of temperature and wind speed near the jet axis are quite similar to those shown in figure 2-23, except that maximum speeds at the top of the nocturnal inversion are significantly stronger with the low-level jet.

The low-level nocturnal jet described here is often present under fair weather conditions, but there are exceptions, especially in the spring. Perhaps the most dramatic situation is when the jet occurs with a developing cyclone over the Great Plains. A common severe weather pattern is shown on the right of figure 2-34. In this case, the low-level jet stream supplies moist, unstable air from the Gulf of Mexico for the severe weather in the shaded area. The low-level southerly flow is accompanied by strong west winds aloft. The high frequency of low-level jets and cyclones in Texas, Oklahoma, and Kansas in the spring is the primary reason for the frequent occurrence of severe weather in that area.

Low-level jets also occur ahead of cold fronts in other geographical areas of the U.S., resulting in similar, but less frequent, severe weather activity. The formation of those low-level jets is related more to the macroscale development of the cyclone rather than the local terrain.

When the low-level jet occurs in combination with thunderstorms, the potential for turbulence and wind shear increases markedly. The details of severe convection will be discussed in the next chapter.

COASTAL JETS

Low-level jet streams occur in many coastal areas of the world. As described earlier, a low-level jet caused by land-water temperature differences is commonly found in the elevated inversion just off the coast of Northern California (near 125°W). This northerly jet is present both day and night. Wind speeds as large as 50 knots have been observed and large vertical wind shears are often found near the inversion base, just above the tops of stratus or stratocumulus clouds commonly found in that area. Shear and occasional turbulence may be critical when operating in and out of airports along the coast and while flying near the coastal mountains. At San Francisco International Airport, remote wind sensors have been established on the coastal hills to help monitor the vertical shear for departing aircraft.

A northerly low-level jet of 15 to 30 knots occasionally develops over the east slopes of the Appalachians when cold air is pushed up against mountains. The process is called "cold air damming" and is associated with mesoscale coastal fronts discussed in the next section.

COASTAL FRONTS

A **coastal front** is a mesoscale airmass boundary that occurs in the late fall and winter between the Atlantic coast and the Appalachian Mountains. It is more frequent in the north where it has been called the "New England Coastal Front." The front develops when a high pressure center associated with a macroscale cold airmass moves eastward through New England or the Canadian Maritime provinces. Easterly flow on the south side of the high traps cold air next to the mountains. As seen in figure 2-35, the north-

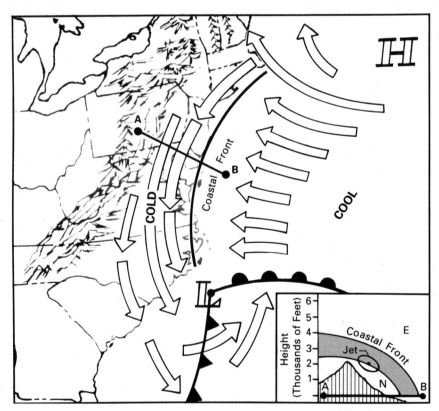

Figure 2-35. The mesoscale circulation near a New England coastal front. The inset shows a vertical cut through the front along line A-B. Wind shear is common in the frontal zone (shaded).

south coastal front separates warmer maritime air along the coast from very cold continental air along the east side of the mountains. The direction of surface airflow is shown with arrows. Horizontal temperature differences as large as 5°C or 10°C over a few miles are common in the frontal zone.

The inset in figure 2-35 shows a cross section through the coastal front along line A-B. The wind commonly shifts from a light northerly (N) flow at the surface to an easterly (E) flow above the front. The location of the northerly low-level jet is shown in the base of the transition zone. The wind shear in the frontal zone is often significant to aviation. Also, the front is usually accompanied by low clouds and precipitation (which may be freezing). The coastal front is of such small dimensions that it may not show up very well on normally available weather maps. The condition should be suspected when a cold high pressure area is in the position shown. It is often intensified by a developing cyclone that is located to the south along the coast.

LOCAL BREEZES

Local breezes are mesoscale circulations that are caused by horizontal temperature differences over distances of a few to a few hundred miles. The temperature differences, in turn, are caused by differences in the heating and cooling of the surface by radiation. Local breezes include sea/land breezes, mountain/valley breezes, and slope circulations. Because they depend on radiational heating and cooling, most local breezes are better developed in mid-latitudes in the warmer part of the year. In low latitudes, they may be well-developed in any season. Their dependence on radiational heating and cooling causes directions and intensities of the circulations to be linked closely to local time of day.

Low-level turbulence and wind shear are caused by interactions of local breezes with terrain and by the development of mesoscale fronts and shear lines. A **shear line** is simply an elongated zone where winds of different speeds and/or directions converge at the surface. It is sometimes called a "convergence zone." The importance of a shear line is the presence of horizontal wind shear and updrafts due to convergence. A shear line is often the source of LLT. If there is a temperature difference across the shearline, it is identified as a mesoscale front. In that case, vertical wind shear is present in the frontal zone.

SEA BREEZE

Along coastlines, daytime heating brings land areas to higher temperatures than nearby water surfaces. The pressure falls over the land, establishing a horizontal pressure gradient. Often, this pressure difference is so small that you won't see it in the isobar patterns on a surface analysis chart. However, it will frequently be seen as a difference in altimeter settings between coastal and inland airports. In any event, the pressure difference will be large enough to cause cool air to begin moving across the coastline in late morning. This is the **sea breeze**. In the sea breeze (and other circulations of this scale and smaller), Coriolis force is usually much less important than the horizontal pressure gradient force and frictional forces. Therefore, the wind tends to blow directly from high to low pressure.

The sea breeze continues to intensify during the day, reaching typical speeds of 10 to 20 knots in mid- or late afternoon and decreasing thereafter. At the peak of its development, the sea breeze is usually 1,500 to 3,000 feet deep and capped by a **return flow** that is weaker and deeper than the sea breeze. (Figure 2-36) The combined sea breeze and return flows are called the **sea breeze circulation**.

The sea breeze circulation is sometimes made visible by dramatic differences in visibility at various altitudes. For example, over some urbanized coastlines, clear marine air moves inland at low levels with the sea breeze, while the return flow aloft is made visible by the offshore movement of polluted urban air. Within the sea breeze, turbulence and wind shear usually are not strong, except possibly near rough terrain and near the sea breeze front.

SEA BREEZE FRONT
The boundary between the cool, inflowing marine air and the warmer air over land is often narrow and well-defined. This feature is known as the **sea breeze front**. (Figure 2-37) The frontal location is often identifiable by differences in visibilities between the moist and dry airmasses, and/or a broken line of cumulus clouds along the front.

Warm air is lifted in a narrow zone by the front. If there is weak convection, it is strengthened by this frontal lifting. The most turbulent part of the sea breeze front is a few hundred feet wide with updrafts of a few hundred feet per minute, occasionally reaching 700 to 1,000 f.p.m.

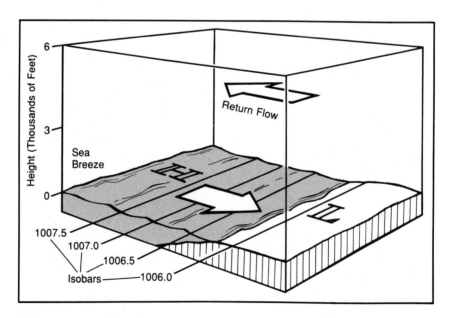

Figure 2-36. Sea breeze circulation. Sea level pressure pattern is shown by isobars labeled in millibars (mb).

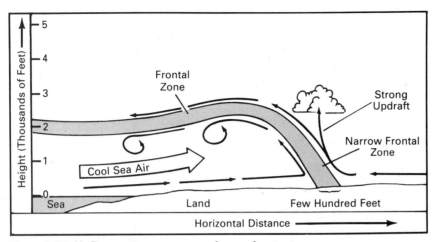

Figure 2-37. Air flow patterns near a sea breeze front.

The narrow sea breeze frontal zone is steep close to the ground with slopes of 1:15 or more. The slope decreases and the front becomes relatively flat over the marine air on its seaward side. Significant shears show up as rapid changes in speed and/or direction across the frontal zone. Vertical shears through the frontal zone at the top of the marine air may cause shearing-gravity wave activity.

The sea breeze front moves inland more slowly than the winds behind it. Frontal speeds vary over a wide range (2 to 15 knots) depending on macroscale wind conditions and terrain. In some areas, the inland movement of the front is limited to a few miles by coastal mountains. In contrast, over regions with broad coastal plains, the front can move a hundred miles or more inland during the course of the day.

Interactions between sea breeze fronts may produce strong shear lines, sometimes well inland from the water. This is especially true with certain coastline shapes and favorable distributions of coastal mountains and hills. One example is the convergence of sea breezes from both sides of the Florida Peninsula. A similar convergence of sea breezes, although on a smaller scale, occurs over Cape Cod.

Near coastal hills or mountains, gaps in the terrain will allow the sea breeze front to move farther inland in those areas. Isolated hills may split the sea breeze into two parts which then move around the barrier and converge on its inland side forming a shear line. Two well-known examples of this are the San Fernando and Elsinore Convergence Zones in Southern California. (Figure 2-38) LLT in convergence zones is often strengthened by convection.

LAND BREEZE

After sunset, the land surface near a coastline cools much more rapidly than the nearby water surface. This causes the pressure gradient across the coast to reverse so that the lower pressure is offshore. The low-level flow which begins to move from land to sea under the influence of this pressure difference is called the **land breeze**. (Figure 2-39) The **land breeze circulation** is made up of a ground level breeze and an oppositely directed

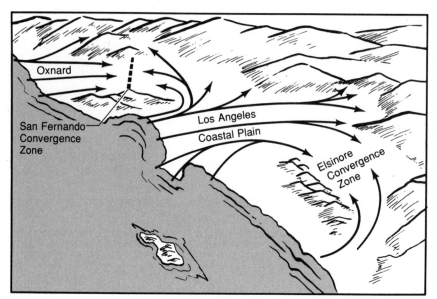

Figure 2-38. Convergence zones created as the sea breeze splits around topographical barriers.

return flow aloft, similar to the sea breeze circulation. In fact, the return flow is characteristic of all thermally driven circulations, although it may not be very obvious at times.

The land breeze continues to strengthen throughout the night, reaching its greatest intensity about sunrise. Because of the strong stability typical of nighttime conditions over land, the depth of the land breeze circulation is considerably less than that of the sea breeze, normally reaching only a few hundred feet above the surface.

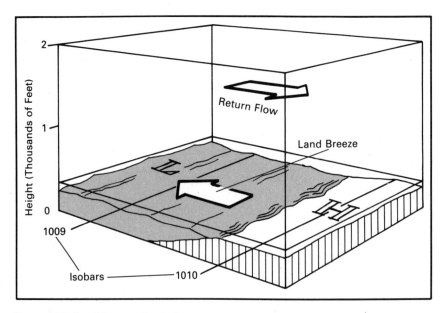

Figure 2-39. Land breeze circulation.

The land breeze is normally weaker than the sea breeze. Typical maximum speeds reach five knots. The land breeze may be significantly stronger if there is a mountain range paralleling the coast. In that case, the offshore flow is combined with the nighttime downslope flow from the mountains. LLWS can develop under such conditions.

A land breeze "front" is not as well documented as the sea breeze front because it occurs over water. However, in many coastal areas a shear line is found offshore at night. The location of this shear line can vary from 5 n.m. or less to over 100 n.m. from the coast. The actual distance will depend on the strength of the land breeze. If the water is warm, the convergence zone may be identified by a line of convective clouds or thunderstorms.

Noticeable land and sea breeze circulations are not restricted to ocean coastlines. For example, land and lake breezes are generated by both Lake Superior and Lake Tahoe. The strength of such breezes is proportional to the areas of the water surfaces and the land-water temperature difference.

VALLEY BREEZE

As noted in the discussion of dry convection, thermal activity is intensified over high terrain. This occurs during the day in fair weather conditions because hills and mountains act as "raised heat sources." Air over the high terrain heats up more than the air at the same level over nearby valley areas. Similar to the sea breeze, a horizontal difference in temperatures causes a horizontal pressure gradient with the lower pressures over the mountains. Air flows toward the slopes of the warmer mountain. The hillside deflects the air, producing an **upslope** or "anabatic" wind. As expected, a return flow is found above the mountain. (Figure 2-40)

If the mountainside is part of a valley, the upslope flow may be part of a larger scale **valley breeze** which is also directed toward higher terrain. (Figure 2-41) Above the mountain tops, a weak return flow known as an "anti-valley wind" is found. Together with the valley breeze, this is called the **valley breeze circulation**.

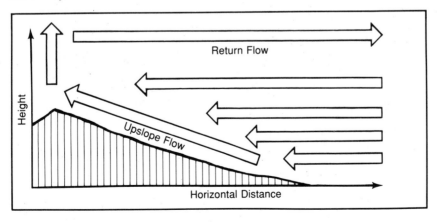

Figure 2-40. Upslope circulation.

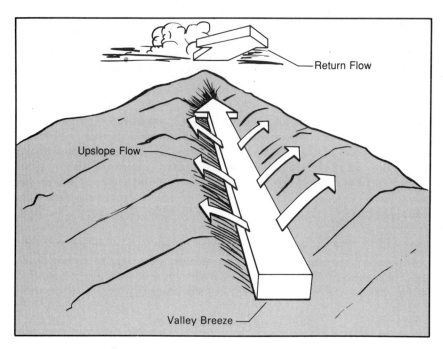

Figures 2-41. Valley breeze circulation.

The precise time an upslope or valley flow begins depends on local sunrise. The time of local sunrise is determined not only by latitude and time of year, but also by the depth and orientation of the valley. In many valleys, upslope flow begins on one side, while the other side is still in shadow. The circulation persists longer on sun-facing slopes.

Usually upslope and valley breezes begin a few hours after sunrise reaching their maximum in mid-afternoon. Typical up-valley wind speeds reach 5 to 20 knots with the maximum winds occurring a few hundred feet above the surface.

Updrafts due to upslope flow can exceed 500 f.p.m. if the terrain slopes are steep (greater than about 1:2). This is especially true along sun-facing slopes with the development of narrow thermals in an unstable boundary layer. LLT is also favored where a valley narrows, changes orientation, or intersects a side canyon.

Strong winds in the atmosphere above the mountain peaks may disturb valley and slope circulations depending on the direction and speed of the upper winds and the orientation and depth of the valley. When wind speeds above the mountains exceed about 15 knots, irrespective of their direction, the valley circulation is affected. Gustiness in the valley increases when strong winds aloft are carried down into the valley via mechanical mixing and/or by afternoon convection.

Over snow-covered terrain, heating of the high slopes is minimized due to the reflection of solar radiation by the snow. Therefore, over bare slopes, the daytime upslope flow stops at the snow line. However, if the hillsides are tree covered, this does not necessarily occur. If the tree tops are snow-free, they absorb solar radiation and can produce a well-defined upslope circulation despite the presence of snow on the ground.

MOUNTAIN BREEZE

At night, when the high terrain cools off, the pressure gradient reverses and **downslope** or "katabatic" winds develop along the hillsides. (Figure 2-42) On the larger scale of the valley, a mountain breeze blows down the valley together with return flow, or "anti-mountain wind," above the mountain tops. This configuration is known as the **mountain breeze circulation**.

Just as upslope and valley breezes are intensified by convection, cold dense air sinking down the slopes strengthens the downslope and mountain breezes. These are sometimes called **drainage flows**.

The mountain breeze should not be confused with the Bora, a larger scale katabatic wind that is capable of producing hurricane-strength winds in some parts of the world. The Bora and related winds will be discussed in Chapter 5.

As with the valley breeze, the strength of the circulation is determined by the size, depth, orientation of the valley, and the steepness of the slopes. Prior to sunrise, speeds of 5 to 15 knots are common. It is not unusual to find greater speeds (exceeding 25 knots) at the mouth of the valley. Maximum mountain wind speeds will occur some distance above the surface because of frictional influences.

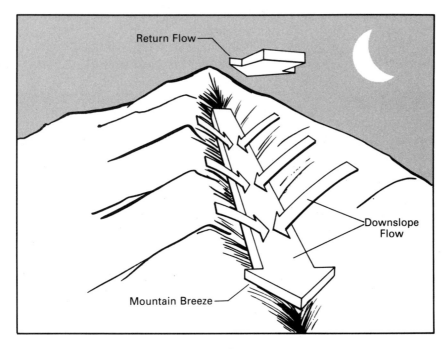

Figure 2-42. Downslope or katabatic wind flow.

The stability of the boundary layer can produce LLWS in connection with mountain breezes, especially if there are shallow drainage winds from nearby slopes. Strong drainage flows are common in mountainous areas with permanent snow and ice fields. Where bare ice slopes are many miles long as in Antarctica, drainage winds can attain speeds of more than 50 knots with severe LLWS and LLT.

In his paper describing the experiences of Lufthansa pilots, (Dreyling, 1973) lists some "critical airports" where LLWS is relatively frequent and contributes to "turbulent approaches." The LLWS in these cases is caused by the common occurrence of stable layers, the influence of the local terrain on the large scale airflow, and/or drainage winds. The airports listed are Anchorage, Tokyo, San Francisco, Buenos Aires, Athens, Genoa, Madrid, Geneva, Zurich, Milan, Prague, and Munich.

In a similar paper describing British Overseas Airways Corporation (BOAC) experiences, Chambers (1973) discusses the combined influence of the nocturnal inversion, drainage flow, and the land breeze on low-level wind shear. He illustrates his concern with the following report from a BOAC Captain of a LLWS experience at Kingston, Jamaica.

> "On arrival at Kingston (2330 local time) on 4 January 1973 the surface wind was given as 270/07, so I went downwind for runway 29. At 1500 feet, the wind was 085 degrees at 18 knots and this persisted down to 100 feet when we entered turbulence and the IAS increased by 25 knots. The tower wind on landing was 270/08. Similar conditions existed two days previously when I found myself too high at final approach and overshot."

In this incident, not only was LLT encountered in the shear layer, but LLWS was 25 knots in the lowest 100 feet. You should compare this with the values given in figure 2-22 and note that the surface wind gave absolutely no indication of the existence of low-level wind shear.

SUMMARY

Low-level turbulence is probably the most complicated turbulence topic in this book. It is complicated because of the wide variety of possible interactions between the atmospheric boundary layer and the earth's surface, and because of the wide range of scales over which those interactions can take place. It is also complicated because LLT and wind shear can be produced outside the boundary layer by several processes that are initiated within the boundary layer.

However, these complications are not so great that we cannot find some unifying concepts. For example, we have seen that the production of LLT and wind shear depends primarily on three conditions: wind, stability, and surface roughness. These three items interact to produce turbulence directly (mechanical turbulence and thermals); to produce phenomena that may become turbulent (atmospheric gravity waves); or produce phenomena that are not turbulent, but are important flight hazards (strongly sheared stable layers). We have also seen that low-level turbulence and wind shear may be found in a wide variety of recognizable macro- and mesoscale circulations.

In order to assist you in understanding LLT, you have been introduced to several more conceptual models, including mechanically generated eddies, thermals, thermal waves, local breezes, fronts and frontal zones, shear lines, and turbulent wakes. These models, together with several rules of thumb and certain macroscale weather patterns favorable for LLT production, should help you anticipate and interpret occurrences of low-level turbulence and wind shear.

KEY TERMS

Adiabatic Layer
Boundary Layer
Capping Stable Layer
Coastal Front
Cold Front
Convergence Zone
Drainage Flow
Dry Convection
Dust Devil
Elevated Stable Layer
Entrainment
Friction
Frontal Zone
Horizontal Wind Shear
Local Breezes
Low-Level Jet
Low-Level Wind Shear (LLWS)
Mechanical Turbulence
Mixed Layer
Mountain/Valley Breeze
Nocturnal Stable Layer
Occluded Front
Pressure Gradient
Roughness
Sea Breeze Front
Sea/Land Breeze
Shear Line
Slope Breezes
Snow Devil
Stable Layer
Superadiabatic Layer
Thermals
Vertical Wind Shear
Warm Front
Wind Shear

CHAPTER QUESTIONS _____

1. Two different airports report identical surface observations at 1300 LST. Surface temperatures are both 86°F (30°C) winds are 8 knots. On approach to airport A, turbulence is encountered from 4,000 feet (AGL) to the ground. On approach to airport B, turbulence doesn't occur until passing through 3,000 feet AGL. Give a reasonable explanation. Draw a simple, but realistic sounding that supports your explanation.

2. Five accidents are listed in the section on wake turbulence. Explain very clearly why each of the first four aircraft encountered turbulence. Draw schematic diagrams showing the aircraft, their paths, the runways, and the probable trajectories of the vortices. Be sure you consider the role of the wind and the typical behavior of wake vortices.

3. In question 10 of Chapter 1, what is the intensity of LLWS.

4. Figure 1-16 summarizes a number of processes related to the production of LLT. What are the processes? What is missing?

5. Obtain a surface analysis chart with a well-defined surface warm front (preferably over level ground where there are plenty of surface and upper air data). Obtain a 700 mb chart for the same time. Find both speed and vector wind shears between the surface and the 700 mb level at the locations indicated by your instructor. If the shear you calculated was concentrated in the lowest 1,000 feet of the atmosphere, what intensity classification would you give LLWS?

6. Obtain surface and 850 mb analysis charts for a location where a well-defined sea breeze is present. Is there any evidence of the presence of vertical shear? Discuss. Repeat for an area with a well-defined mountain breeze.

7. Draw a perspective diagram of a warm front similar to figure 2-29. Make the slope of the front 1:200. Give the diagram the identical vertical exaggeration of the cold front in figure 2-29 (assume the cold front slope is 1:50). Make the warm frontal zone twice as wide. Use the diagram to explain why an airport under the influence of a warm front would be subjected to LLWS for a longer period than with a cold front.

8. Local study. Carefully document the most important forms of LLT and wind shear which occur in your local flying area. Use a local aeronautical chart to illustrate locations. Don't forget the influence of obstacles on and near the airport during strong winds. From your own experience, your knowledge of meteorology, and interviews with more experienced pilots and meteorologists, answer the questions: what? where? when? and why? Document all local rules of thumb, critical large scale weather conditions, and sources of information.

Chapter 3

TURBULENCE IN AND NEAR THUNDERSTORMS (TNT)

INTRODUCTION

In this chapter, we will examine the causes and characteristics of all types of **turbulence in and near thunderstorms (TNT)**. TNT includes turbulence and wind shear within thunderstorms, in the vicinity of thunderstorm tops and wakes, in downbursts and gust fronts.

Our concentration will be on turbulence related to cloudy convection versus the dry convection of the previous chapter. First, we briefly review the cloud formation process. Next, thunderstorm types, life cycles, circulations, and TNT are examined in detail. Finally, the discussion turns to the description of meso- and macroscale environments which favor thunderstorm development.

CLOUDY CONVECTION

Discussions of turbulence experiences among pilots do not proceed very far before the conversation turns to thunderstorms. Why? The reasons are many.

Although there are no extensive statistics for general aviation aircraft, it is estimated that about 30% of turbulence encountered by air carriers is due to thunderstorms (Dreyling, 1973). An important characteristic of thunderstorm turbulence is that it is more likely than other types to be of moderate intensity or greater. This flight hazard is made worse by IFR conditions commonly associated with thunderstorms and is reflected in accident statistics. For example, of 32 serious/fatal weather-related accidents involving air carriers from 1962 to 1984, 23 were related directly to thunderstorms (Rudich, 1986). In his book on *Thunderstorms and Airplanes,* Collins (1982) describes no less than 24 serious/fatal general aviation accidents caused by thunderstorms in a single year in the U.S.

While such statistics are impressive, personal experience provides a more dramatic statement of the problem. A study of thunderstorms with instrumented aircraft nearly 50 years ago provided the following postflight report after a particularly rough thunderstorm penetration at 15,000 feet.

> The pilot stated that "The jolt was so severe that I thought I had collided with another plane. I was unable to keep my hands on the controls, they banged around so much." Postflight analysis of the altitude record indicated that the aircraft entered an updraft which carried it from 14,800 feet to 20,000 feet in 70 seconds. This required an average climb rate of more than 4,400 f.p.m. The peak rate of climb was 6,200 f.p.m. Although the aircraft incurred no major structural damage, skin cracks of up to two inches in length were found on the horizontal stabilizer at the conclusion of the flight.

Without question, the thunderstorm offers the pilot a formidable turbulence hazard. Knowledge of thunderstorms is an important first step in avoiding, or at least, minimizing, the impact of thunderstorm turbulence. We are fortunate because, since "Project Thunderstorm" (Byers and Braham, 1949), enormous resources have been invested in the study of thunderstorms and other forms of convective weather. Efforts have been particularly intense in the last thirty years as satellites, radar, and other remote sensing instruments have been developed and improved. A well-known benefit of this research has been an increased knowledge of wind shear caused by downbursts. This information has resulted in a large amount of highly informative pilot training material on that particular thunderstorm hazard. (FAA, 1988; Kupcis, 1989). However, the downburst is only one important aspect of thunderstorm turbulence.

In the previous chapter, we examined the processes which cause dry (cloudless) convection. In this chapter, we continue to examine convective motions, only now we concentrate on **cloudy convection** which produces various forms of cumulus clouds. In order to better describe and explain TNT, it is necessary to begin by briefly reviewing the general process of convective cloud formation and growth.

CLOUD FORMATION

If an initially cloud-free, convective updraft contains a sufficient amount of water vapor, a cloud will form as the air rises. A brief explanation of this process is essential to the understanding many of the details of cloudy convection.

When the air contains the maximum amount of water vapor (a gas) it can hold, it is said to be in a state of **saturation**. A useful term for describing the degree of saturation of the air is **relative humidity**. It is expressed as a percent. For example, at saturation, the relative humidity is 100%; if the air contains only half the water vapor needed for saturation, the relative humidity is 50%. When the relative humidity exceeds 100%, excess water vapor changes to water or ice, forming a cloud.

The saturation point for a given mass of air depends primarily on the air temperature; that is, the capacity of air to hold water vapor is less at lower temperatures. Therefore, a cloud will form in an initially cloud-free, convective updraft because the air expands and cools adiabatically to saturation as it rises.

CLOUD GROWTH

The distinct appearance of cumuliform clouds reflects not only the saturation, but also the instability of the convective updraft. The characteristic flat bases of the clouds occur at the altitude where the rising, unstable air first reaches saturation, This is called the **convective condensation level**. (Figure 3-1) Above the convective condensation level, upward

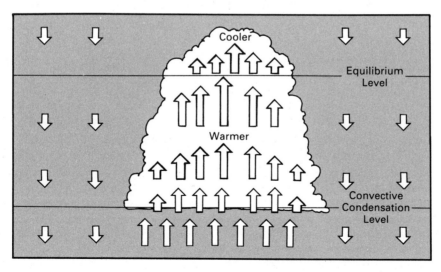

Figure 3-1. Schematic cross section of a growing cumulus cloud. Lengths of arrows are proportional to speeds of up and downdrafts. "Warmer" and "cooler" refer to the temperature of the updraft relative to the temperature outside the cloud at the same altitude.

moving air cools at the moist adiabatic lapse rate. You should recall that that rate is less than the dry adiabatic lapse rate because of the continued release of latent heat as the cloud forms. For this reason, an unstable updraft will often become more unstable (the vertical acceleration will increase) when the cloud begins to appear. This important influence of moisture on the intensity of convection is reflected in the extreme heights reached by cloudy convection. In many areas of the world, thunderstorms reach altitudes of more than 65,000 feet while over the hottest deserts, the extreme altitudes attained by dry convection are closer to 20,000 feet.

As shown in figure 3-1, above the convective condensation level, the cloudy updraft continues to accelerate upward. Clear air sinks around the cloud to compensate for the upward motion. Similar to dry thermals, the sinking is usually much weaker than the updrafts, typically taking place over a much wider area than the cloud. The updraft is similar to a jet of fluid pointed vertically. The strong shears between the updraft and the weak downdrafts outside the cloud produce turbulence scale eddies which are seen as cauliflower-like protuberances on the edges of the cumulus cloud.

The cloudy updraft continues its upward acceleration until it reaches an altitude where the updraft temperature is equal to the temperature of its surroundings. This is called the **equilibrium level**. Above that level, the air continues to rise, but decelerates because it is cooler than its surroundings. The top of the cloud will be at the level where the updraft speed decreases to zero. Because the cloud top is colder than its surroundings, it finally collapses and spreads out around the equilibrium level.

The upper limit of convective clouds depends strongly on the presence or absence of stable layers above the convective condensation level. A strong tropospheric inversion may stop the vertical growth of cumulus clouds at any stage. We have already discussed this effect in Chapter 2 in regard to fair weather cumulus clouds at the top of the boundary layer under a capping stable layer. Those cumuli last only a few minutes because the bases of the clouds and the equilibrium level are close together. The clouds are characterized by a diffuse appearance and shallow depths.

In cases where atmospheric stability changes with time, appearance of the cumulus clouds also changes. For example, as the ground is heated early in the day, increasing instability will transform a smooth layer of stratus clouds into a distinctively convective layer of stratocumulus. In contrast, as the ground cools and stability increases late in the day, convective activity decreases, and existing cumuli often spread out into a stratocumulus layer. (Figure 3-2)

Another example of limited cloud development is often found in a cold airmass following a cold frontal passage. Although the convection may be strong in these circumstances, the vertical development of the clouds is frequently limited by the stable layer near the top of the shallow cold airmass.

The extreme state of cloudy convection is evidenced by the presence a cumulonimbus cloud. (Figure 3-3) Here, the equilibrium level is frequently

Figure 3-2. Stratocumulus clouds form from cumulus as the cloud layer stabilizes. Photo courtesy of A. Rangno.

above the tropopause where the convection overshoots into the lower stratosphere. The smooth cirriform appearance of the upper part of the cloud reflects its very stable and cold environment and identifies the cloud as a cumulonimbus even before an anvil is fully formed. In fact, the entire cumulonimbus cloud provides a knowledgeable observer with a large amount of information about the orientation and intensity of its turbulent internal circulation. These and other details are presented in a later section.

DOWNDRAFTS

As the cloudy convection grows, downdrafts begin to develop within the cloud. These internal downdrafts are caused by precipitation and are significantly stronger than the sinking motions outside the cloud.

Figure 3-3. Cumulonimbus cloud with an anvil top behind a line of developing cumulus clouds. Photo courtesy of A. Rangno.

The downdraft begins to develop with the rapid growth of cloud particles in the updraft. This process is particularly efficient in that part of the cloud where temperatures are just below freezing. Cloud particles that are too heavy to be supported by the updraft begin to fall as snow then, at lower levels, as rain. Hail may also develop in response to the very strong updrafts.

The downdraft is produced as the precipitation drags air downward. In addition, negative buoyancy develops where dry air is mixed across the boundaries of the cloud. This causes evaporation of cloud and precipitation particles and cools the downdraft. As snow turns to rain in the lower levels, the melting contributes to the cooling of the downdraft. As we will see in the next section, this precipitation-induced downdraft is a major component of the life cycle of the thunderstorm and in the production of TNT.

THUNDERSTORM STRUCTURES

The thunderstorm represents the extreme of convection. By definition, a **thunderstorm** is a local storm invariably produced by a cumulonimbus cloud, and always accompanied by lightning and thunder. It normally produces strong wind gusts, heavy rain, and sometimes hail. It is usually of short duration, rarely over two hours for a single storm (Huschke, 1959).

This definition is based on surface observations. If we were to include airborne observations, we would add turbulence, wind shear, and icing.

Special weather observations are taken to mark the beginning and end of a thunderstorm, and to report significant changes in its intensity. Besides the standard coded information about sky condition, weather, visibility, pressure, temperature, and wind, evidence of the presence of thunderstorms is also found in the plain language remarks of surface weather reports. Some examples are given in the following sequence. An aircraft crashed in a downburst over the runway within about two minutes of the last report.

1555	SA	45 SCT 300-BKN 7 92/66/2515/995
1636	SP	E45 BKN 160 BKN 6TH /2812/991/T B35 3 MI W
		MOVG E OCNL LTGICCG
1655	RS	E30 BKN 160 BKN 300 OVC 1/4TRW+A
		82/68/3020G32/982/T B35 OHD MOVG E OCNL
		LTGCCCG RB43 AB50

Fortunately, cloudy convection is usually visible. We will take advantage of this fact throughout the chapter by stressing the relation between the visible characteristics of thunderstorms and TNT. In this regard, it is not too early to be reminded of a practical and very important rule of thumb related to thunderstorms: if a convective cloud reaches the cumulonimbus stage, it should be considered a thunderstorm, whether or not any other evidence of thunderstorm activity is present.

THUNDERSTORM TYPES

In order to understand turbulence production in and near thunderstorms, thunderstorm structure and development must first be understood. This requires a careful examination of thunderstorm models. The "models" used here are typical mid-latitude thunderstorm structures derived from detailed field studies using instrumented aircraft, radar, and mesonetworks of surface observations. These models may be looked upon as extensions of the simpler eddy and thermal models described in Chapters 1 and 2.

The current scientific literature identifies two basic thunderstorm types: an **airmass thunderstorm**, and a **severe thunderstorm**. From your initial studies in aviation meteorology you are most familiar with the airmass thunderstorm. A severe thunderstorm is differentiated from an airmass thunderstorm by its greater intensity, larger size, longer lifetime, and the severity of the weather it produces: wind gusts of 50 knots or more, hail 3/4" or more in diameter, and/or strong tornadoes.

The basic component of a thunderstorm is the **cell**; that is, the updraft region of the thunderstorm. Thunderstorms may exist as single cell, multicell, or supercell storms. A single cell airmass thunderstorm lasts less than an hour. In contrast, a **supercell** thunderstorm (always severe) lasts two hours or more. In some aviation meteorology texts, the supercell thunderstorm is also called a "steady state" thunderstorm.

A **multicell** storm is a compact cluster of thunderstorms. It is usually composed of airmass thunderstorm cells in different stages of development. These cells interact and cause the duration of the cluster to be much longer than any individual cell.

Multicell and, occasionally, supercell thunderstorms may be organized into large groups of thunderstorms known generally as **mesoscale convective systems**. These include squall lines and nearly circular clusters known as mesoscale convective complexes.

Some aviation meteorology texts and manuals refer to a "frontal thunderstorm." This phenomenon is described as more severe and longer lasting than the (single cell) airmass thunderstorm. It is often found along fronts and squall lines. The use of this terminology is somewhat ambiguous because it does not differentiate between what are now identified as multicell and supercell thunderstorms. It also omits reference to the organization of thunderstorms into areas as well as along lines. In order to avoid confusion, we will not use the term, "frontal thunderstorm."

Mesoscale convective systems and other macro- and mesoscale environments favorable for thunderstorm development will be discussed at the end of this chapter. First, the structure and life cycle of the thunderstorm cells will be examined together with the turbulence they produce.

AIRMASS THUNDERSTORM

The life cycle of a single cell airmass thunderstorm is illustrated in figure 3-4. The cycle is divided into three stages: cumulus, mature, and dissipating.

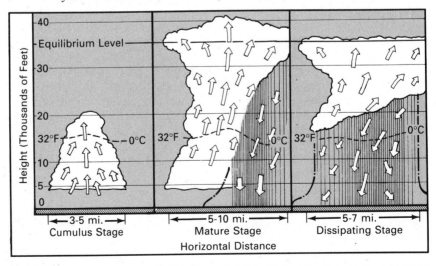

Figure 3-4. The three stages in the life cycle of a single cell, airmass thunderstorm (Doswell, 1982).

CUMULUS STAGE

When atmospheric moisture and instability are sufficient, the evolution of the thunderstorm cell will begin. In the initial, or **cumulus stage**, the circulation develops rapidly, reaching the next stage in about 15 minutes.

The cumulus stage is characterized by a rapidly growing **towering cumulus** cloud which is typically three to five miles in diameter. (Figure 3-4) An important change in the nature of the convection occurs as the cumulus stage develops; there is a marked increase in the scale of the convection. The size of the updraft is much larger than any individual thermal. This change can be observed in the decrease of the number of small cumuli in the immediate area of the towering cumulus. Smaller scale thermals are swept into the general cloud updraft in a pattern of convergence below the cloud base. Sinking around the cloud produces an unfavorable environment for the smaller clouds.

In the cumulus stage, air initially rises throughout the cloud, although the upward growth is much greater in some portions of the cloud than others. The cloud grows in an unsteady succession of upward bulges as thermals arrive at the top. These can be seen as turrets on the top of the cloud in figure 3-5. Variations in the strength of updrafts are also produced by turbulent mixing of cooler, drier air from outside the cloud. As the cloud continues to grow, precipitation develops, initiating a downdraft within the cloud late in the cumulus stage.

MATURE STAGE

As shown in figure 3-4, the mature stage begins when the precipitation-induced downdraft reaches the ground. Lightning and thunder begin as the thunderstorm cell grows to about 5-10 miles in diameter.

Figure 3-5. Towering cumulus cloud. Note growing turrets at the top of the cloud.

As the rain-cooled air approaches the ground, it spreads out, causing horizontal gusts which often extend beyond the edges of the thunderstorm cell. Both downbursts and gust fronts are related to the downdraft. They will be described in detail in later sections.

The circulation of the thunderstorm cell is well-organized in this stage. The warm updraft and the precipitation-induced downdraft exist side-by-side. The downdraft reaches its greatest velocity near the base of the cloud, while the updraft reaches its maximum speeds near the equilibrium level in the upper part of the cumulonimbus.

The top of the mature cell reaches and overshoots its equilibrium level, usually within a few thousand feet of the tropopause. Above that level, upward motions decrease and the cloud spreads out horizontally, finally forming the well-known anvil shape. (Figure 3-6) The anvil may not be developed in the early part of the mature stage, but the cirriform appearance of the cloud top is usually identifiable.

When upward motions are very strong at the top of the storm, overshooting tops produce cumuliform bulges on the top of the anvil. This effect is shown schmetically in figure 3-4 and visually in figure 3-6.

Although the beginning of the mature stage of the airmass thunderstorm cell is indicated by the arrival of precipitation and wind gusts at the ground, there are exceptions. For example, a developing cumulus cloud may not reach the mature stage, even if it grows to the point that precipitation is produced within the cloud. In this case, a shower and an associated downdraft can occur without any lightning or thunder.

Another exception to the model of the mature stage is found in the arid regions of the western U.S., especially during summer. The dry surface air

Figure 3-6. The cumulonimbus cloud in the background is moving to the left. Note the overshooting tops. In the foreground are growing cumuli.

in that region causes thunderstorm bases to be as high as 10,000 feet AGL or more. In these storms, lightning and thunder occur, but precipitation may evaporate completely before reaching the ground. Only a veil of precipitation known as **virga** may be observed immediately below the cloud base. (Figure 3-7) Despite the lack of rain, the associated downdraft and gusty winds can still produce flight hazards at the surface. Also, this combination of lightning and gusty winds in the absence of precipitation is often a cause of forest fires. These variations on the ideal airmass thunderstorm model will be discussed in more detail in a later section in connection with the formation of downbursts.

DISSIPATING STAGE

Thirty minutes or so after its initiation, the single cell airmass thunderstorm reaches the dissipating stage. As shown in the right hand panel of figure 3-4, precipitation and downdrafts have spread throughout the lower levels of the thunderstorm cell cutting off the updraft. Since the source of energy for thunderstorm growth is the supply of heat and moisture from the surface layer, the loss of the updraft spells the end of the storm. Precipitation decreases and the entire thunderstorm cloud takes on a stratiform appearance, gradually dissipating. Because the anvil top is an ice cloud, it often lasts longer than the rest of the cell. Therefore, an observation of an anvil alone may not be conclusive as to the stage or even the presence of a thunderstorm.

Figure 3-7. Virga below a thunderstorm base is an indication that precipitation is evaporating before it reaches the ground. Photo courtesy of A. Rangno.

The lifetime of a single cell airmass thunderstorm is typically less than an hour. But odds are that you have encountered thunderstorms that have lasted much longer. How can this be? In such cases, the explanation is that you were actually observing a multicell thunderstorm or a supercell thunderstorm, both of which last longer and affect larger areas than an airmass thunderstorm

MULTICELL THUNDERSTORM

The **multicell thunderstorm** is a tight cluster of thunderstorm cells. It occurs when individual cells interact with each other and with the environment to cause new cells to form as old cells dissipate.

The multicell has its roots in the downdraft caused by precipitation in a mature thunderstorm. A sharp boundary known as a gust front forms when the downdraft spreads out beyond the edges of the thunderstorm. The gust front separates cool, gusty downdraft air from the air outside the storm. This mesoscale version of a cold front is particularly well-defined when it is formed by the outflow from more than one thunderstorm cell.

The strongest portion of the gust front typically moves several miles out ahead of the thunderstorms; that is, in the direction the storm cells are moving. (Figure 3-8) As a rule, the cells move with the velocity of the average wind through the troposphere. The 700 mb wind speed and direction can be used for a rough estimate of that average.

As shown in figure 3-8, the updraft usually enters the storm from either the front or the right side of the cell (looking in the direction of the cell motion). The updraft is located just above the gust front at low levels,

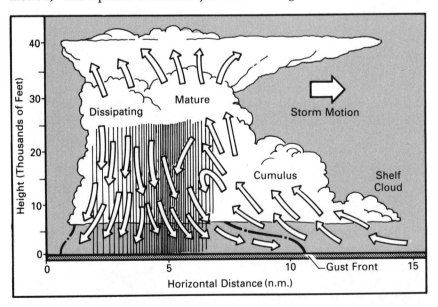

Figure 3-8. Multicell thunderstorm with cells in various stages of development. Arrows indicate airflow. The vertical lines on the left indicate precipitation. The boundaries of cool, downdraft air are shown by heavy dashed lines below the thunderstorm base. Note, the right hand boundary is the gust front.

slanting upward toward the back of the storm. The downdraft is generated in the precipitation area of the mature cell in the rear.

New cells develop as the gust front systematically lifts unstable air. At the same time, the gust front is maintained by a supply of cool air from the downdrafts of several mature and dissipating cells. This process of cell regeneration explains why the multicell thunderstorm influences a larger area and lasts longer than a single cell airmass thunderstorm.

Figure 3-9 shows visual evidence of both the downdraft and the updraft. The primary thunderstorm downdraft is seen as a **rainshaft** under the cloud, while a smooth **shelf cloud** is located where the updraft is entering the growing cell just above the thunderstorm outflow.

As noted above, the movement of an individual storm cell will be in the direction and with the speed of the average wind through the depth of the cell. However, the cluster of cells that makes up the multicell storm will not necessarily move in the same direction. The motion of the clusters will be toward the updraft, where new cells are forming. This is often to the right of the cell motion.

Multicell storms vary widely in intensity. They can produce severe convective weather when they are organized into mesoscale convective systems. These structures will be discussed in the last section of this chapter.

Figure 3-9. The smooth arch-shaped cloud feature is the shelf cloud where the updraft is entering the storm. Near the ground, cool air is flowing out from the downdraft area of the thunderstorm, indicated by the rainshaft in the background. Photo copyright C. Melquist.

SUPERCELL THUNDERSTORM

While the multicell thunderstorm will occasionally produce severe weather, the supercell almost always produces one or more of the extremes of convective weather: very strong horizontal wind gusts, large hail, and tornadoes. The difference in the frequency of severe weather associated with these two thunderstorm types is due primarily to differences in their thunderstorm structure.

The supercell storm can occur almost anywhere in mid-latitudes, but the favored area is in the southern Great Plains of the U.S., in spring. This is because the supercell requires extreme instability and a special combination of boundary layer and high-level wind conditions that are most frequently found over Texas, Oklahoma, and Kansas at that time of year.

The internal structure of the supercell is more complicated than either the single cell or multicell thunderstorms. This complication is, in fact, what makes the supercell large, intense, and long-lasting. Specifically, the supercell forms in an environment that tilts and twists the thunderstorm updraft. In order to illustrate the details of this airflow, it is necessary to use a three dimensional model of the storm. (Figure 3-10)

The updraft enters the storm with the low-level flow from the southeast. The air rises in a strong, steady updraft which slants upward toward the back of the thunderstorm (toward the northwest in this case). Overshooting tops, indicated by bulges on the top of the anvil, show the location of the updraft at that level. Under the influence of the strong westerly winds at upper levels, the former updraft, now mainly horizontal, twists toward the east where it exits the thunderstorm through the anvil.

A major precipitation-induced downdraft occurs north of the updraft where the rainshaft can be seen in figure 3-10. Another downdraft (not visible) also spreads around to the west of the updraft as the supercell develops. The gust fronts caused by these two downdrafts are indicated by the heavy dashed lines at the surface. The "flanking line," which parallels the gust

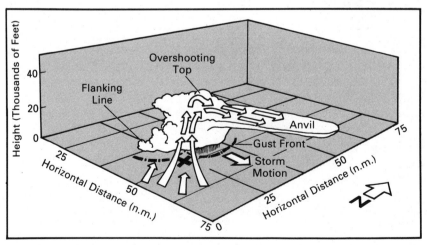

Figure 3-10. Perspective diagram of a supercell thunderstorm. For clarity, only the updraft is shown. The direction of movement of the supercell is to the east in this example.

front to the southwest of the updraft, is composed of growing cumulus towers.

There are two important differences between the structures of the single cell and the supercell. First, the supercell is much larger and, second, its updrafts and precipitation-induced downdrafts remain separated. (Figure 3-10) The large scale wind field in which the supercell is embedded is the reason for this separation. The winds change from surface southerlies to upper westerlies. Because of this vertical shear, the precipitation-induced downdraft occurs where it cannot interfere with the updraft as happens in the airmass cell. This structure allows the supercell to develop a strong, steady updraft. This is the reason why supercells last longer and reach a much greater size and intensity than airmass thunderstorm cells.

The horizontal separation of vertical drafts in a supercell can be better appreciated when observing the storm from the ground. Consider an observer looking at a supercell from the southeast (point X in figure 3-10). The view reveals the cloud features shown in figure 3-11.

Below the cloud to the northwest (right side), the downdraft area is indicated by precipitation. In the southwest (left side) is the rain-free base of the flanking line. The area of the storm immediately to the west (middle) is very close to the main updraft. As illustrated in the diagram, in that area, a portion of the rain free base of the clouds may appear lower in what is called a "wall cloud." Significant rotation of this cloud is often seen. In fact, it is the location in the severe supercell where the strongest tornadoes occur.

Supercells may occur in isolation or in mesoscale convective systems with multicells and other supercells. These large lines and clusters of thunderstorms will be discussed in a later section.

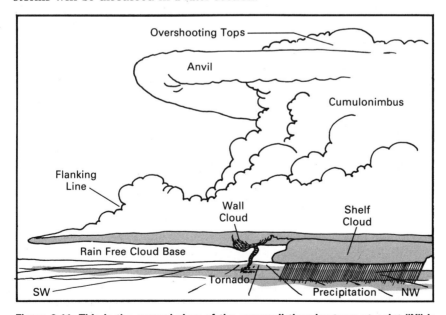

Figure 3-11. This is the ground view of the supercell thunderstorm at point "X" in figure 3-10. This view shows the anvil, the main storm tower, the flanking line, and expected weather under the storm. (Doswell, 1985)

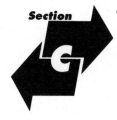

THUNDERSTORM TURBULENCE

The development of a thunderstorm can be viewed as an explosive instability in an initially undisturbed environment. Within the thunderstorm, air moves both rapidly upward, where it spreads out at the base of the stratosphere, and rapidly downward, where it spreads out near the ground. These vertical drafts produce turbulence not only within the storm, but also outside, as the vertical drafts interact with the surrounding air.

In the following paragraphs, we will describe and explain that turbulence as it occurs over a variety of scales, ranging from large updrafts and downdrafts to turbulent eddies smaller than the wingspan of your aircraft. The preceding review of thunderstorm structure has provided important background for our examination of TNT, and we will refer to it often. For convenience, the broad topic of TNT has been broken down into discussions of turbulence and wind shear in the thunderstorm, below the thunderstorm base, and outside, but near the thunderstorm.

IN THE THUNDERSTORM

In this section, we are concerned with turbulence caused by the strong up- and downdrafts within the thunderstorm cloud boundaries. It is the most frequent and, typically, the most intense TNT (although turbulence below the cloud may have more disastrous consequences). Furthermore, it is made worse because it occurs in IFR conditions with heavy rain, hail, icing, and lightning. The combination of these hazards increases the possibility of disorientation and loss of control, major factors in many fatal general aviation accidents in thunderstorms (Collins, 1982). Examples of such encounters are given below.

> Cessna 182. No injuries. Substantial damage. Thunderstorm reported at site. Aircraft in normal cruise at 4,000 feet AGL. Encountered turbulence, lost control, and entered spin upon entry into cloud. Recovery assisted by FSS. Precautionary landing. Wings and stabilizer damaged.

> Cessna 195. Four fatalities. Aircraft destroyed. Pilot continued flight into known area of thunderstorms, severe turbulence. Aircraft suffered overload fatigue, separated in flight.

> B-707. Two serious, eleven minor injuries. No aircraft damage. Aircraft encountered 4.5 minutes of severe turbulence in the vicinity of strong thunderstorm activity. Some passengers were not wearing seat belts.

> Electra. 85 fatalities. Aircraft destroyed. Attempted recovery from an unusual attitude caused by thunderstorm turbulence. Aircraft separated in flight. The right wing (in two pieces), the empennage, and the two left engines were recovered separately from the major part of the aircraft.

Turbulence inside thunderstorms has at least two different scales. Gusts occur on a relatively large scale comparable to the size of the major up- and downdrafts. Turbulence is also produced by smaller scale eddies caused by strong shears on the edges of the vertical drafts.

The effects of the variety of scales of thunderstorm turbulence on a particular aircraft depend on aircraft design and speed and where the aircraft is relative to the primary up- and downdrafts. For example, in the mature stage, updrafts are often exceptionally smooth in lower levels of the storm. An aircraft penetrating a strong thunderstorm updraft in straight and level flight might experience a rapid, but smooth altitude gain for ten seconds or so. But, as the aircraft crosses the boundary between an up- and downdraft, it could suddenly encounter a burst of the worst small scale turbulence imaginable. Disorientation becomes a distinct possibility if the aircraft is in a turn, and if there is hail, heavy rain, and frequent lightning.

In the next few paragraphs, we examine the development, location, and intensity of turbulence in an airmass thunderstorm, stage by stage.

CUMULUS STAGE

When a thunderstorm cell is in the cumulus stage, the primary turbulence inside the storm is due to the updraft. A rule of thumb based on the experiences of glider pilots is that, in its early stages, a towering cumulus cloud has an updraft just below the cloud base of at least 500 f.p.m.

Within the cloud, the speeds of the vertical gusts vary across the updraft. The primary updraft of a typical towering cumulus usually occupies less than 50% of the cloud area and is characterized by sharp edges. It is neither steady nor smooth in the cumulus stage because of varying intensities of individual thermals carried into the cloud by the larger scale updraft, and because of the diluting effects of cooler outside air mixed into the sides of the cloud.

The updrafts intensify with height within the growing cloud. Maximum updraft speeds are found in the growing turrets near the top of the thunderstorm.

MATURE STAGE

In the mature stage of the thunderstorm, the maximum updrafts in the cell are found in the upper part of the cloud at the equilibrium level; that is, near the tropopause. Because of the rapid rate of rise of the cloud tops, aircraft flying just below the tropopause are occasionally surprised with a strong burst of turbulence as the cloud top intersects the flight level. An example follows.

> DC-10. 12 injuries. Minor damage. Northbound at 37,000 feet, the aircraft experienced a few minutes of light to moderate chop, and then passed through the top of a cumulus cloud. Within the cloud, severe turbulence was encountered for about 30 seconds. Vertical accelerations deviated more than 1.5g from normal, and vertical gusts exceeded 4,800 f.p.m.. No echoes were visible on the aircraft's radar.

Although the updrafts weaken above the equilibrium level, intense thunderstorms may produce very strong updrafts well into the stratosphere. Two good clues as to the intensity of a thunderstorm are:

1. The overall height. If the height exceeds 35,000 feet, the thunderstorm should be regarded as extremely hazardous.

2. The maximum distance that the cloud tops penetrate the stratosphere. A severe thunderstorm storm will typically overshoot the tropopause by 3,000 to 10,000 feet.

Updraft speeds in the mature stage of the airmass thunderstorm normally vary from 400 to 1,200 f.p.m. near the base of the thunderstorm to 4,000 f.p.m. near the equilibrium level. Extreme vertical gusts of more than 10,000 f.p.m. have been reported.

Typical updraft areas at the tops of airmass thunderstorms are one to two miles on a side versus five or more for supercells. Updraft areas in moving thunderstorms are commonly elongated, with their shortest dimension in the direction of storm movement. Supercell cases have been reported where the dimensions of the updraft were only 2.5 n.m. along the track, but more than 10 n.m. across the track.

Thunderstorm downdrafts are strong in the areas of precipitation. However, they may also exist away from the main precipitation area, driven mainly by evaporation of cloud particles as dry outside air is entrained into the cumulonimbus. Downdrafts typically reach their greatest intensities near the base of the thunderstorm. Maximum downdraft speeds are about half of the speed of the maximum updraft. Extremes of near 5,000 f.p.m. have been reported.

The smaller scale turbulence within the thunderstorm is superimposed on the large up- and downdrafts that define the thunderstorm. Measurements indicate that the intensity of this turbulence generally increases with the stage of development of the thunderstorm. In the typical thunderstorm this means light to moderate intensities in the cumulus stage, and moderate to severe (or worse) in the mature stage. Measurements in the middle and upper troposphere show that in the mature stage, turbulence levels are at least light to moderate in the updraft, and moderate to severe near the precipitation-induced downdraft and its interface with the updraft.

DISSIPATING STAGE

When the thunderstorm cell begins to dissipate, the associated turbulence weakens. Late in the dissipating stage, as precipitation decreases throughout the thunderstorm and the remnants of the updraft in the upper portion of the storms exit the anvil or mix with the surroundings, turbulence diminishes markedly. Subsequently, the spreading out and general disorganization of the cumulonimbus cloud is an indication of the stabilization of the atmosphere.

In the absence of radar, a high degree of caution should be exercised in evaluating the turbulence potential of a dissipating cell. There is no clear point of separation between the mature and dissipating stage. Early in the dissipating stage, turbulence in some locations of the thunderstorm will be as intense as in the mature stage. Near the end, isolated patches of turbulence may persist.

An assumption of moderate or greater turbulence is a good one while the cumulonimbus cloud continues to show some degree of organization. Also, the possibility of a multicell thunderstorm being present should always be considered; it is possible that a nearby mature cell in the vicinity of the dissipating cell could be obscured.

WEATHER RADAR

Thunderstorm detection is the primary application of weather radar. The FAA (1983) cites four important rules concerning thunderstorms and airborne radar:

1. Don't fly into a cloud mass containing scattered embedded thunderstorms without airborne radar. (Here, "embedded" refers to thunderstorms that cannot be identified visually because they are obscured by stratiform clouds.)

2. Don't trust visual appearance to be a reliable indicator of turbulence inside a thunderstorm.

3. Avoid by at least 20 n.m. any thunderstorm that gives an intense radar echo (or is identified as severe). This is especially true under the anvil of a large cumulonimbus.

4. Circumnavigate any area where the thunderstorm coverage is 6/10 or more.

Although these rules relate to turbulence outside the cloud as well as in the cloud, they depend on locating the primary convective activity, preferably, by radar. For this reason, it is useful to pause briefly and examine the main capabilities and limitations of radar, especially with regard to TNT.

Conventional airborne radar does not detect clouds, it detects precipitation. Some precipitation provides more substantial targets than other. For example, large water droplets and wet hail give better echoes than snow or drizzle. Cloud particles are generally too small to cause significant reflection. This means that echo tops are not cloud tops, which are generally higher than the thunderstorm echoes. Thunderstorm bases may also be difficult to detect by radar because the echo often extends to the ground with the precipitation.

Currently, turbulent motions can only be determined by operational weather radar if the turbulence occurs in the same area as the precipitation. Conventional weather radar (radar that does not have doppler capabilities) does not actually sense turbulence. It is used to identify certain precipitation echo patterns with which turbulence occurs. For example, within a thunderstorm, moderate and severe turbulence is often found in the middle and upper troposphere near strong echoes on the boundary of the updraft core.

Airborne doppler weather radar offers an advantage over conventional airborne radar with regard to turbulence detection. Whereas both conventional and doppler radar provide echo intensity information, doppler radar can also identify turbulence. It does so by sensing the small scale motions of precipitation-size droplets.

Similar to conventional radar, if there is no precipitation, then the turbulence cannot be identified by either type of radar. This is a problem with some strong updrafts within well developed thunderstorms. They may be echo-free because cloud particles within the updraft are too small to be detected. For example, a substantial portion of the updraft region in a supercell is usually echo-free. Another example is the case of the DC-10 described in a previous section. Without warning, the aircraft encountered severe turbulence in the top of a rapidly growing thunderstorm that was not detected by radar.

As the radar signal propagates away from its source, it undergoes a process known as **attenuation**. This occurs when the signal is absorbed or reflected along its path. Precipitation is an efficient attenuator of weather radar signals. For example, in heavy rain, a radar signal may be partially or totally absorbed by the target (the rain) in the foreground, so that targets in the background cannot be seen very clearly, if at all. In more than one case, a pilot decided to cross what appeared (by radar) to be a narrow band of bad weather. Since the band was narrow, it seemed reasonable that it could be crossed quickly, minimizing the turbulence. Unfortunately, upon penetration, it is often discovered that attenuation by heavy rain has caused the echo to appear narrower than it actually is. The crash of a passenger aircraft in a thunderstorm a few years ago was caused when a crew misinterpreted an attenuated radar return and flew into a supercell.

Thunderstorm hazards are observed continuously by the network of ground-based weather radars maintained by National Weather Service, the armed forces, and FAA. A radar intensity scale that relates to turbulent level is in common use by these agencies. These "video integrator and processor" (or **VIP) levels** are listed in figure 3-12 (FAA, 1983).

VIP Level	Turbulence
1 Weak	Light to Moderate possible
2 Moderate	Light to Moderate possible
3 Strong	Severe possible
4 Very strong	Severe likely
5 Intense	Severe with organized surface wind gusts
6 Extreme	Severe with extensive surface wind gusts

Figure 3-12. Video integrator and processor (VIP) levels with estimated turbulence intensity. The probability of lightning increases above VIP level 1, and the likelihood of large hail increases above VIP 4.

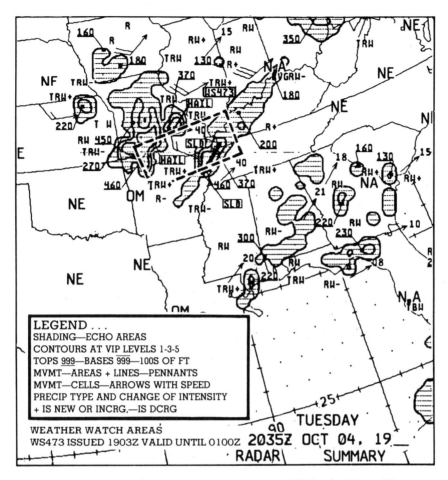

Figure 3-13. Weather Radar Chart. Contours represent VIP levels 1, 3, and 5.

An example of the display of VIP information from the national radar network is shown on a weather radar summary chart in figure 3-13. You should have been introduced to the format and use of these charts in your first aviation meteorology course, and/or through publications such as *Aviation Weather Services* (FAA, 1985).

The use of contoured VIP levels on radar summary charts is analogous to identifying terrain as "rough" or "very rough." The contours only tell you in broad terms where the turbulence associated with thunderstorms was at map time, and then only on a fairly large scale. For that reason, a cautious interpretation is recommended: the maximum reported VIP level should always be used to estimate the turbulence intensity (FAA, 1975).

You should also be aware that surface weather radar signals can be blocked by mountainous terrain. The result is that some nearby thunderstorms cells may be missed. Other modes of detection such as surface observations, satellite data, or lightning data should also be used in those areas.

BELOW THE THUNDERSTORM

The environment below a thunderstorm cloud base is truly a "no man's" land. The applicable rules of thumb (FAA, 1983) are:

1. Don't land or takeoff in the face of an approaching thunderstorm.

2. Don't attempt to fly under a thunderstorm even if you can see through to the other side.

Beneath the thunderstorm, intense and rapidly changing winds and weather produce turbulence, wind shear, low ceilings, and poor visibilities to make flight conditions difficult at best. The worst problems develop when precipitation and cool air reach the surface in the mature stage. The key to understanding the production of TNT below a cloud base is the knowledge of the structure and behavior of this downdraft and its interaction with the updraft. Figure 3-14 shows the main features of the region below the cloud base of an idealized multicell thunderstorm.

Turbulence and wind shear are found within the main downdraft; in smaller, stronger downbursts occasionally embedded in the main downdraft; at the boundary of the downdraft (the gust front); in strong winds near the ground; and in vortexes such as tornadoes.

DOWNBURST

Comprehensive field studies and aircraft accident analyses by T. Fujita at the University of Chicago during the 1970's made it very clear that the intensity and scale of downdrafts varies widely. Furthermore, there exists a class of downdrafts that are particularly hazardous to flight operations because of their severity and small size. Fujita coined the term **downburst** for a concentrated, severe downdraft that induces an outward burst of

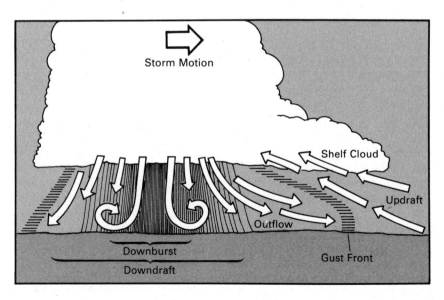

Figure 3-14. Composite of turbulence-producing phenomena that can occur below a thunderstorm cloud base. Note all phenomena may not occur simultaneously.

damaging winds at the ground. He also introduced the term **microburst** for a downburst with horizontal dimensions of 2.2 n.m or less. (Fujita, 1985) Downbursts form by the same processes that produce the larger and less intense downdrafts; that is, by precipitation drag and cooling due to the evaporation and melting of precipitation particles.

Strong downbursts may occur in airmass thunderstorms as well as in multicell and supercell thunderstorms. In fact the isolated, single cell storms present a greater hazard to aviation for several reasons. They are common summertime phenomena, small scale, develop rapidly, and may have very strong outflows. In contrast, the larger multicell storms are usually easier to avoid because they are less frequent, larger scale, have longer lifetimes, and are often already identified as severe (Wolfson, 1988).

A perspective view of the downburst is shown in figure 3-15. The downburst circulation is similar to that of a so-called vortex ring. There is strong descent in the core of cool, dense air which is surrounded by a ring of air which rolls upward on the outside, much like a smoke ring. A similar pattern occurs in dry thermals, except that thermals are warm updrafts with air descending on the outside. The downburst takes only a few minutes to descend from the base of its parent cloud to the ground.

A cross section through an idealized microburst at the ground is shown in figure 3-16. The lifetime of a downburst ranges from 5 to 30 minutes, once it reaches the ground. Most microbursts weaken significantly in only a few minutes as they spread out. There is evidence that some longer downburst

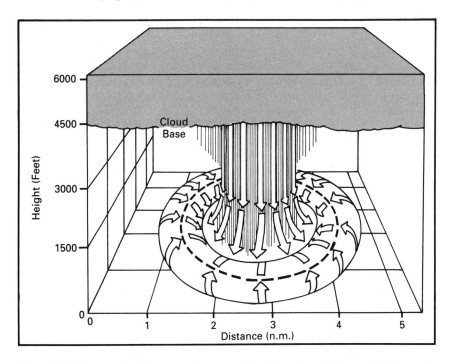

Figure 3-15. Perspective diagram of a symmetrical downburst. The axis of the vortex ring is indicated by a heavy dashed line. The arrows indicate airflow. The vertical lines indicate precipitation.

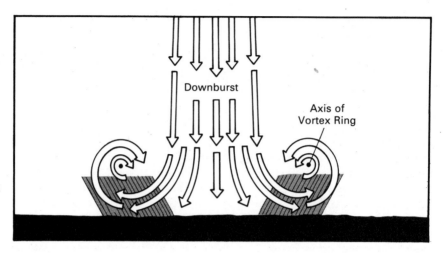

Figure 3-16. Cross section of an idealized microburst after it has reached the ground. Shaded areas are regions of strongest winds. Note the strong horizontal wind shear (reversal of wind direction) between the shaded areas. Precipitation is not shown.

events are a combination of successive downbursts that occur a few minutes apart in the same location. Microburst flight hazards include the strong downdraft (often with heavy precipitation), gusty horizontal winds (shaded), strong horizontal wind shear from one side of the downburst to the other, and turbulence.

Studies of a large number of microbursts at airports found typical peak speeds of 25 knots, although it is estimated that microburst winds well in excess of 100 knots are possible. The typical wind speed change (wind shear) across a microburst is about 45 knots. This means an aircraft crossing through the center of a microburst would experience a headwind change of 45 knots. The effect is illustrated in figure 3-17. This is about the maximum LLWS that can be tolerated by heavy jet transports. In seven

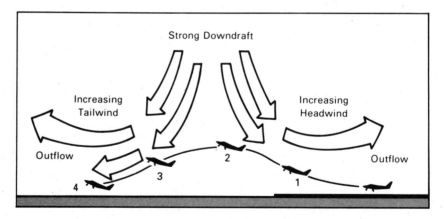

Figure 3-17. During a takeoff into a microburst, an aircraft experiences an increasing headwind (position 1), followed by a decreasing headwind and downdraft (position 2), and finally a tailwind (position 3). The most severe downdraft will be encountered between positions 2 and 3. Together with the loss of airspeed due to the tailwind, it can result in terrain impact or operating dangerously close to the ground (position 4).

microburst accidents involving jet transports, maximum wind speed changes ranged from 30 to 75 knots (FAA, 1988).

You should be aware of several variations in the formation and appearance of downdrafts and downbursts. For example, a downdraft does not require a thunderstorm. As discussed previously, showers are common from cumulus clouds that do not reach the cumulonimbus stage. Therefore, downdrafts and, given the right conditions, downbursts may occur.

Another variation on the ideal downburst is that it may be moved and distorted by the large scale airflow in which the thunderstorm is embedded. Such "traveling" downbursts have stronger winds on the downwind side and weaker winds on the upwind side. Here "downwind" and "upwind" refer to the direction the downburst is moving.

There are several visual indicators of the presence of a downburst. In humid climates, convective cloud bases tend to be low. These conditions produce "wet downbursts" which are closely associated with a visible rainshaft. (Figure 3-18) In dry climates, such as in the deserts and mountains of the western U.S., thunderstorm cloud bases are often high, and the complete evaporation of the rainshaft can occur. In this case, a "dry downburst" may be produced. All that may be visible is virga at the cloud base and a characteristic dust cloud on the ground. Fortunately, dry downbursts occur mainly in the afternoon when these visible features can be identified.

Figure 3-18. Photograph of a wet downburst. Photo courtesy of A. Rangno.

Because of the low-level wind shear hazards of downbursts and gust fronts, **low-level wind shear alert systems (LLWAS)** have been installed at many large airports around the U.S. where thunderstorms are frequent. This system continuously monitors surface winds at remote sites around the airport and communicates the information to a central computer. The computer evaluates the wind differences across the airport to determine whether a wind shear problem exists. Wind shear alerts are issued on the basis of this information. In the near future, terminal doppler radar systems will provide a major improvement in airport wind shear monitoring capabilities. More detail on this topic will be provided in Chapter 7.

As we leave this brief discussion of downbursts, it is important to note that a wide variety of information regarding downbursts and related flight techniques is contained in the *Pilot Windshear Guide* (FAA, 1988) and the *FAA Windshear Training Aid* (Kupcis, 1988).

GUST FRONT

A **gust front** is found on the edge of the pool of cold air flowing outward from the downdraft. When several multicell storms are present, their outflows combine, forming a single gust front. The gust front is best defined in the direction of the storm motion. In that location, the front moves several miles out ahead of the thunderstorms, leaving the rain behind. (Figure 3-19) The steepest slope of the front is along the leading edge of the outflow. The location of this feature is sometimes indicated by the presence of a **roll cloud**. In very moist conditions, cloud base will be low and the shelf cloud and roll cloud may merge.

The gust front also is the location of TNT caused by horizontal wind shear and gusty winds. On the ground, a passage of the gust front produces

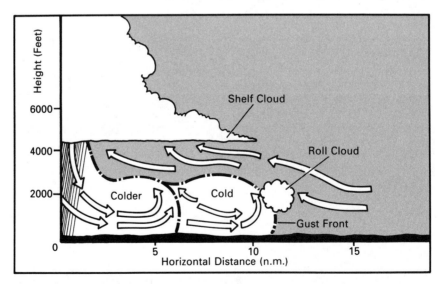

Figure 3-19. Detailed view of a gust front. Heavy dashed lines indicate the boundary of the cold air generated by precipitation on the left. Note the secondary gust front with a new surge of cold air from the thunderstorm. A roll cloud is not always present with a gust front.

changes much like a cold front. It is typically marked by a wind shift, gusty winds, a pressure increase, and a temperature decrease.

Successive surges of cold air often occur behind the gust front. These are caused by variations in the timing and intensity of the precipitation from the thunderstorms. Each new surge is preceded by a turbulent region followed by an increase in the depth of the cool air.

The turbulence and shear associated with the gust front does not only exist at low levels. As shown in figure 3-19, the frontal zone of an active multicell thunderstorm stretches all the way back into the cloud. Although the updraft may be exceptionally smooth, significant turbulence and wind shear occurs along the frontal zone.

An **outflow boundary** is the remnant of a gust front that continues to exist long after the thunderstorms that created it have dissipated. On some occasions, outflow boundaries generated by thunderstorms late in the day have been observed to continue moving throughout the night, often covering well over a hundred miles. New convection may be triggered hours later due to lifting along an outflow boundary as it moves into unstable areas or intersects fronts or other outflow boundaries. The downburst responsible for the crash of a B-727 at New Orleans in July, 1982 was associated with thunderstorm activity at the intersection of an outflow boundary, a lake breeze front, and a sea breeze front (Purdom et al. 1983).

TORNADOES AND OTHER VORTEXES

Tornadoes are violently rotating columns of air which are found below some cumulonimbus clouds. (Figure 3-20) They may or may not reach the surface. The latter case is termed a "funnel cloud." Wind speeds associated with tornadoes generally range from 100 to 150 knots with a maximum of about 260 knots. Most tornado diameters are 300 to 2000 feet although extremes of a mile have been reported. Tornado lifetimes are usually only a few minutes, however, cases of over three hours have been documented. The flight hazards of these so-called "twisters" are obvious.

The strongest tornadoes are usually associated with severe thunderstorms. The supercell produces strong, damaging tornadoes in the vicinity of the wall cloud. (Figure 3-11) Tornadoes also occur with nonsevere thunderstorms, although they are usually weaker.

Tornadoes that occur over water are called **waterspouts**. They are usually weaker than tornadoes over land. "Fair weather" waterspouts are very common near the Florida Keys between March and October. These vortexes form over warm water near developing cumulus clouds. In general, fair weather waterspouts are very weak, short-lived, and slow-moving. They offer hazards to small boats and the unwary pilot.

Near gust fronts and near the edges of downbursts, damaging tornado-like vortexes known as **gustnadoes** sometimes occur. These are caused by the strong horizontal wind shear and strong updrafts that are common at these boundaries.

Figure 3-20. Two examples of tornadoes. The observation of a funnel cloud does not necessarily mean that there is not a tornado on the ground. Sometimes the lower part of the tornado is not visible because of the lack of debris in the funnel. Photos courtesy of J. Monteverdi.

Another related phenomenon that pilots should be aware of is a **cold air funnel**. These are weak vortexes that occasionally develop with rainshowers and nonsevere thunderstorms. Although similar in appearance to tornadic funnel clouds, they rarely reach the ground. Also, cold air funnels do not appear under conditions usually associated with severe weather. For example, outbreaks commonly occur in a cold airmass, a half day or so after the passage of a cold front. Cold air funnels are more frequent in the spring and fall. As with any microscale vortex, they should always be considered a flight hazard.

NEAR THE THUNDERSTORM

Turbulence "near the thunderstorm" refers to that found outside the main convection. This includes turbulence in clear and cloudy air next to the main cumulonimbus cloud and turbulence in and over the anvil.

In general, the downdrafts in the clear air around the towering cumulus or cumulonimbus are spread over a larger area than the updrafts and are comparatively weaker. Downdraft speeds in the clear air are typically a few hundred feet per minute within a lateral distance of six nautical miles from the cloud. Close to the cloud boundary, where evaporation cools the air and intensifies the downward motions, downdraft speeds are larger, but not exceptionally large compared to the downdrafts within the cloud.

These average characteristics of downdrafts in the clear air are somewhat misleading. Experienced pilots have long known that the areas around thunderstorms can be quite turbulent. Significant gusts have been found above thunderstorm tops, in the clear wake, and the cloudy anvil. The following are some examples.

> While circumnavigating thunderstorms at FL350 in clear air, a large passenger aircraft encountered turbulence which caused it to gain 700 feet.

> At FL330, an aircraft encountered severe turbulence and lost several hundred feet of altitude, causing crew and passenger injuries. At the time of the encounter, the aircraft was in cirrus-type clouds 25 miles from nearest cell depicted on radar.

> While deviating around a cell along the route at FL350, the aircraft suddenly encountered severe turbulence. The flight was clear of clouds and precipitation. The aircraft rolled approximately 45 degrees left then 30 degrees right. Minor injuries to crew.

Some well-known rules of thumb have evolved over the years to warn pilots of the dangers of turbulence outside the obviously convective region of the thunderstorm. We saw the most important of these in our previous discussion of in-cloud turbulence and radar applications to TNT.

1. Do not fly within 20 miles of a thunderstorm classified as severe or giving an intense radar echo.

2. Do not fly under the anvil of a large cumulonimbus.

This rule and others given below are extremely useful, but they do not go very far in explaining just what is being avoided outside the thunderstorm. How does strong TNT develop outside the main convective area?

The pattern of weak clear air downdrafts described earlier is probably most representative of an airmass thunderstorm cell that develops under generally light wind conditions. In contrast, the multicell and supercell thunderstorms require vertical wind shear through a deep layer of the atmosphere. For example, with the multicell, the wind speed typically increases from the base to the top of the thunderstorm. This is also true for a supercell, except that there is also a distinct wind direction change with height, usually from southerly at low levels to westerly aloft. In either case, the thunderstorm cloud will move more slowly than the winds at upper levels.

Under these conditions, the thunderstorm will act as a sort of "porous mountain." Part of the airflow will be blocked and part will be mixed into the thunderstorm. The blocking effect is greater with strong thunderstorms and strong winds aloft. In the previous chapter, you learned that obstructions to airflow, whether they are buildings or mountains, cause a variety of flow disturbances near the barrier. These included waves and turbulence upwind, over, and downwind of the obstacle. A thunderstorm can produce an equally wide variety of disturbances when air flows over and around it.

The airflow outside thunderstorms has not received the same scientific attention as the airflow in and below the storms, so only rough approximations of the flow patterns can be given. Figure 3-21 represents a mature thunderstorm cell under the influence of increasing winds with height. Regions where "obstacle effects" have been observed outside the main region of convection are labeled. Note that directions "upwind," "downwind," and "wake" refer to wind direction at the top of the storm.

UPWIND

Just upwind of the thunderstorm, a narrow zone of upward motions has been observed in the clear air. Glider pilots flying in clouds have attained

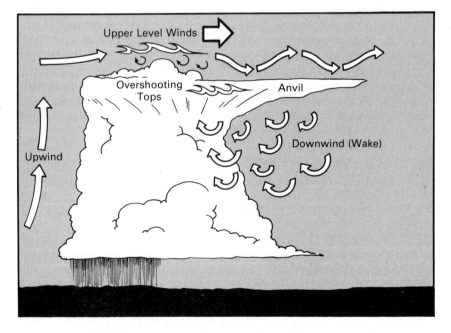

Figure 3-21. Potential turbulent regions outside of a thunderstorm cell. The sawtooth symbols at the top of the storm indicate shearing-gravity waves.

high altitudes by beginning their climb at low levels inside the cumulo-nimbus cloud, and then penetrating upwind of the storm and finishing the climb in clear air. In these cases, the updraft upwind of the storm has usually been steady and smooth at a few hundred feet per minute. The penetration of thunderstorms with a sailplane is an extremely dangerous practice, and is not allowed in the U.S.

SUMMIT

At the top or **summit region** of the thunderstorm, the cloudscape is dominated by the anvil cloud. Although the anvil is typically a smooth cloud, this is not always the case. We have seen that intense thunderstorms produce updrafts that overshoot the smooth top of the anvil. The cumuli-form appearance of the overshooting tops is a warning to pilots that they are a source of significant turbulence due to the convective currents. The following experience illustrates this problem.

> Immediately after emerging from a cirrus deck at 41,000 feet, the pilot turned the aircraft to avoid what appeared to be the top of a cumulonimbus cloud 200 to 300 feet above flight level. The aircraft passed through a portion of the cloud and experienced 5 to 10 seconds of severe turbulence. Passenger and crew injuries.

Near the top of the thunderstorm, partially blocked air flows over and around the anvil and any overshooting tops. When both the wind and convective updrafts are strong, this is similar to airflow over a hill or a group of hills. Since the anvil is in the stable stratosphere, atmospheric gravity wave activity may be generated on several scales when the airflow is disturbed by the storm.

Winds often reach maximum speeds near tropopause height and decrease above that level. This means that the summit region is frequently located in a layer of strong negative wind shear (wind decreases with height). Therefore, given a favorable combination of strong winds, stability, and vertical wind shear, TNT may be produced near the top of the thunder-storm not only by pure gravity waves, but also by enhanced vertical shears, shearing-gravity waves, or some combination of these.

We know that the intensities of the flow disturbances around the summit region depend on the severity of the storm and the strength of the upper winds relative to the moving thunderstorm. However, the rapid changes in the form and strength of the updrafts make it difficult to describe the turbulence in any one storm very accurately. Currently, we must depend on very rough and conservative estimates of the turbulence. These lead to rules of thumb such as the following:

1. If the wind at the top of a thunderstorm is reported to be 100 knots, stay at least 10,000 feet above the storm. Add (subtract) 1,000 feet for each 10 knot increase (decrease) in reported wind speed.

2. Do not fly in the anvil cloud under any circumstances.

DOWNWIND

Turbulence is commonly reported downwind of thunderstorms. (Figure 3-21) In the anvil, the remnants of the updraft exits horizontally in a stabilizing environment. The convective circulation is flattened out. This process can strengthen vertical wind shears in limited areas, leading to the sporadic breakdown of shearing-gravity waves, and patchy turbulence in the anvil, well downstream of the summit region.

Several other airflow patterns are also possible in the wake of a thunderstorm when the airflow is partially blocked. Two of these are shown in figure 3-22.

In the top diagram, air is accelerated as it flows past the sides of the thunderstorm cell. The result of this flow pattern is that two oppositely rotating eddies form on each side of the storm, immediately downwind. The eddies are most likely unsteady; that is, they form, dissipate, and possibly reform, during the lifetime of the thunderstorm. They likely contribute to turbulence below the anvil, although not wholly in the clear air. In fact, horizontal shears of 30 to 50 knots, probably caused by blocking, have been reported within cumulonimbus clouds.

In addition to the turbulence problems below the anvil, flying conditions may be further complicated by the occurrence of hail. Two flight experiences in the wakes of thunderstorms are given below. Note the flight levels. The "overhang" refers to the anvil.

> As the aircraft entered the overhang area, it immediately began to experience severe turbulence, heavy precipitation, and lightning. At 24,000 feet, both pilots were on the controls as airspeed fluctuated from 280 to 310 knots.

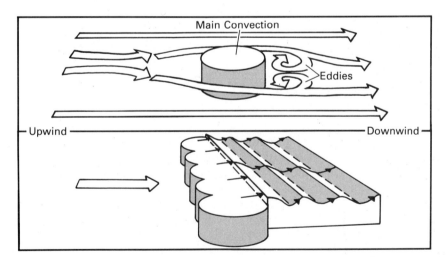

Figure 3-22. Two possible airflow patterns which may briefly develop in the wake of strong thunderstorms with strong winds aloft. For clarity, the anvil is not shown. The main convective regions are shown as cylinders. In the lower diagram, the solid lines represent gravity wave crests and the dashed lines represent wave troughs. The areas of upward motions are shaded and downdrafts are unshaded.

The aircraft encountered turbulence in clear air at 22,000 feet as it flew under the overhang. One crew member injured.

If thunderstorm cells occur in a line more or less perpendicular to the wind, gravity waves, comparable to mountain lee waves, can develop downwind as stable air flows over the thunderstorm tops. This pattern is shown in the bottom diagram of figure 3-22. In Chapter 2, a similar effect was seen when the wind direction at the top of the convective boundary layer was perpendicular to cloud streets.

Although the mechanics of lee waves will not be examined until Chapter 5, it is worthwhile to consider the reports of two pertinent turbulence incidents. In each of these cases, the aircraft was near the tropopause and downwind of a line of thunderstorms.

A DC-10 was eastbound at 37,000 feet across a line a thunderstorms near Hannibal, Missouri. The aircraft was flying downwind at the time. Wind speed at flight level was 140 knots. According to aircrew statements, the aircraft was passing through thin cirrus just prior to the incident. Lightning flashes could be seen below and to the sides. A few moments later, the aircraft exited the cirrus and then encountered a second clearly formed cloud that was illuminated by a lightning flash off to the side and below. At this time, ATC and surface weather radar placed the aircraft downwind of the line of radar echoes from the thunderstorms. Subsequently, several severe gusts were encountered. There were 29 injuries. Post analysis indicated that the turbulence was caused by a gravity wave similar to a mountain wave.

An L-1011 encountered severe turbulence at 37,000 feet just off the coast of South Carolina. There were 24 injuries to passengers and crew. Just prior to the incident, the aircraft was flying on an intersecting track with a line of thunderstorms. It approached the line from the downwind side, below the highest tops. Winds near the top of the storms were about 80 knots. The path of the aircraft took it into an anvil cloud. A few minutes of light to moderate chop was followed by two jolts of severe turbulence about a minute apart. The turbulence was experienced before the aircraft crossed the line of thunderstorms; that is, downwind, but within 20 n.m. Subsequent analysis of the incident provided strong evidence that the turbulence occurred in a lee wave-like disturbance caused when the thunderstorms provided a barrier to the strong airflow aloft.

The occurrence of turbulence outside of the cloudy convection is poorly observed and not predictable. The diagrams presented above give some guidance as to the causes, locations, and configurations of turbulent eddies, but they leave a lot to be desired. For the most part, they are idealized for simple, steady cells. In reality, the thunderstorm is a porous, constantly changing obstacle to the flow. It is often present with several other cells in different stages of development. There are many possible interactions between growing and dissipating cells and the ambient wind. These are not very well understood. This uncertainty is the primary reason why such broad buffer zones are recommended when flying near thunderstorms. Even radar does not always reveal safe paths in the constantly changing thunderstorm environment. As examples of the potential problems, we will leave this topic with two descriptions of flights through "holes" between thunderstorm cells.

We started turning and maneuvering through the hole. We were level at 33,000 feet on speed with autopilot and altitude hold on. Initially the ride was smooth; however, very shortly we encountered severe turbulence. In a matter of seconds, we were climbing, descending, still with autopilot and altitude hold on. . . we went as high as 33,700 feet and as low as 32,500 feet, uncontrollably.

While flying at 37,000 feet, the crew prepared the cabin to cross a line of thunderstorms. The aircraft entered a 40 mile hole between a building cumulus on the right and a dissipating cell on the left and entered an obscured layer between them. Transition was smooth for the first half with no turbulence reported in the area. Then a slight updraft followed by a moderate to severe jolt was experienced, followed by an immediate drop of 250 to 300 feet . . . Light to moderate turbulence was experienced as the aircraft entered a severe downdraft, 2500 f.p.m. Passenger injuries.

THUNDERSTORM ENVIRONMENT

So far, the emphasis of this chapter has been on the description and causes of turbulence in and near thunderstorms in mid-latitudes. Our approach to the "causes" of TNT has assumed that a thunderstorm already exists or is developing. Our basic questions have been where, when, and why is turbulence likely to occur in and near that thunderstorm? Although we have answered this question in some detail, our treatment of TNT would be incomplete without also considering the questions: where, when, and why are thunderstorms likely to occur? Answers to these questions are especially important for flight planning purposes.

REQUIREMENTS FOR DEVELOPMENT

Two basic requirements must be met for the formation of thunderstorms: the air must have strong **potential instability**, and there must be a source of **initial lift**.

Air that is potentially unstable contains adequate moisture for convective cloud formation, but needs to be lifted a sufficient distance to set off convection. If the air is too stable, no amount of moisture or lifting will cause thunderstorms to develop.

"Initial lift" is the minimum amount of vertical displacement necessary to set off potential instability. Sometimes the initial lift will be quite large because a stable layer may have to be overcome or condensation may have to occur before the air destabilizes.

What are the possible sources of initial lift for thunderstorms? Surface heating and mountains are two common sources. Fronts can also provide the initial lift. These include warm and cold fronts, as well as sea breeze fronts, gust fronts, and outflow boundaries. In addition, certain large scale upper air circulations such as troughs and lows promote the lifting of air over very large areas.

When the requirements for thunderstorms are met, they will undoubtably develop. An important point to be made here is that they do not occur by chance. Thunderstorms are organized into distinctive patterns by such things as macro- and mesoscale weather systems and terrain. These provide the moisture, potential instability, and lifting mechanisms needed for thunderstorm development. If you understand the relationships between thunderstorm occurrence, larger scale circulations, and terrain, it is a distinct advantage for flight planning. In the next few paragraphs, we will look at some of the more common examples of these relationships. A useful starting point is thunderstorm climatology.

CLIMATOLOGY

Figure 3-23 shows the number of thunderstorm days in the contiguous U.S. by season. Summer is by far the most active season. Ample solar heating and the supply of moist, potentially unstable air from the Gulf of Mexico at this time of year accounts for many of the thunderstorms which occur from the Rocky Mountains eastward. The highest number of thunderstorm

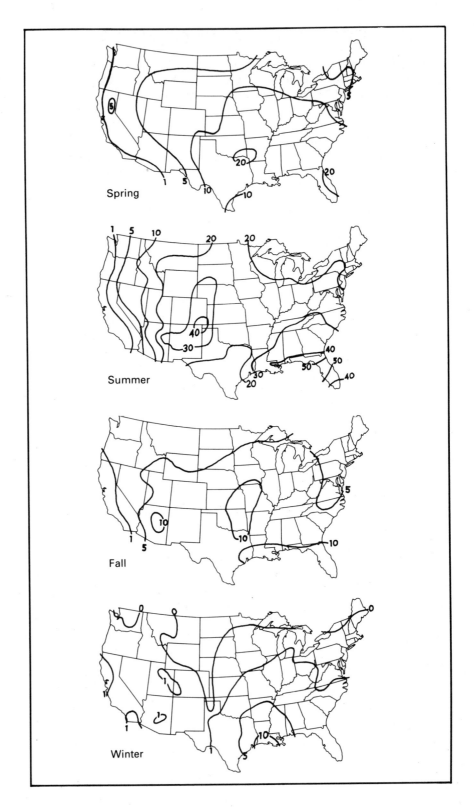

Figure 3-23. Average number of thunderstorm days in each season.

days in Florida and the southern Rockies are, respectively, caused by sea breeze convergence and orographic lifting. An increase in thunderstorm activity in the very hot desert Southwest occurs during July and August as moist air reaches that area from the Gulf.

Thunderstorms are much less common on the West Coast of the U.S. because of the stability of air in that area tends to be much higher. You should recall from Chapter 2 that the West Coast is dominated by a strong elevated inversion during the warmer part of the year. During some winters, locations along the coast actually experience more thunderstorms than in summer.

Thunderstorm activity reaches its peak in the afternoon in most areas because of the influence of solar heating. However, the Great Plains region has a nighttime maximum during the summer. This is caused, at least partially, by the influence of the nocturnal low-level jet in that area.

The tops of thunderstorms tend to be lower in winter than in summer, and lower at high latitudes than at low latitudes. Cumulonimbus cloud bases, on the other hand, are lower in the moist environment of the eastern U.S., and higher over the drier west.

The highest frequency of severe thunderstorms (supercells) occurs in the springtime in the area between the Rockies and the Mississippi and from Texas to the Dakotas. The primary region of activity is northern Texas, Oklahoma, and southern Kansas. That area is particularly conducive to severe weather because of its proximity to the warm, moist air from the Gulf of Mexico; the development of large scale cyclones just east of the Rockies; and, as noted above, the presence of the southerly low-level jet stream.

Thunderstorm climatology provides important information. It alerts you to the likelihood of certain regional and seasonal thunderstorm problems. But caution should be used in its application. Variations from the average picture may be large. In the next few paragraphs, we examine those variations in terms of large scale weather patterns that favor the occurrence of thunderstorms. It is these that you should look for in current and forecast weather information as you prepare your flight plan.

INSTABILITY PATTERNS

The potential instability requirement for thunderstorms can be evaluated with one of several stability indexes. One of the most common is the **lifted index**. It is simply the difference between the observed 500 mb temperature and the temperature that a parcel of air would have if lifted from the boundary layer to the 500 mb level. The lifting process takes into account any condensation and latent heat release that occurs so that the temperature difference at 500 mb also reflects the influence of moisture. If the observed 500 mb temperature is colder than an air parcel lifted to that level, then the lifted index is negative (unstable), and thunderstorms are likely. The relation between the lifted index and thunderstorm severity is shown in figure 3-24.

Lifted Index	Chance of Severe Thunderstorm
0 to -2	Weak
-3 to -5	Moderate
<=-6	Strong

Figure 3-24. The lifted index measures the instability of the atmosphere. A lifted index below minus three is a good indication of moderate to severe thunderstorms.

Keep in mind, however, that airmass (nonsevere) thunderstorms can occur when the lifted index is slightly positive. An alternate stability index, known as the **K index**, has proved useful in determining the probability of airmass thunderstorms. Similar to the lifted index, the K index is determined from a current sounding. It is defined as

$$K = \overset{A}{(T_{850}-T_{500})} + \overset{B}{D_{850}} \overset{C}{-(T_{700}-D_{700})}.$$

T is the air temperature and D is the dewpoint temperature in degrees Celsius at the pressure levels indicated by the subscripts (850 mb, 700 mb, 500 mb). The K index may seem a bit complicated at first glance, but it has a simple physical interpretation.

Term A is the lapse rate between the 850 mb and 500 mb levels. If it is a large positive number, then it contributes to instability. Term B measures the moisture at 850 mb. If the 850 mb dewpoint temperature is high, the contribution to instability is large. Term C (including the minus sign) simply measures the dryness of the air at 700 mb. When the difference between the air temperature and the dewpoint temperature is large, the air at that level is dry. The contribution to instability is negative.

Therefore, if the atmosphere has plenty of moisture and the lapse rate is large, the K index will be large and the probability of airmass thunderstorms will be high. Figure 3-25 shows the relationship between K and airmass thunderstorm probability.

K Index	Thunderstorm Probability (%)
<15	near 0
15 to 20	20
21 to 25	20 to 40
26 to 30	40 to 60
31 to 35	60 to 80
36 to 40	80 to 90
>40	near 100

Figure 3-25. The K index is another useful measure of atmospheric stability. As the K index increases, the probability of thunderstorms increases.

The lifted and K indexes are computed twice-a-day for all soundings made across the U.S., Canada, and Northern Mexico. Stability maps which

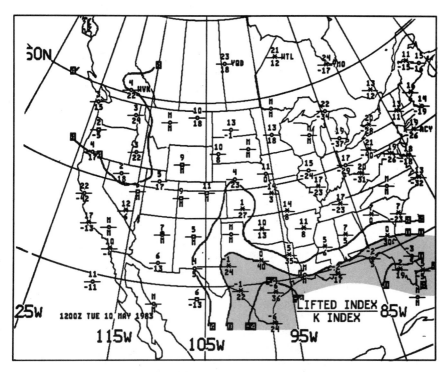

Figure 3-26. A stability panel from a composite moisture stability chart. Areas with a lifted index of less than zero are shaded.

display both indexes are prepared and are regularly available. An example is shown in figure 3-26. Note, only the lifted index is contoured.

As a first approximation of the location of thunderstorm activity, use a lifted index value of zero or less and a K index of 28 or more (50% probability or greater). When these numbers are applied to figure 3-26, one or both of the criteria are met in southern Texas, along the Gulf Coast, and in northern Florida.

The thresholds you use may vary slightly depending on the geographical area or season. Also, as the pilot, you may choose a different probability for your "go, no-go" decision. For example, suppose you choose 20% (K = 20) instead of 50% as the critical probability for the stability pattern shown in figure 3-26. In that case, western Idaho and eastern Washington would also be identified as thunderstorm areas.

The regions of thunderstorm activity are located where critical stability index values and adequate initial lifting coexist. In some cases, the "lift" is simply afternoon heating. In other cases, the initial lift, and/or the subsequent organization of the thunderstorms into lines and areas is provided by common macro- and mesoscale airflow patterns. These are discussed in the following sections.

THUNDERSTORM LINES

Multicell thunderstorms often form along convergence lines that are much longer than the diameter of any single storm. The concept of a convergence line was introduced in Chapter 2. Such lines include fronts, squall lines, and a number of mesoscale phenomena. They may contain either (or both) nonsevere and severe thunderstorms.

MACROSCALE FRONTS

Fronts often produce lines of thunderstorms due to the convergence and lifting of unstable air. This process is particularly efficient when cold air is present aloft. A cold front is more often the location of a line of thunderstorms because it is fast moving and has a relatively steep slope.

However, all cold fronts will not necessarily produce thunderstorm activity. The variations are large. For example, depending on the moisture and the stability, some cold fronts may be dry (cloudless), while others will produce mainly stratiform clouds, or showers without thunderstorms. Because of these variations, it is important to examine information other than the surface weather map analysis to determine if thunderstorms are associated with a front. Weather radar data, satellite imagery, and surface weather data provide many useful clues as to thunderstorm presence.

Thunderstorms may also be aligned along warm fronts when unstable air overruns the wedge of retreating cold air at lower levels. Over land, this occurs more frequently in the warmer months of the year. It is a particularly troublesome situation because the thunderstorms are often embedded in stratiform clouds and cannot be easily seen from the ground or from the air. This problem is also likely in occlusions.

SQUALL LINES

A **squall line** or "instability line" can be either a broken or continuous line of nonfrontal thunderstorms. It is typically a hundred to several hundred miles long. Depending on the degree of instability and the wind variation through the troposphere, thunderstorms in squall lines may be ordinary multicell, supercell, or a mixture.

A squall line frequently develops along or ahead of a cold front in the warm sector of a cyclone. The ability of multicell thunderstorms to regenerate new cells helps to maintain the line. The squall line generally moves in the direction of the winds at 500 mb. When the squall line approaches and passes a particular location, the effect is similar to an idealized cold front. Examples of squall lines on a surface analysis chart, a radar summary chart, and a satellite image are given in figure 3-27.

Additional flight hazards occur when squall lines are long and fast moving. Small aircraft may not be able to fly around or over the thunderstorms. Two related aircraft accidents are described in the following paragraphs.

B-75. No injuries. Substantial damage. Pilot misjudged approaching squall line. Unable to return to airport. Crashed. Winds to 70 knots.

BAC-11. 42 fatalities. Aircraft destroyed. The accident cause was determined to be in-flight structural failure during the operation

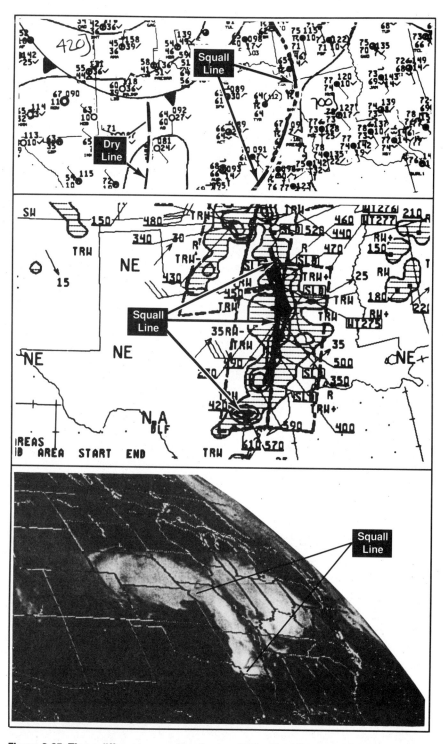

Figure 3-27. Three different examples of a squall line. Top: Section of surface analysis. Middle: Radar chart showing the alignment of echoes along a squall line. Bottom: Infrared satellite image of a north-south squall line. Note bright (cold) cloud tops associated with the most intense thunderstorm activity. The squall line is in the warm air just ahead and parallel to a cold front.

of the aircraft in an area of avoidable hazardous weather. Aircraft was seen to fly into or over a roll cloud preceding a thunderstorm. It exploded with major portions of the right wing and the empennage falling separately from the main part of the aircraft. The crash was followed shortly by a squall line passage.

OTHER MESOSCALE LINES

There are several other mesoscale phenomena that are known to contribute to the formation of thunderstorms along narrow bands. For example, you have seen the lifting that is generated at a sea breeze front. If potentially unstable air is present, thunderstorms will form in a line along that boundary. Similarly, outflow boundaries from thunderstorms produce favorable conditions for the formation of thunderstorm lines when they move into unstable regions.

In west Texas and Oklahoma during late spring and early summer, there often exists a north-south boundary between moist tropical air flowing northward from the Gulf of Mexico and dry air over the higher terrain to the west. The moisture boundary, which is called a **dry line**, is apparent in the distribution of surface dewpoint temperatures. Weather radars in this area may show a long, narrow clear air echo known as a "fine line." This is where the moisture content of the air changes rapidly from one side of the dry line to the other. The dry line is often the initial location of eastward moving lines of thunderstorms in that area. A dry line appears to the west of the squall line in the top diagram in figure 3-27. Note dewpoints fall from the sixties east of the dry line to less than 10°F to the west.

Dry lines are also important in the development of severe thunderstorms. In those cases, the dry line is usually present near or ahead of the cold front.

THUNDERSTORM CLUSTERS

Under certain circumstances, thunderstorms will develop in large clusters that are more circular than linear. These include both macroscale and mesoscale clusters which may contain both nonsevere and severe thunderstorms.

MACROSCALE CLUSTERS

There are many macroscale upper air circulations that can cause thunderstorm outbreaks over areas of many thousands of square miles. A few of the more common patterns are described here.

Large areas of thunderstorms are often caused when a developing upper level disturbance moves over an unstable area. The "disturbance" in this case is usually a cold trough or a low (a closed cyclonic circulation) in the upper troposphere. As viewed from a meteorological satellite, the associated thunderstorm cluster often appears as a **comma**-shaped cloud mass below and slightly ahead of the upper disturbance. This pattern is visible more often over oceans where the surface and the moisture distribution do not vary greatly.

Other macroscale regions of thunderstorms are observed to develop without any obvious frontal structure. These may also occur when upper air disturbances traverse the southwestern U.S. from the west (cool season) or from the south (warm season). It is useful to keep in mind that although upper level disturbances may provide good initial lift, they will only produce thunderstorms if the air has strong potential instability.

MESOSCALE CONVECTIVE COMPLEXES

Mesoscale convective complexes are nearly circular clusters of thunderstorms that develop primarily between the Rockies and the Appalachians during the warmer part of the year. Heavy rains and severe weather are not unusual. The complexes, as viewed by satellite are typically a few hundred miles in diameter. Their favored area of development moves from the south central to the north central U.S. between May and August.

Mesoscale convective complexes typically develop in late afternoon as the result of interactions and mergers of smaller groups of thunderstorms. They generally move eastward, reaching their maximum development about midnight, then weaken in the early morning hours. An example of a mesoscale convective complex is shown in the satellite image of figure 3-28.

Figure 3-28. A large MCC covers Missouri and portions of Kansas, Oklahoma, and Arkansas. The area of major activity appears larger than it actually is due to the blow-off of anvil cirrus.

SUMMARY

The purpose of this chapter has been to give you a better understanding of the mechanisms and dangers of thunderstorm turbulence and wind shear. Thunderstorm developmental processes, the circulations they generate, and the turbulence they produce are, in fact, fairly easy to understand. However, even with this improved knowledge, thunderstorms must still be treated cautiously. There are several reasons for this. First, the internal structures of thunderstorms vary widely in both space and time. In contrast, the models presented above only describe average structures. Second, our current forecast capabilities do not allow us to specify just how much a particular storm will deviate from our models once it develops. Even after the storm does develop, radar and other measurements do not give us a complete picture of the rapidly changing distribution and intensity of TNT. Finally, the thunderstorm presents many other aviation hazards (icing, lightning, hail) that only add to the problem of TNT, especially in IFR conditions.

Many visual indicators of the thunderstorm circulation have been described (towering cumulus, anvil, overshooting tops, shelf cloud, roll cloud, etc.). Although these should help you observe a thunderstorm more knowledgeably, they do not give conclusive information on the intensity of TNT. In no way should the visual indicators or any other information given here be interpreted as advice on how to "thread your way through" a thunderstorm. The FAA warning "avoid! avoid! avoid!" is well taken. In fact, most aviation weather forecasters would agree that if they could give only one piece of weather advice to a pilot, it would be

"NEVER FLY THROUGH A THUNDERSTORM."

KEY TERMS _____

Airmass Thunderstorm
Anvil
Attenuation
Barrier Effect
Cloudy Convection
Cold Air Funnel
Comma
Convective Condensation Level
Cumulus Stage
Dissipating Stage
Downburst
Dry Downburst
Dry Line
Equilibrium Level
Gust Front
Gustnado
Initial Lift
K Index
Lifted Index
LLWAS

Mature Stage
Mesoscale Convective Complex
Mesoscale Convective Systems
Microburst
Multicell
Outflow Boundary
Potential Instability
Radar Summary Chart
Relative Humidity
Roll Cloud
Saturation
Severe Thunderstorm
Shelf Cloud
Single Cell
Squall Line
Summit Region
Supercell
Thunderstorm
Thunderstorm Wake
TNT
Tornado
Towering Cumulus
VIP Level
Virga
Waterspout
Wind Shear

CHAPTER QUESTIONS _____

1. What are the visible clues of the following thunderstorm components?

   Gustnado
   Mature thunderstorm
   Cumulus stage
   Thunderstorm updraft
   Gust front

2. Turbulence in thunderstorms occurs on at least two different scales. Explain.

3. Winds of 65 knots are reported at tropopause level (FL320) in an area of strong thunderstorms. Assuming your aircraft has the capability to overfly the storms, what is the minimum height you should cross them?

4. What is the difference between a gust front and a microburst?

5. Develop a thunderstorm climatology for your local flying area. What is the month with the greatest number of thunderstorm days? Least thunderstorm days? Explain the differences in monthly frequencies in terms of the availability of moisture (sources?), instability (causes?), and initial lifting (what provides it?).

6. Assume you are approaching a wet microburst at an altitude of 1,000 feet AGL. What visible indications (outside the cockpit) would you have of the presence of the microburst? What if the downburst was dry? What indications would you have inside the cockpit that you are approaching a downburst?

7. Document a thunderstorm event in your flying area. Obtain the following information for the period of the event: Surface Analysis, Radar Summary Chart, Stability Chart, and 500 mb Chart and the hourly weather observations. Write a brief description of the event (date, time, local weather changes), describe the pertinent features of the stability pattern (thunderstorm intensity and probability), explain echo movement and intensity, and identify the source of lifting.

8. Figure 1-16 pictorially summarizes TNT. Are all TNT processes represented? If not, modify or redraw the diagram to include those that are missing.

Chapter 4

CLEAR AIR TURBULENCE (CAT)

INTRODUCTION

Clear air turbulence (CAT) is that turbulence which occurs in the free atmosphere away from visible convective activity. "Free atmosphere" in this context means outside of the atmospheric boundary layer and primarily above 15,000 feet AGL. CAT includes what some texts and training manuals refer to as "high level turbulence," "high level frontal turbulence," and "jet stream turbulence." This definition recognizes that CAT mechanisms can also operate in nonconvective clouds.

The chapter begins with a description of the large scale environment of CAT. Next, the characteristics of clear air turbulence are examined and the mechanisms of its production are explained. In the last part of the chapter, some useful indicators of the presence of CAT are presented.

Section

THE ENVIRONMENT OF CLEAR AIR TURBULENCE

Clear air turbulence did not receive much attention prior to WWII because most aircraft did not fly high enough. The following is the recollection of Professor P.A. Sheppard, a noted British meteorologist, of his first experiences with high altitude turbulence in 1942.

> "Prior to 1941 they had meteorological flights in the vertical up to about 24,000 feet as a routine, but nothing above. Then they got some Spitfire flights going to about 40,000 feet, and within a short time began to get pilots' reports of severe gustiness at cirrus levels" (Hislop, 1951).

One of the most obvious and troublesome characteristics first noticed about this turbulence was that it often occurred in clear air. This was in sharp contrast to other turbulence types that were associated with distinct visible indicators such as convective clouds. Because CAT and its causes were often invisible, it was not very well understood when pilots first began to experience it.

With the emergence of the jet aircraft after the end of World War II, the nature of CAT became better defined. Over the last 40 years, a clear description of the large scale environment of CAT has developed from the experiences of pilots and from a number of formal scientific studies. For example, we know that CAT occurs more often in the upper troposphere and lower stratosphere than elsewhere in the free atmosphere. Furthermore, in that layer there are four important meteorological features that play significant roles in the production of CAT. They are macroscale waves, the tropopause, jet streams, and jet stream fronts. The purpose of this section is to describe and explain these features as important background for the understanding of CAT.

WEATHER MAPS AT CAT LEVELS

The upper troposphere and lower stratosphere is the layer between about 15,000 and 65,000 feet MSL. We will focus mainly on the region up to about 45,000 feet, where most of the air traffic is concentrated. Constant pressure analysis charts are the most common sources of information about meteorological conditions in this region. These charts include 500 mb (18,000 feet), 300 mb (30,000 feet), 250 mb (34,000 feet), and 200 mb (39,000 feet). Each number in parentheses is the approximate altitude of the respective pressure level. The 300 mb, 250 mb, and 200 mb analyses are often called **jet stream charts** because of the frequent occurrence of the jet stream near those levels.

Many general aviation pilots do not fly at such high levels and are not immediately familiar with these charts which are only treated briefly in elementary aviation meteorology courses (for example, see section 12 in *Aviation Weather Services, AC 00-45C*: FAA, 1985). Since we will make frequent references to jet stream charts in the remainder of this chapter, it is useful to pause briefly and review their format.

As an example, a portion of a 300 mb chart is shown in figure 4-1. This and other constant pressure analyses are available twice-a-day at 0000 and 1200 UTC. Observational data used in the analyses are plotted on the chart for individual reporting stations and aircraft. These data are indicated in the figure.

There are three sets of lines on each jet stream chart. These are labeled in figure 4-1. The lines represent analyses of the reported 300 mb heights (**contours**: every 120 meters, solid lines), temperatures (**isotherms**: every 5°C., heavy dashed lines), and wind speeds (**isotachs**: every 20 knots, thin dashed lines).

The interpretation of each set of lines on a jet stream chart is straightforward. The contours show the "topography" of that pressure level. For example, the height of the 300 mb level can vary from less than 28,000 feet to more than 32,000 feet on a 300 mb analysis for North America. These small height variations are critical for determining wind speed and

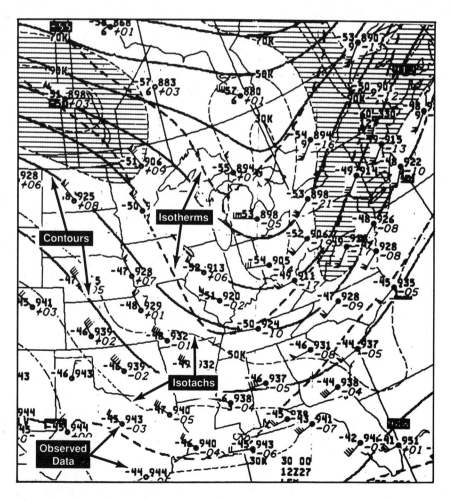

Figure 4-1. A portion of an analyzed 300 mb chart is shown as an example of a jet stream chart.

direction; however, for flight planning purposes, the chart can be assumed to be flat. Therefore 300 mb represents about 30,000 feet.

Contours on a constant pressure chart are parallel to the wind with the lower heights on the left looking downwind (in the Northern Hemisphere). Wind speeds are strongest where the contours are packed closely together. This pattern can be seen in figure 4-1 by comparing plotted wind reports and the contour pattern.

The isotherms show the temperature distribution at the 300 mb level at the time of the analysis. (Figure 4-1) Notice the regions of strong isotherm gradients (isotherms closely packed). Such areas may be associated with turbulence. More on this topic is presented below.

In figure 4-1, isotach patterns are alternately shaded and unshaded at 40 knot intervals for speeds greater than or equal to 70 knots. This makes it easy to locate the jet stream. Note that regions of strong horizontal shear are located where isotachs are close together. A detailed discussion of the relation of these features to turbulence is given in a later section.

MACROSCALE WAVES

Contours on upper air charts usually form wavy patterns. For clarity, we will refer to these patterns as **macroscale waves**. Not to be confused with mesoscale gravity waves which oscillate vertically, macroscale waves are much larger scale waves that oscillate primarily in a horizontal plane. A simple example is shown in **figure 4-2**.

As with any wave form, descriptions of macroscale waves are concerned with the wave troughs and crests. (Figure 4-2) In general, the trough receives more attention than the wave crest because it is frequently related to poor weather (including turbulence). Meteorologists frequently use terms such as "trough aloft," "upper trough," or "upper disturbance" to describe the trough portion of the macroscale wave.

The crest of the wave, where the heights of the pressure level are relatively high, is more often called a "ridge." (Figure 4-2) While the ridge is not generally associated with bad weather, it can be a location of CAT under certain circumstances.

A 500 mb chart with several macroscale wave disturbances is presented in figure 4-3. A few of the waves have been highlighted. Note that there is a large variation of wavelength from wave to wave. Globally, the range of wavelengths is about 500 n.m. to 5,000 n.m.

All of the waves usually move from west to east, but the waves with the shortest lengths move much faster than the longer waves. For example, a typical short wave will move eastward at about 600 n.m. per day (25 knots) while one of the longest waves may only move 100 n.m. or so in the same period. The fast-moving (shorter) macroscale waves contribute to the development of surface low pressure systems, especially when the upper wave trough is located just upwind (usually west) of the surface low. (Figure 4-4)

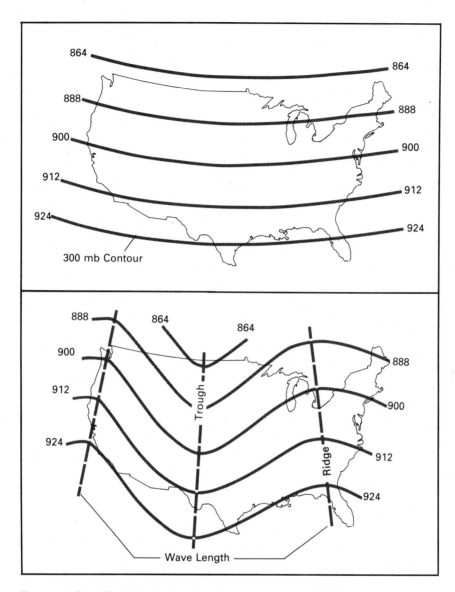

Figure 4-2. Simplified 300 mb chart showing contours only. Heights are in decameters. In the top diagram, the 300 mb contours are east-west lines. No macroscale waves exist. In the bottom diagram, a macroscale wave is present.

Macroscale wave troughs and ridges have many variations in shape and orientation. We will give several examples that are related to CAT in a later section.

THE TROPOPAUSE

Clear air turbulence has an affinity for the tropopause, so it is important that we know just what and where the tropopause is and how it behaves. The **tropopause** is defined simply as the boundary between the troposphere and the overlying stratosphere. A temperature sounding through the

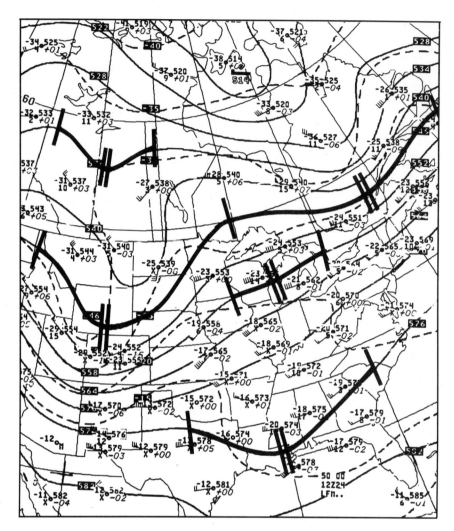

Figure 4-3. Typical constant pressure chart with macroscale waves. The contours have been emphasized in some areas to show the location and wavelength of some selected waves. Trough lines are indicated with double lines. Contours at 60 meter intervals and the isotachs are not shown because this is a 500 mb chart.

tropopause is illustrated in figure 4-5. In the lower part of the sounding, the upper troposphere is identified by temperature generally decreasing with height. Just above the tropopause (usually located above 25,000 feet MSL), the lapse rate decreases abruptly through a deep layer, reflecting the more stable environment of the stratosphere. In the standard atmosphere, the tropopause level is at 227 mb (about 36,000 feet) at a temperature of -56.5°C.

The dependence of the tropopause height on the temperature of the troposphere is illustrated in a pole-to-equator cross section in figure 4-6. Notice that the tropopause height rises from less than 30,000 feet (300 mb) near the pole to just above 34,000 feet (250 mb) in mid-latitudes to more than 53,000 feet (100 mb) near the equator.

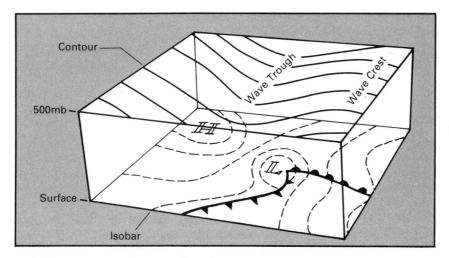

Figure 4-4. Perspective view of macroscale short wave aloft over surface cyclone. The contours are thin solid lines on the upper chart and sea level isobars are dashed on the lower chart. Note the wave trough is to the west of the surface low.

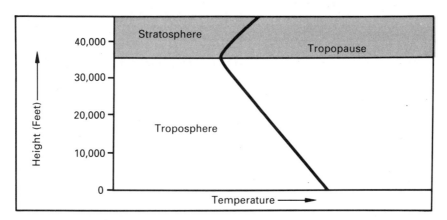

Figure 4-5. Temperature sounding. Tropopause location appears as a kink in the temperature curve between 30,000 and 40,000 feet MSL.

The tendency for the tropopause to be higher over warmer portions of the troposphere is also reflected in the seasonal variation of tropopause height. At a given location the tropopause is generally higher in summer and lower in winter. This is especially noticeable in middle and high latitudes.

Another important property of the tropopause is that it varies in height in the vicinity of macroscale waves such as those that are shown in figure 4-3. The tropopause is higher over tropospheric ridges and lower over tropospheric troughs. This means that as a macroscale wave moves from west to east across your location, the tropopause will fall with the approach of the upper trough and then rise after it passes.

Because of the slope of the tropopause between trough and ridge, a level flight path near the tropopause may pass from the troposphere to the

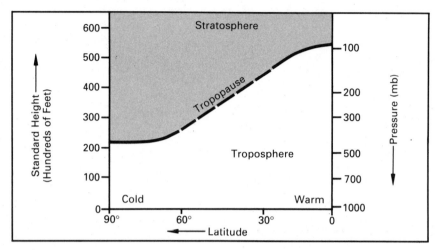

Figure 4-6. North-south cross section from pole (left) to equator (right). The troposphere, tropopause, and lower stratosphere (shaded) are shown.

stratosphere one or more times, depending on the location of the flight path relative to the macroscale wave. Since the chance of turbulence is greater at the tropopause, it is helpful to be able to anticipate such intersections.

In figure 4-6, the line that represents the tropopause in mid-latitudes is dashed to indicate that the tropopause height is more variable in that region compared to regions north and south. In fact, the tropopause will often exhibit a discontinuity in mid-latitudes, showing a low northern tropopause and a high southern tropopause that do not connect. This feature is called a **tropopause break** and is illustrated in figure 4-7. The tropopause break is important because the jet stream, another focus for CAT, is commonly found in that region.

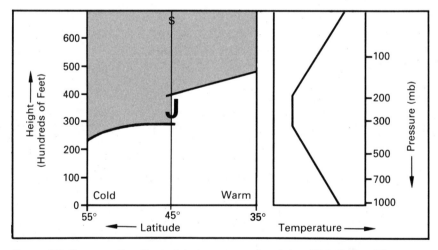

Figure 4-7. Cross section through a tropopause break in mid-latitudes. The stratosphere is shaded. The troposphere is warm to the right (high tropopause), and cold to the left (low tropopause). The jet stream directed into the page is usually found in the break between the two tropopauses ("J"). A temperature sounding along line "S" is shown on the right hand side. Note the signature of the double tropopause.

JET STREAMS

In a few latitude zones around the world, westerly winds increase markedly with height to the tropopause where narrow bands of high speed winds called **jet streams** are found. Not to be confused with the mesoscale low-level jet streams discussed in preceding chapters, these jet streams are located at high altitudes, are macroscale in length, and are usually much stronger than their low-level counterparts.

Jet streams are typically thousands of miles long, hundreds of miles wide, and five or six miles thick. The minimum speed of jet streams is about 60 knots. Maximum wind speeds in jet streams range to more than 250 knots. The highest jet stream speeds in the world have been observed near southern Japan. In the United States, the highest speeds normally are found from Texas through the southeastern states in the cooler months of the year.

A perspective diagram of a jet stream is shown in figure 4-8. The concentric circles around the **jet core** (the zone of maximum winds) are isotachs. This diagram is greatly exaggerated in the vertical to show details in that dimension.

More familiar representations of jet streams are found on jet stream charts described earlier. These correspond with horizontal cuts through the three-dimensional jet stream structure shown in figure 4-8. An example is given in figure 4-9 where the isotach pattern gives a good indication of the location of the jet stream. As a reference, the **jet axis** has been added to the standard analysis. This feature is the intersection of the jet core with a particular jet stream chart (300 mb in this case). It is a line which corresponds with the strongest winds in the jet stream at that level.

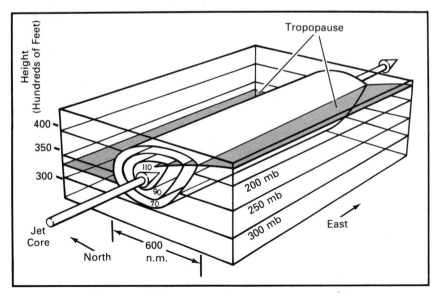

Figure 4-8. Perspective diagram of the jet stream showing the isotachs and tropopauses. Note the location of the jet stream in the break between the high tropopause on the warm side of the jet and the low tropopause on the cold side.

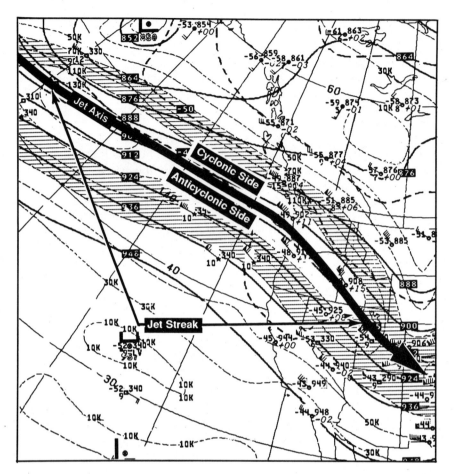

Figure 4-9. 300 mb constant pressure analysis. Jet axis is indicated by the heavy solid line with the arrowhead.

There is no guarantee that a jet core will lay exactly at the level of one of the jet stream charts (300 mb, 250 mb, or 200 mb). The strongest winds in a jet core may, in fact, be between two chart levels. Also, jet stream cores are not necessarily straight or horizontal. As seen in figure 4-9, they follow the macroscale wave patterns. Additionally, they are located at lower altitudes around troughs and higher altitudes around ridges.

When describing the jet stream, it is common practice to refer to the left side of the axis (looking downwind) as the **cyclonic side** of the jet stream and the right side as the **anticyclonic side**. This nomenclature is also illustrated in figure 4-9.

The properties of the jet stream are not necessarily the same on both sides of the jet axis. As illustrated in figure 4-9, wind speeds often decrease more rapidly with distance from the jet axis on the cyclonic side than on the anticyclonic side. Put another way, horizontal wind shear is typically stronger on the cyclonic side of the jet stream.

Other features common to jet streams are **jet streaks**. These are segments of the jet stream axis where the wind speeds are stronger than elsewhere. An example is shown in figure 4-9. Jet streaks are typically 1,000 n.m. long. They travel along the jet axis at speeds of about 600 n.m. per day (25 knots); that is, much slower than the observed jet stream winds.

Jet streaks often occur in the vicinity of macroscale waves. We will see that their stronger wind speeds and associated wind shears increase the likelihood of significant turbulence.

In wintertime, there are frequently two westerly jet streams over the continental U.S. as shown in figure 4-10. The northern jet stream is the **polar front jet stream** which is found near an altitude of about 30,000 feet (about 300 mb). In the south, the **subtropical jet stream** is located closer to 40,000 feet (near 200 mb).

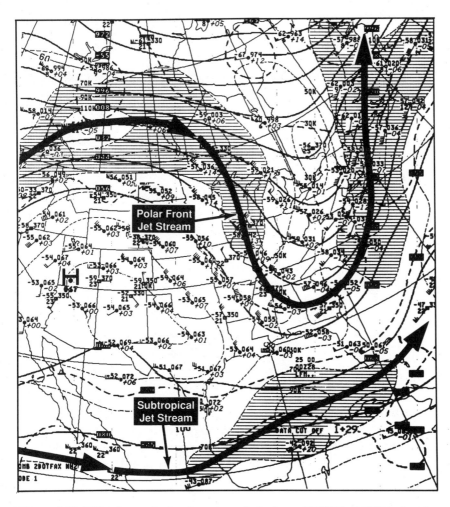

Figure 4-10. 250 mb constant pressure analysis (near 34,000 feet MSL) showing subtropical and polar front jet streams.

The polar front jet stream is closely related to the polar front and it tends to parallel the mid-latitude storm track. The latitude of this jet stream varies from day-to-day in response to the movement of warm and cold airmasses. At any time in the winter, a polar front jet stream may be found between about 30°N and 60°N.

In contrast, the subtropical jet stream is usually found between 20°N and 35°N over North America. Also, there are no surface weather fronts associated with the subtropical jet stream.

On some occasions, there may be more than two polar front jet streams across the contiguous 48 states. For example, there are situations when a polar front jet stream moves southward from Canada with a fresh outbreak of cold air while at the same time, an old polar front jet stream approaches the Gulf coast where the subtropical jet is often located. As the old polar front jet stream moves into the southern part of the U.S., it is often difficult to distinguish it from the subtropical jet when looking only at a jet stream chart. However, the presence of the two different jet streams can often be seen in a wind sounding for the area. An example is shown for a sounding from Cape Canaveral, Florida. (Figure 4-11) The polar front jet stream core is at a lower altitude than the core of the subtropical jet stream. This particular jet stream configuration is capable of creating multiple wind shear layers with a high potential for CAT. For example, the sounding shown in figure 4-11 was taken a few minutes after the Challenger disaster (Endlich, 1991). It has been hypothesized that CAT contributed significantly to the Challenger explosion.

In the summer, the subtropical jet stream is not present. A higher and weaker polar front jet occupies an average summer position near 45°N.

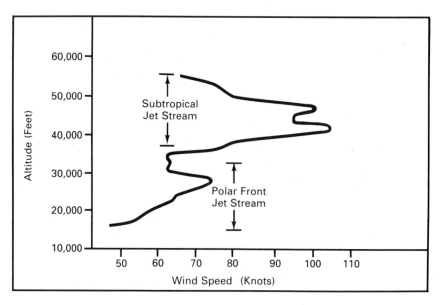

Figure 4-11. Wind sounding showing double speed maximum associated with the polar front jet stream moving under the subtropical jet stream.

Evidence of jet streams is found in satellite images as well as on constant pressure charts. So-called "jet stream cirrus" bands are often easy to identify on infrared images because of their large size and unique shape. As shown in figure 4-12, the jet stream axis parallels the cirrus band and is positioned in the clear, just to the left of the sharp edge (looking downwind).

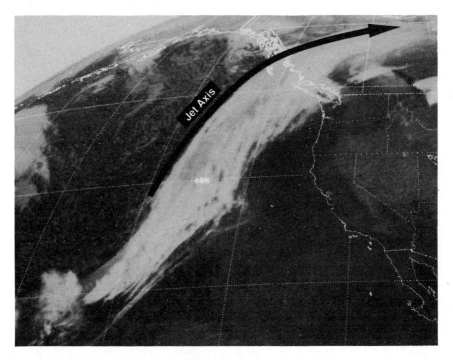

Figure 4-12. Jet stream cirrus band. The approximate position of the jet stream axis is indicated by the solid line with the arrowhead.

JET STREAM FRONTS

As described in Chapter 2, fronts in the lower troposphere are zones of transition between airmasses of different temperatures. Furthermore, frontal zones are stable layers which often contain horizontal and vertical wind shears and turbulence. Frontal zones with similar properties also occur in the upper troposphere whenever a jet stream is present. These **jet stream fronts** or "jet fronts" can be locations of significant CAT. It is important to know where they are located with respect to jet streams.

HORIZONTAL STRUCTURE

If you were to fly from the anticyclonic side to the cyclonic side of a jet stream at 20,000 feet, you would observe a rapid decrease in winds and temperatures as soon as you crossed the region of maximum winds (the jet axis). This transition zone is a jet stream front. It is 60 to 180 n.m. wide and is always located on the cyclonic side of the jet axis.

If you made the same flight at successively higher levels, you would find that although the horizontal wind shear would remain strong in the frontal zone (a change of one knot per nautical mile is possible), the horizontal temperature difference would become smaller until you reached the level of the maximum winds where there is no horizontal temperature difference. Above the core (in the stratosphere) the temperature is usually colder on the anticyclonic side of the jet than on the cyclonic side.

Jet stream fronts are not shown on constant pressure analysis charts (unlike surface fronts on a surface analysis chart). However, the transition zones of jet stream fronts are often obvious on jet stream charts as narrow bands of large temperature gradients and/or strong, horizontal wind shears paralleling the jet stream on its cyclonic side. The stronger the jet stream, the better defined the jet stream frontal zone. Examples of these zones are shown for the polar front jet at 500 mb and at 250 mb in figure 4-13.

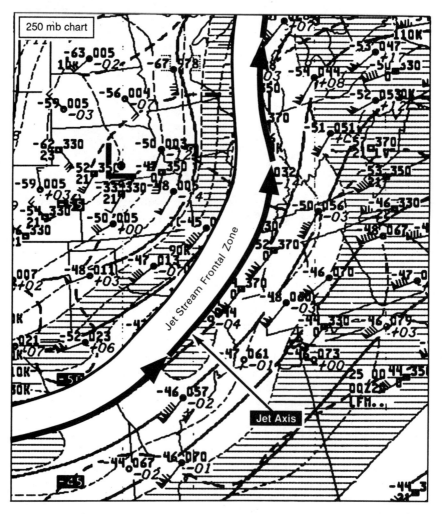

Figure 4-13. 250 mb (above) and 500 mb (next page) constant pressure analyses with added jet axes (heavy solid lines with arrowheads) and jet stream frontal zones labeled. Note the temperature change across the frontal zone is large at 500 mb but small at 250 mb. Wind reports indicate strong horizontal shear across the frontal zone at both levels.

VERTICAL STRUCTURE

Although constant pressure charts provide useful information about the structure of jet stream fronts, additional detail can be found by examining a vertical cross section of the jet stream. Such a diagram is shown in figure 4-14.

The jet stream frontal zone slopes downward from the tropopause break, below the jet core and between the warm and cold air in upper troposphere. Because the vertical scale of figure 4-14 is greatly exaggerated, the slope of the front also appears to be much greater than it actually is.

There are two important features in the cross section that are related to CAT. One of these is the region of strong shear just above the section of the tropopause that slopes downward over the jet core. The second is the zone of relatively strong horizontal and vertical wind shears in the jet stream front. Notice that the maximum winds at each level below the core are on the warm (anticyclonic) side of the frontal zone. As described earlier, this means that a flight that crosses the front from the anticyclonic to the

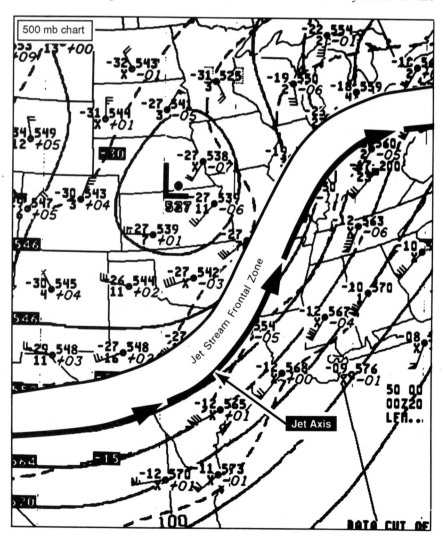

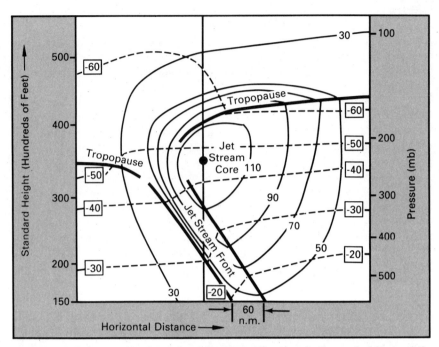

Figure 4-14. Cross section through a jet stream. The view is downwind (toward the east) with the cyclonic side of the jet on the left (north) and the anticyclonic side on the right (south). The cross section shows isotachs (knots), isotherms (°C), tropopauses, and the boundaries of the jet stream frontal zone. The vertical line is the location of the temperature and wind sounding shown in Figure 4-15.

cyclonic side of the jet stream will encounter the strongest winds before entering the frontal zone.

Figure 4-15 is a temperature and wind sounding through the jet stream front. The sounding location corresponds with the vertical line in the

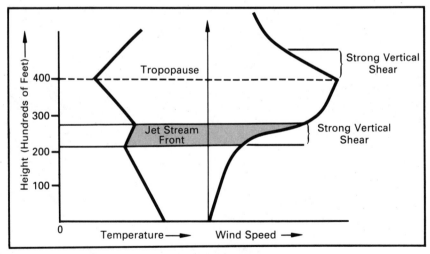

Figure 4-15. Temperature (left) and wind (right) soundings along the vertical line in the center of figure 4-14. Note the location of the jet stream front (lowest inversion), the tropopause, and the regions of strongest vertical wind shear.

center of figure 4-14. The frontal zone (stable layer) is clearly visible in the temperature sounding, as is the tropopause. The wind speed sounding shows significant vertical wind shears in the frontal layer and just above the tropopause.

Only the most common upper tropospheric jet streams and jet stream structures have been discussed in this brief description of the large scale environment of CAT. Keep in mind that other jet streams exist in the atmosphere. For example, a westerly jet stream is found at high latitudes and at very high altitudes in the stratosphere during wintertime. Also, an easterly jet is found near the tropical tropopause to the south of the Himalayas in the summer. Descriptions of these and other jet streams not mentioned here may be found in the References and Recommended Reading section of this book (see Palmen and Newton, 1969).

THE NATURE OF CLEAR AIR TURBULENCE

The impact of clear air turbulence on the aviation industry is large. It accounts for about 45% of all turbulence reported by air carriers. Many studies have been carried out over the last 40 years to better understand and predict CAT. Research efforts have included the collection and analysis of pilot reports; special field measurements by instrumented aircraft; studies using radar, lasers, and satellite observations; and theoretical studies. The results of this research together with the experience of pilots have provided a variety of information about the characteristics and causes of CAT. In this section, we will review that information.

OBSERVED CHARACTERISTICS

In the next few paragraphs, average CAT characteristics are described. These include frequency of occurrence, dimensions of turbulence regions, and durations. Finally, characteristics of severe and extreme CAT are illustrated with a few incident descriptions.

SOME STATISTICS

The analysis of many thousands of aircraft reports from around the world (Endlich and Mancuso, 1968; Colson, 1969; Vinnechenko, et al, 1980) has produced a large amount of information about the location, intensity, and frequency of CAT occurrences. Researchers, forecasters, and aircraft designers use these statistics to describe the average characteristics of CAT. You should note that in such descriptions, the terms "frequency" and "probability" are often used interchangeably. This simply means it is assumed that the sample of CAT observations on which the frequencies are based represents all future CAT observations. Since the statistics presented here are based on large samples, this is not a bad assumption.

The probability of randomly encountering CAT of any intensity along a 100 n.m. segment of flight path somewhere in the upper troposphere or lower stratosphere is about 15%. The probability decreases to about 6% for moderate or greater CAT and to less than 1% for severe or greater. Although the small probabilities of significant turbulence (moderate or greater) may seem to minimize the importance of this turbulence type, three important points must be kept in mind when interpreting them.

1. While not life-threatening, light turbulence contributes to passenger and crew discomfort, and prolonged exposure to turbulence of any intensity may cause pilot fatigue. Avoidance is advisable whenever possible.

2. Clear air turbulence does not occur "randomly." With certain meteorological flow patterns, probabilities of all intensities can be significantly higher than those quoted above. These meteorological situations must be recognized in order to minimize turbulence encounters.

3. While the probabilities of severe or greater clear air turbulence are small, they are not zero. Such incidents do occur causing injuries and occasional aircraft damage. Avoidance is of prime importance.

CAT occurs more frequently in winter than in summer. Some studies also suggest that it is generally more frequent over continents than oceans; however, this tendency only becomes very clear over mountainous regions. The more numerous occurrences of CAT near mountains are due to the added influence of mountain waves. This effect will be discussed in the next chapter under the topic of mountain wave turbulence (MWT).

The frequency of clear air turbulence generally increases with height from the midtroposphere to a maximum between 30,000 to 45,000 feet, then decreases rapidly. These altitudes are typical of the tropopause and the jet stream.

DIMENSIONS

Clear air turbulence commonly occurs in strongly sheared stable layers; the shape of the turbulence patches reflects the layered structure of their stable environments. CAT usually occurs in thin layers that are stretched in the direction of the wind. The patches average less than 2,000 feet in depth, 10 to 40 miles in the crosswind direction, and 50 miles or more downwind. The flat appearance has led some Russian investigators to describe CAT layers as "blini" (pancakes).

Dimensions of the turbulence patches are smaller where the air is very stable (for example, in the stratosphere) and larger where the turbulence is more intense. Turbulent regions several thousand feet deep and more than a hundred miles in length have been observed.

The typical structure of CAT regions leads to two helpful rules of thumb (FAA, 1988).

1. If jet stream turbulence is encountered with direct tailwinds or headwinds, a change of flight level or course should be initiated since these turbulent areas are shallow and elongated with the winds.

2. If jet stream turbulence is encountered in a crosswind, it is not so important to change course or flight level since the turbulent areas are narrow across the wind.

DURATIONS

The time that an aircraft spends in turbulence usually decreases as the intensity of the CAT increases. For example, the average continuous flight time in a patch of light or greater CAT is about 16 minutes while the typical duration for severe or greater CAT is only a few minutes. The longest continuous episodes of light or greater CAT reported by a large group of airline pilots were mostly in the 20 minute to 2.5 hour range, although a few pilots reported continuous events of 4 hours or more. (Dreyling, 1973)

Another characteristic of CAT related to duration is its intermittency; that is, encounters are typically described as "burst-like." This is especially true of the most intense turbulence. Similar patchiness was noted with turbulence in the stable boundary layer.

Average durations of CAT described above (along the flight path) should not be confused with the length of time that CAT persists at a specific location. CAT outbreaks in a particular area may last for several hours although an aircraft may be exposed to CAT for only a few minutes as it passes through the turbulent layer.

The knowledge that CAT layers tend to persist is useful when interpreting PIREPs. Put another way, a practical question is: For what area and for how long is a single CAT PIREP valid? Studies have shown that, on the average, a PIREP of moderate or greater CAT represents conditions within about 80 n.m. of the report location for a period of three to four hours. These averages do not apply to other types of turbulence.

CAT INCIDENT DESCRIPTIONS

While a description of the average characteristics of CAT is useful for developing a model of a "typical" CAT occurrence, it does not include details that give insight into the extremes of CAT. Some examples are given below with excerpts from actual reports.

> Just before reaching Gander, ATC released the airliner to climb from FL330 to FL370. At FL360 the Mach number increased rapidly and the aircraft assumed an exaggerated nose-up pitch. Rate of climb exceeded 4,000 f.p.m. and FL380 was reached before the aircraft could be brought smoothly to a straight-and-level condition when a rapid return to FL370 was made and Gander ATC was informed of the excursion. Severe turbulence in clear air was experienced during this time, but the main concern was the excess of airspeed and rate-of-climb. The aircraft was subsequently cleared to FL310 where conditions were smooth (Chambers, 1973).

> Cleared to FL240, the aircraft encountered light turbulence at 21,000 feet. At 23,000 feet, it was like hitting a brick wall. Severe clear air turbulence, power to idle, speed breaks extended, aircraft shaking violently. Unable to see cockpit and instruments. Aircraft stopped climbing at 24,700 feet. Aircraft was cleared to lower altitude, FL230, which was then assigned by ATC. First officer had a hard time communicating as the mike was flying around the cockpit on its flex cord. Unable to see it or reach the transponder. Aircraft pitched 10 degrees nose down to 20 degrees nose up while rolling 50-70 degrees right and left. No aircraft damage or passenger injuries.

> After leveling off at FL230 and while on autopilot, aircraft was cleared to climb to FL330. Out of approximately FL240, it encountered severe turbulence which disengaged the autopilot and pitched the aircraft nose down 14 to 20 degrees. Turbulence was

of such intensity that instruments were difficult to read. Aircraft recovered after 3,000 to 4,000 foot loss in altitude.

Crew reported encounter with strong "rolling" clear air turbulence at 31,000 without warning. Aircraft rolled to the right with yawing motion. Autopilot was disconnected and manual control inputs were used to right the aircraft. Some moments later, a second encounter with the same type of turbulence was handled in the same manner. Center had no reports of turbulence. One passenger and one flight attendant were injured.

As Mach 1.3 was reached, approach control passed a message from another (fighter) aircraft that turbulence in clear air was encountered between 25,000 and 28,000 feet. This message was acknowledged, but flight remained smooth until reaching Mach 1.7 at 31,000 feet. The entry into turbulence was very sudden, and for several seconds the pilot could do nothing but hang onto the stick and throttles. During this period it was impossible to control the aircraft which was bucking violently in every direction. The actual deviations from the flight path were thought to be small, but the sharpness, random nature, and high frequency of the bumps were disorienting. At this stage the pilot thought the aircraft might disintegrate. A determined effort was required to place the aircraft in a climb and to throttle the engine. The buffeting ceased on passing through 36,000 feet (Roach, 1969).

CAUSES

In the following paragraphs, we will describe a number of possible atmospheric causes of CAT. Since wake turbulence and maneuvering may also be a source of bumpiness in flight, a brief description of those influences will also be given.

SHEARING-GRAVITY WAVES

Our previous descriptions of the statistical characteristics and environment of CAT have shown that it occurs in relatively thin layers and displays a high degree of intermittency. Furthermore, it is found in the upper troposphere and lower stratosphere where strongly sheared stable layers are common. This evidence, in addition to some special observations and theoretical studies, has led investigators to the conclusion that a major cause of CAT is the breakdown of shearing-gravity waves.

Shearing-gravity waves associated with CAT have wave heights (vertical distance from wave trough to crest) of 100 to 1,500 feet. Wavelengths range from a few hundred feet to a few miles. Bumpiness in flight is caused by up- and downdrafts created by the wave motions, especially if the waves actually "break." The latter process occurs when the waves are subjected to strong vertical wind shear. In the idealized case, the shear causes the more dense air in the wave crest to move over the less dense air in the wave trough. This is an absolutely unstable situation, so the air "turns over." The entire process usually takes 5 to 30 minutes. An example of the wave-breaking pattern in the atmosphere is given in figure 4-16 where clouds just happened to be present to show the relative motions of the air.

The existence of such cloud forms has been recognized by pilots for many years, although their meaning has not always been known. The following is a description of an encounter with shearing-gravity wave clouds and turbulence experienced more than 40 years ago by Capt C.D. Wilson of British European Airways (Hislop, 1951).

> . . . On that occasion during a descent from 35,000 feet, the crew noticed a curious cloud formation near 25,000 feet. The most remarkable feature of the cloud was a series of corrugations like teeth isolated in clear air. Those "teeth" appeared singly and in groups of two or three and were from 50 to 100 feet high and some 200 feet apart. Generally the outlines . . . were well defined, although in one or two cases, the peaks of the teeth seemed to be shrouded in wispy clouds. Quite marked turbulence was experienced on flying through some of the teeth and also in the clear air outside them. (Figure 4-17)

Related "Herring Bone" cloud patterns often appear in decks of high and middle clouds which lay in sheared layers near the jet stream. (Figure 4-18) The bands are caused as clouds thicken in the updrafts and dissipate in the downdrafts of the shearing-gravity waves. Such banded cloud forms are known generally as **billow clouds**.

When observed from the ground, a group of billow clouds will show an overall movement that corresponds with the average wind speed and direction in the cloud layer. The smaller scale wave motions will usually be more difficult to see, but if the clouds are observed for five or ten minutes, wave motions and breaking will often be evident in the formation and dissipation of individual cloud bands.

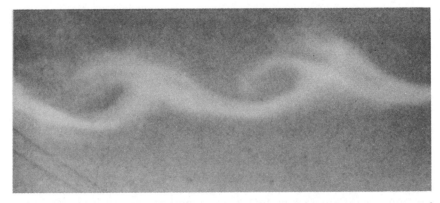

Figure 4-16. Breaking shearing-gravity waves are made visible by the presence of clouds. Vertical wind shear has caused the crests of the waves to move over the troughs. The wind shear is directed from right to left. Two wind profiles that could produce such shear are wind from the right with speeds increasing with height, or wind from the left with speeds decreasing with height.

Figure 4-17. A side-on view of clouds in shearing-gravity waves after the waves have "broken"; that is, they have started to overturn. The clouds resemble "teeth" as described by Captain Wilson.

Figures 4-18. Billow clouds indicate vertical wind shear in a high level cloud deck near the jet stream. (Photo courtesy of A. Rangno)

All billow clouds do not necessarily indicate the presence of shearing-gravity waves. They may also be caused by a number of other small scale circulations. However, if billows are observed in the vicinity of a known wind shear layer or the cloud forms are similar to those shown in figures 4-16 through 4-18, then it is very likely that shearing-gravity wave activity is present in the layer.

Even with a positive identification of billow clouds, it is not a simple matter to infer the magnitude of either the turbulence or the shear from visual observations alone. Similar cloud forms may be caused by different combinations of vertical shear and stability. There is some evidence that the probability of significant CAT is greater when related billow clouds have a spacing of 2 to 3 n.m. Regardless of their appearance, a conservative interpretation of billow clouds is recommended when they are observed. Layers of such clouds should always be approached with caution.

Perhaps a more important point about billow clouds is that the occurrence of these clouds in the vicinity of clear air turbulence is the exception, not the rule. You cannot depend on them to be present to provide a visual warning of CAT.

The recognition of shearing-gravity waves as a primary cause of CAT raises a question. Why do 50 mile-long pancake-shaped turbulent layers form when the waves are at the most only a few miles in length? The answer is that the vertically sheared stable layers which provide a favorable environment for the development of CAT are produced by much larger scale phenomena such as the jet stream. Associated shear layers typically measure hundreds of miles on a side and have lifetimes of a day or more (versus 5 to 30 minutes for a shearing-gravity wave).

Within these larger scale sheared layers, there is often a variation in the strength and stability of the shear from one location to another. Under these conditions, groups of shearing-gravity waves will grow and break-down into turbulence where the local shear is large enough to overcome the stability of the layer. Thus, a turbulence patch which is significantly smaller than the large scale sheared layer (but larger than an individual wave) will develop and be swept downwind, mixing with its surroundings and weakening. This process acts to reduce shear and stability in some parts of the large scale sheared layer and to strengthen them in others.

Since the larger scale sheared layer has a much longer lifetime than a single shearing-gravity wave, the processes described above will cause turbulence intensity to vary throughout that layer as turbulent patches develop and dissipate. This behavior explains why an aircraft can experience intermittent CAT whether it penetrates a sheared layer just briefly or flies within one for a considerable length of time. This patchiness is illustrated in figure 4-19.

In figure 4-19, the local vertical shear in layer 1 is insufficient to cause the shearing-gravity waves to overturn. In contrast, shear in layer 2 causes waves to break producing turbulence. The turbulent mixing in layer 2 increases shear in layer 3, causing waves to break, producing yet another turbulent region.

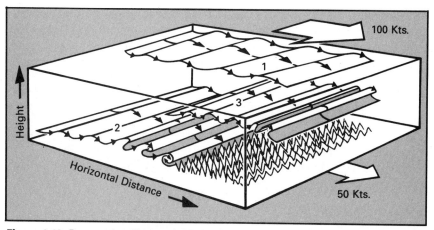

Figure 4-19. Perspective diagram of intermittent turbulent patches produced by the overturning of shearing-gravity waves within a vertically sheared stable layer. Large scale winds are indicated by broad arrows at the top and bottom of the diagram. Vertical shear and stability within the layer will vary as individual turbulent patches develop and dissipate.

The idealized wave patterns in figure 4-19 are the result of variations in speed shear alone. This ensures that the wave crests and troughs have the same orientations in the three sublayers. However, it is important to note that directional shear is also common in the real atmosphere. Since shearing-gravity wave fronts are perpendicular to the wind shear vector, only slight changes in wind directions in figure 4-19 could cause the waves to be oriented differently in each sublayer.

The processes described in figure 4-19 stress the important role of the larger scale flow features in producing CAT. This is a fortunate state of affairs, because it allows the presence of microscale CAT (which is not observed well) to be implied from large scale flow patterns (which are observed well). More on this will be presented later in the chapter.

OTHER ATMOSPHERIC GRAVITY WAVES

Although shearing-gravity waves are thought to be the primary cause of CAT, there are other mechanisms that can also contribute to CAT occurrences. These include internal gravity waves generated by boundary layer convection, mountains, thunderstorms, and jet streaks. Such waves are typically much longer than shearing-gravity waves. Their potential influence on aircraft is demonstrated by the following example (Roach, 1969).

> Airliner enroute over the North Atlantic at FL350, Mach 0.8, and ground speed 530 knots. During cruise in clear air, there was a very rapid fall in temperature from about -63°C to -72°C followed by the onset of moderate turbulence with appreciable IAS fluctuations. Pilot recognized cyclic character of the turbulence, disengaged altitude hold and "rode the waves" for an hour. The aircraft rose (as much as) 2,000 feet in the wave. It descended as rapidly as 1,500 f.p.m. Wavelength as recorded in the altitude trace was about 40 n.m. with an average wave height of 3,500 feet. Flight was just below tropopause in "fairly" stable air.

Besides the production of such cyclical and smooth motions, atmospheric gravity waves may contribute to smaller scale turbulence by increasing vertical wind shear, or by breaking when the wave heights become very large.

As illustrated in the above example, gravity waves (including shearing-gravity waves and mountain waves) in very stable environments may also cause large temperature variations in short distances along the flight path. Research aircraft flying in the lower stratosphere have recorded temperature changes of more than 19°C in one nautical mile (Nicholls, 1973). Such fluctuations have potentially serious influences on engine performance at high altitudes.

CONVECTION

Other sources of clear air turbulence (usually light) are layers of convection at high levels in the troposphere. Such instability can be caused when a layer of cooler air is carried (advected) over a layer of relatively warm air. If the lapse rate becomes unstable, convective currents will develop. If the moisture supply is sufficient, altocumulus or cirrocumulus will form. (Figure 4-20)

Light CAT can also be experienced in the vicinity of cirrus uncinus ("mare's tails" or "hooked cirrus") where vertical gusts of 400 f.p.m. have been measured. (Figure 4-21) This turbulence is due to convection that forms the upper part (the "head") of the cloud. The convection generates ice crystals that fall out and form the long feathery "tail" which often appears bent because of vertical wind shear.

Figure 4-20. A layer of high level convection is indicated by cirrocumulus clouds. Cumulus clouds are also visible over the hills to the left.

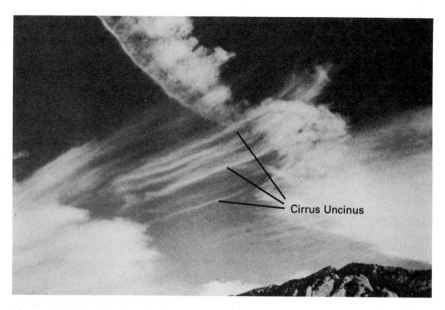

Cirrus Uncinus

Figure 4-21. Hooked cirrus indicates potential regions of light turbulence and wind shear.

WAKE TURBULENCE

Wake turbulence was discussed in Chapter 2 in regard to its impact on the critical phases of takeoff and landing. As illustrated below, wake vortexes continue to be generated while the aircraft is in flight.

> Commuter aircraft failed to maintain adequate separation, encountered wake turbulence at 27,000 feet. Turbulence caused aircraft to momentarily climb 300 feet above assigned altitude.

Although significant wake effects have been observed as far as 15 miles behind large jet aircraft, it is more common for wake vortexes to dissipate a few miles behind the generating aircraft as they interact and descend. Breakdown finally (and often suddenly) occurs when outside air is mixed (entrained) into the vortexes. Their persistence at high altitudes depends on aircraft design and atmospheric conditions. Atmospheric turbulence will hasten the dissipation of the vortexes. Vortex breakdown is often visible in condensation trails (**contrails**) behind the aircraft.

MANEUVERING

The strongly sheared stable layers in the vicinity of the jet stream can be the source of heavy g-loads on aircraft, even when atmospheric turbulence is insignificant. Such loads are often caused by control inputs (**maneuvering**) to adjust for rapidly changing wind conditions. Although a comprehensive treatment of this problem is beyond the scope of this text, it is important to know that vertical accelerations due to maneuvering can be as large as those experienced in severe atmospheric turbulence. The potential problem is illustrated with the following example.

A DC-10 was descending from 41,000 feet when it reported a "turbulence" upset at 40,000 feet. Vertical accelerations deviated from normal by more than 1.0g. The incident occurred as the aircraft (flying downwind) was descending into a jet stream. After a brief period of increasing tailwinds, the wind suddenly decreased over a layer about 500 feet deep and then increased again as the aircraft continued its descent. The reported "turbulence" incident occurred where the wind shear reversed. Analysis of flight recorder data revealed that the strong vertical accelerations were the result of control inputs made to compensate for vertical wind shear. Several passengers were injured, although atmospheric turbulence intensities were actually very small.

ESTIMATING CAT POTENTIAL

The preceding discussion has explained why CAT favors the upper troposphere and lower stratosphere. That environment is characterized by sheared stable layers. The vertical shear, in particular, promotes the development of shearing-gravity waves and their breakdown to microscale turbulence.

Although this conceptual model has helped us understand CAT, there is a problem when it comes to its practical application. CAT is not observed well and, except for an occasional PIREP, its presence and intensity must be estimated from larger scale measurements and analyses. Because this procedure introduces uncertainties, it is more accurate to describe CAT occurrences in terms of probabilities rather than a simple yes or no.

When using macroscale information (for example, jet stream charts) to estimate the likelihood of microscale CAT, it is important to realize that even in the most favorable circumstances CAT probabilities will be much less than 100%. What is important in the interpretation of such probabilities is how they compare to the chance of randomly encountering turbulence. For example, if the chance of moderate or greater CAT is estimated to be 20% along a 100 n.m. segment of flight track near a jet stream front, that probability would be considered "large" compared to the 6% chance of randomly encountering CAT of that intensity. In the following discussion, we will describe such areas as being "more likely" to have moderate or greater turbulence, or as having a "higher probability" of moderate or greater CAT, even though there may only be a one-in-five (or smaller) chance.

In this section, we review macroscale patterns related to the occurrence of clear air turbulence. Knowledge of these will help you identify potential CAT regions on commonly available analysis and forecast maps. Furthermore, this background will help you interpret CAT forecasts issued by NWS and other agencies.

A USEFUL MODEL

When examining weather maps (usually jet stream charts) for evidence of CAT, it is helpful to have a model that relates microscale CAT to the relevant features of the larger scale environment: the tropopause, jet stream, and jet stream front. Such a model is shown in figure 4-22.

The important turbulence features of figure 4-22 are described by several well-known rules of thumb (Serebreny, et al, 1960; Chandler, 1986; FAA, 1988; Stack, 1991)

In general:

1. Jet streams stronger than 110 knots (at the core) are apt to have areas of significant turbulence near them in the sloping tropopause above the core and in the jet stream front below the core.

2. CAT is a minimum near the level of maximum winds where the vertical shear is a minimum.

In the frontal zone:

3. The most intense CAT in the jet stream frontal zone lies about a third of the distance between the level of the jet core and the ground.

   The colder the airmass, the lower the CAT regions in the frontal zone. general, CAT is located at lower levels in frontal zones in high ..titudes and in winter.

Near the tropopause:

5. CAT at tropopause level will be moderate or greater when tropopause temperatures are cold (below standard), winds are strong, and a strong temperature inversion exists just above the tropopause. Probabilities of CAT decrease with warmer temperatures and lighter winds at tropopause levels, and with weaker stability above the tropopause.

6. The probability of moderate or greater CAT at the tropopause is small when the tropopause is low (less than about 31,000 feet). Significant CAT is observed primarily when the tropopause level exceeds 34,000 feet.

7. If turbulence is expected with a sloping tropopause, watch the outside air temperature. The point of coldest temperature along the flight path will indicate the tropopause penetration. Turbulence will be most pronounced on the stratospheric (upper) side of the sloping tropopause.

The caveat, "If turbulence is expected," in the last rule should remind you that the tropopause is nonturbulent much more often than it is turbulent. Additional conditions (to be discussed below) must be met for the occurrence of turbulence at that level.

Probably the most important aspect of figure 4-22 and the associated rules of thumb is that they focus our attention on specific regions of the jet stream that are favorable for CAT. The model also helps us not only to anticipate CAT, but also to explain reported CAT incidents. The following are two examples.

In Chapter 1, a crash of a Learjet was given as an example of an extreme effect of CAT. Postflight analysis of that case revealed that a second Learjet crossed the same airspace 16 minutes after the crash. The pilot reported the worst turbulence he had ever experienced as a Learjet pilot. The sky was clear with light haze at FL450. With autopilot engaged, his aircraft encountered three successive events in which the aircraft violently pitched up, down, and up again, with successive altitude gains and losses of 300 to

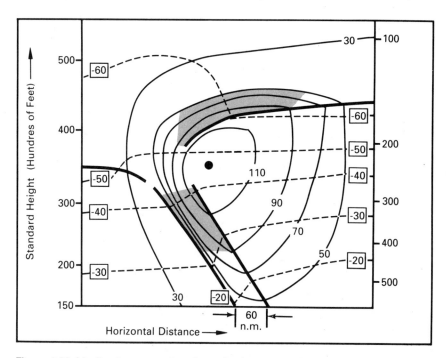

Figure 4-22. Idealized cross section through a jet stream. Thin solid lines are isotachs. Heavy solid lines are tropopauses and boundaries of the jet stream frontal zone. The most likely zones of significant turbulence are shaded. Note: the slope of the front is greatly exaggerated, and altitudes of various features may be significantly different depending on latitude and season.

800 feet. The meteorological analysis showed that the accident occurred in a jet stream front with significant vertical wind shear. (McLean, 1986)

An independent investigation of the explosion of the Space Shuttle Challenger concluded that turbulence in a jet stream frontal zone contributed strongly to the loads which caused the second rupture of the O-ring seal leading to the final structural breakup. (Endlich, 1991)

Although the main characteristics of the model in figure 4-22 will always exist in the presence of the jet stream, there will be differences depending on the strength of the jet stream. That strength depends to a large degree on the location of the jet stream relative to macroscale waves. It follows that the likelihood of CAT will be greater with some macroscale wave patterns than with others. We examine these variations next.

MAP PATTERNS AND CAT

Over the last 30 years or so, meteorologists have identified several patterns on constant pressure charts that are favorable for the occurrence of CAT. Since about two-thirds of all severe clear air turbulence incidents occur near the jet stream, our concentration is on that phenomenon.

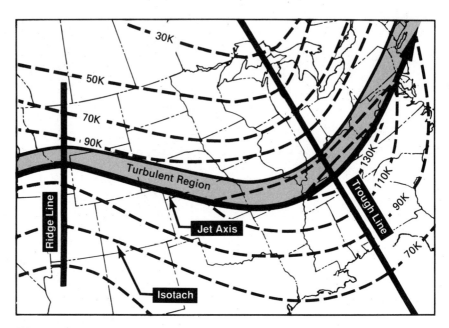

FIG 4-23. 300 mb analysis with isotachs (dashed, in knots) and jet stream axis (solid, with arrowhead) in the vicinity of a macroscale wave. Favored regions of CAT occurrences are shaded.

BASIC PATTERNS

Figure 4-23 is a simplified 300 mb chart showing the isotach pattern in a macroscale wave. Jet stream and wave features that are important in the diagnosis of CAT are labeled. Note that the axis of the jet stream has been added for clarity.

Earlier, we saw that the probability of randomly encountering moderate or greater CAT along a 100 n.m. portion of the flight path in the upper troposphere and low stratosphere is only about 6%. In the general vicinity of the jet stream, that probability can be more than double, depending on the strength of the jet stream and just where the flight path is relative to the jet stream axis.

With reference to figure 4-23, CAT is more likely to occur in a narrow band on the cyclonic side of the jet stream axis. From previous discussions, we recognize this region as the jet stream frontal zone. Note also, that along the cyclonic side of the jet axis, significant CAT is more frequent in the ridges.

SPECIFIC PATTERNS

The probability of CAT increases as the curvature of the jet stream axis and jet stream speeds increase. This often occurs as macroscale waves intensify. Under these conditions, certain unique flow patterns develop that are conducive to CAT outbreaks and are easily identified on jet stream charts. Some of the most common patterns are illustrated and discussed in the following paragraphs. In all the patterns presented below, unless otherwise noted, the turbulence typically occurs in the layer from about 6,000 feet below the tropopause to 2,000 feet above (FAA, 1975, 1988; Hopkins, 1977; Vinnechenko et al, 1980; USAF, 1982; Chandler, 1986).

Figure 4-24 indicates areas of increased probability of moderate or greater CAT associated with a sharp upper level ridge. In the top diagram, if jet stream winds are 140 knots or greater in the ridge, severe CAT can be expected in the area indicated. If the ridge is rapidly growing, it is particularly susceptible to CAT. As illustrated in the lower part of figure 4-24, if the ridge becomes very narrow, the probability of turbulence increases along the ridge line. The intensity of the turbulence depends on the amount of horizontal wind shear across the ridge line.

The following report is a description of CAT experienced in a ridge (Chambers, 1973).

An airliner was enroute over the North Atlantic at FL330 when severe turbulence was suddenly encountered and a flight attendant was injured. The flight recorder showed a 1.15g deviation from normal acceleration. The turbulence was severe over a distance of about 150 n.m. in anticyclonic flow near a 150 knot jet stream.

Sharply curved flow in a macroscale wave trough is also conducive to moderate or greater CAT. The larger the horizontal wind shear across the trough line, the more intense the turbulence. An example is shown in figure 4-25.

CAT probabilities are generally greater wherever jet streams undergo **diffluence** (splitting) or **confluence** (joining). There are many situations where these patterns occur; however, one of the best examples is a cutoff low. (Figure 4-26) As the cutoff develops, moderate or greater CAT is favored upwind of the cutoff low where the flow is diffluent. It is also favored downwind where the flow is confluent. Once the low completes the process of cutting off, the turbulence diminishes to light near the low. However, if the "neck" of the low is narrow, turbulence will persist there after the cutoff low is fully developed in a pattern similar to a sharp trough.

An example of a turbulent incident near a cutoff low is presented below (Chambers, 1973).

The airliner was descending from FL410 in the clear with a tailwind of 130 knots when, at FL350, severe turbulence was suddenly encountered for a period of about 30 seconds causing the aircraft to pitch and roll violently. The maximum vertical acceleration increment was 1.25g. A passenger sustained a broken leg. The turbulence occurred near the polar front jet which had moved across the top of a cutoff low.

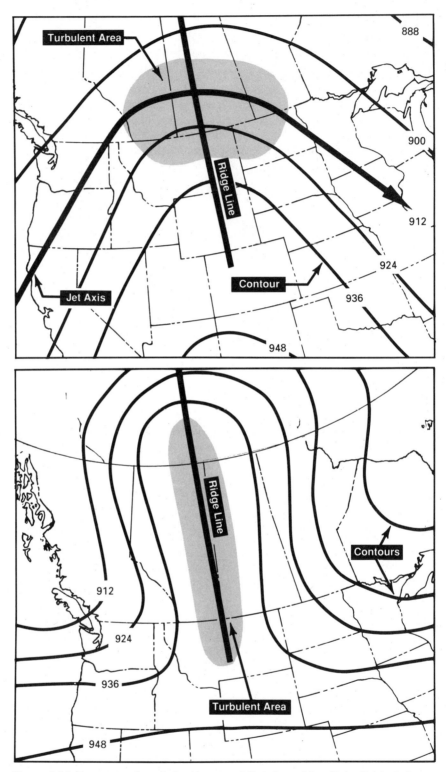

Figure 4-24. Two examples of sharply curved flow in a ridge. Potential turbulence regions are shaded. Thin solid lines are 300 mb contours. Thick solid line is the jet stream axis.

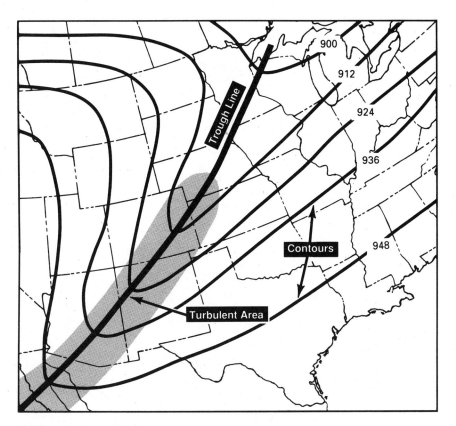

Figure 4-25. Sharp trough near tropopause level. Potential turbulence region is indicated by the narrow shaded zone along the trough line. Thin solid lines are 300 mb contours.

When two jet streams are in close proximity, turbulence outbreaks are favored in the region between the jet axes, as shown in figure 4-27. This pattern often develops when a polar front jet stream moves southward toward a subtropical jet stream over the southeastern U.S. When the axes are within about 300 n.m. of each other, turbulence probabilities increase within the confluence region.

If the polar front jet stream continues to move southward, its core may actually move under that of the subtropical jet stream, leading to several layers of strong vertical wind shear and CAT. An example of this pattern in a wind sounding was given in figure 4-11.

When a strong jet streak is moving southward in the rear (west) of a macroscale trough, the probability of significant CAT is greatest between the jet streak and the downstream trough line. (Figure 4-28)

The region to the north and northeast of a developing surface cyclone is also susceptible to CAT outbreaks as shown in figure 4-29. The intensity of the CAT is greater for rapidly occluding systems.

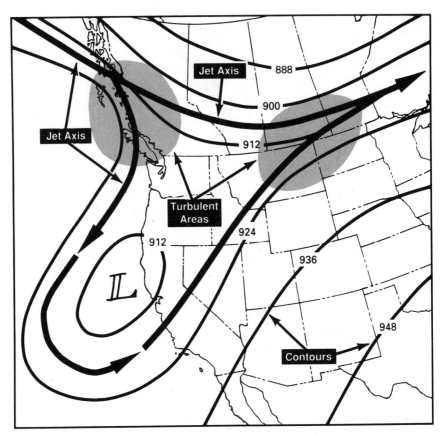

Figure 4-26. Potential turbulence regions (shaded) near a cutoff low. Thin solid lines are 300 mb height contours. Thick solid line is jet stream axis.

WIND SHEARS

Estimating the likelihood of turbulence is more precise if suspected areas can be quantified in some way. We have already seen this where the application of some the rules and patterns for CAT required that the jet stream speeds attain some minimum value. Other useful quantifying parameters are horizontal and vertical wind shears. Some critical values for significant turbulence are given in figure 4-30 (FAA, 1988).

Keep in mind that these values apply to CAT and high level wind shear. They do **NOT** apply to low altitudes (LLWS). Two important rules of thumb about the interpretation of wind shear information are given below.

1. The turbulence intensity for a given value of wind shear will be greater with greater wind speeds.

2. Wind shear is a useful but not a perfect indicator of turbulence. Strongly sheared layers may exist without turbulence.

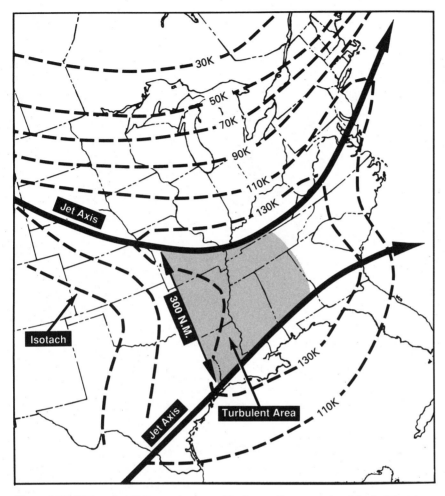

Figure 4-27. CAT probabilities are increased in the confluence region (shaded) between two jet streams when their axes are within about 300 n.m. of each other.

SATELLITE IMAGES

In a previous section, you saw that the jet stream axis is often identified on infrared satellite images by the sharp poleward edge of a broad cirrus band. One value of such an image is the ability to specify the approximate location of the zone of potential turbulence on the cyclonic side of the jet stream axis. Other indications of turbulence near the jet stream are smaller scale cloud patterns which interrupt the general smoothness of the cirrus band. There are two easily identifiable types: billow clouds, which were introduced earlier, and **transverse bands**. Transverse bands are usually longer and broader than billows. They typically occur when maximum speeds of the jet stream exceed 110 knots. Examples of these features are shown in figure 4-31.

Transverse bands are associated with strong vertical shear and possibly turbulence. The broader the transverse bands, the greater the likelihood of significant CAT.

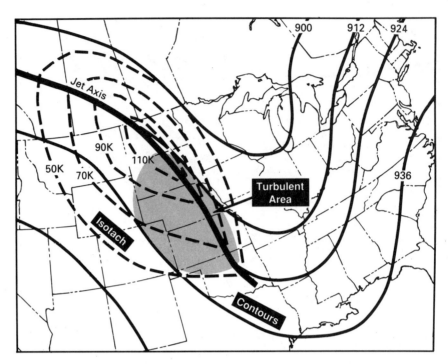

Figure 4-28. A jet streak is located in northerly flow on the west side of a macroscale trough at 300 mb. The turbulence potential is large in the shaded area located just downwind of the region of highest winds in the jet streak. The greater the rate of decrease of wind speed along the jet axis, the greater the probability of significant turbulence.

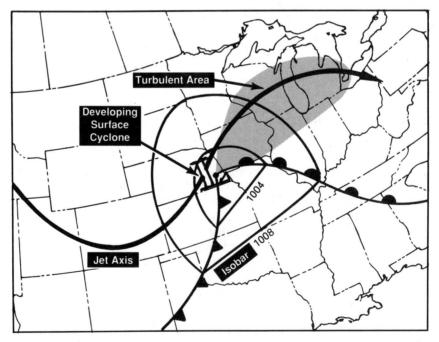

Figure 4-29. Region of increased probability of CAT located to the northeast of a developing surface cyclone.

Horizontal Shear (knots/150 n.m.)	Vertical Shear (knots/1000 feet)	Turbulence Intensity
20-40	5-6	Moderate
>40	≥6	Severe

Figure 4-30. Critical horizontal and vertical shears for significant (moderate or greater) CAT.

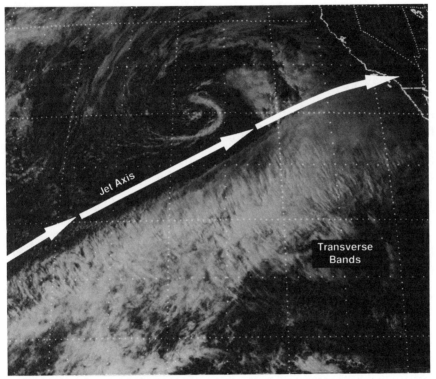

Figure 4-31. Visible satellite image of a cirrus cloud band near a jet stream. Jet axis has been added. Note transverse bands.

SUMMARY

In the current chapter, we have examined the environment, causes, and characteristics of CAT, as well as some large scale indicators of its presence. You now have a basic understanding of why the jet stream, jet stream front, and tropopause are prone to CAT outbreaks: the presence of strong stability and strong shears provides favorable conditions for the development of shearing-gravity waves and turbulence.

The study of map patterns and satellite images related to CAT should enhance your understanding of turbulence-producing processes. Knowledge of the patterns should also help you to identify potentially turbulent regions, understand forecast reasoning, and communicate with the aviation forecaster. Remember, only the most common patterns have been shown here, further details will be found in the references.

We have concentrated our attention on the jet stream because most CAT is observed near that flow feature. However, about one third of CAT is observed outside of the influence of the jet stream. A large portion of such incidents happen over mountains and in the presence of mountain lee waves. These will be considered in the next chapter. The remaining CAT reports are most likely associated with high level convection, atmospheric gravity wave activity set off by thunderstorms (discussed in the previous chapter), and by strong vertical shears outside jet stream regions.

Although we have a good understanding of the processes that generate clear air turbulence, the task of determining whether or not CAT is, or will be, present in a particular airspace remains a frustrating problem. The microscale of CAT combined with the inadequacy of CAT observations introduces a high degree of uncertainty in describing or predicting the details of CAT below a certain minimum scale. For this reason, predicted CAT regions are significantly larger than the airspace where CAT actually occurs. In other words, probabilities of occurrence of significant turbulence in a given forecast area will be small, even when the forecaster knows that the large scale conditions are favorable.

Potential improvements in current observation and forecast systems are on the drawing boards and are being tested. Research continues in the development of onboard remote CAT detection systems as well as satellite, radar, and other ground- and space-based remote CAT sensing systems. Automated PIREP collection and dissemination systems are already operating on a limited basis. These and other future observation and forecast systems will become operational over the next few years. More details are given in Chapter 7.

KEY TERMS

Altocumulus
Anticyclonic Side
Billow Clouds
Cirrocumulus
Clear Air Turbulence
Confluence
Contour
Contrail
Critical Patterns
Critical Shears
Cutoff Low
Cyclonic Side
Diffluence
Intermittency
Isotachs
Isotherms
Jet Axis
Jet Core
Jet Streak
Jet Stream
Jet Stream Charts

Jet Stream Cirrus
Jet Stream Front
Macroscale Wave
Maneuvering
Mare's Tails
Polar Front Jet
Ridge
Shearing-gravity Wave
Subtropical Jet
Transverse Bands
Tropopause
Tropopause Break
Trough
Wake Turbulence

CHAPTER QUESTIONS _____

1. Why are "frequencies" or "probabilities" used so often to describe the occurrence of CAT under various large scale conditions?

2. If the probability of severe or greater CAT along a 100 n.m. segment of your flight track is 8%, would you consider the probability large or small? Why?

3. Compare figures 2-22 and 4-30. Discuss.

4. Compute the slope of the upper front in figure 4-22.

5. Does figure 1-16 show a clear picture of the sources of CAT? What is missing?

6. The following are two rules of thumb for "minimizing or avoiding clear air turbulence" (FAA, 1988). Explain why the recommended actions minimize exposure to CAT. (Hint: See Figures 4-22 and 4-25.)

    1. If possible, when crossing the jet, climb with a rising temperature and descend with a falling temperature.
    2. If turbulence is associated with a sharp pressure trough line, establish a course across the trough rather than parallel to it.

7. For 0000 or 1200 UTC on a winter day, obtain the following constant pressure analysis charts for the continental U.S.: 500 mb, 300 mb, 200 mb, and if possible, a satellite image.

    1. Locate a macroscale wave.
    2. Locate the jet stream axis on each chart for winds exceeding 60 knots.
    3. Where are the jet streams the strongest?
    4. Locate a jet streak.
    5. Find evidence of a jet stream front.
    6. Locate the area of strongest horizontal wind shear.
    7. Compute the maximum horizontal shear on the chart (knots per 150 n.m.). Compare it with figure 4-30.

8. You are flying eastward at FL350. You begin your flight on the ridge line of a macroscale wave, just below the tropopause. Your flight takes you across the wave trough located 500 n.m. to the east, then to the next ridge line another 500 n.m. to the east. You cross the tropopause twice.

   1. Draw a simple 250 mb chart showing the macroscale wave and your flight track.
   2. Draw a flight cross section that shows the location of the tropopause intersections.
   3. Where will the strongest winds along the flight track be experienced? What will be their direction(s)?
   4. Where will you have the greatest chance of encountering turbulence? Why?

Chapter 5

MOUNTAIN WAVE
TURBULENCE (MWT)

INTRODUCTION

Mountain wave turbulence (MWT) is defined as turbulence produced in connection with mountain lee waves. It includes turbulence caused by high amplitude mountain waves, rotors, wind shear, wakes, and strong downslope windstorms.

This chapter begins with an explanation of the essential causes and characteristics of lee waves. Next, this information is integrated into a useful model of the "lee wave system." These preliminary topics provide the foundation for a detailed discussion of the production of mountain wave turbulence. The final section is devoted to a description of some useful guidelines for anticipating the occurrence of mountain waves and MWT from macroscale weather patterns.

LEE WAVES: SOME BASICS

In this section we will examine the causes of lee waves, their basic characteristics, and some of their more common variations in time and space.

BACKGROUND

Lenticular clouds are unique cloud forms that are frequently observed downwind of mountains. (Figure 5-1) Although these clouds have been recognized for hundreds of years, it was not until the 1920s and 1930s that scientists began to understand how they formed (Alaka, 1960). Led by the explorations of glider pilots in Europe, it was discovered that substantial upward motions occurred downwind of mountain barriers under certain meteorological conditions. Furthermore, the upward motions were coupled in a wave-like pattern with downward motions of similar strength. The updrafts were occasionally strong enough to carry gliders to very high altitudes (over 37,000 feet MSL was attained as early as 1939). The periodic up- and downdrafts were soon identified with a particular type of atmospheric gravity wave known as a **mountain lee wave**, **mountain wave**, or **lee wave**.

Figure 5-1. The smooth clouds with the bright edges at the center and top of the picture are wave clouds. A stratocumulus layer is seen at low levels over the mountains. Cirrus appears in the background. Photo courtesy of A. Rangno.

Although mountain waves proved to be an excellent source of lift for gliders, they also provided conditions favorable for the occurrence of turbulence. Research studies (Alaka, 1960; Nicholls, 1973; and many others) have clarified the relationship between mountain lee waves and turbulence and have provided guidelines for pilots. In the remainder of this chapter, we will draw on that information to describe the causes and effects of lee waves and MWT.

CAUSES OF LEE WAVES

When a stable airstream flows over rough terrain, it behaves in many ways like water flowing past rocks in a stream. There are three possible results: the air can be blocked; it can flow around a barrier; or it can flow over a barrier. Some combination of these flow patterns is also possible. What actually happens depends on the size and shape of the barrier, and on the width, depth, speed, and degree of stability of the airstream. In order to sort all of these effects out, especially with regard to the causes of lee waves, we will begin by considering the simple case of airflow across a long ridge.

Air streaming toward a mountain ridge will be displaced vertically as it crosses the ridge. As shown in figure 5-2, this can happen either because the upwind side of the ridge actually lifts the air, or because air flowing horizontally above the ridge suddenly descends on the downwind (lee) side. In either event, if the air is stable, atmospheric gravity waves develop in the lee of the mountain as air parcels are swept downstream and oscillate around their original (equilibrium) level.

Because the mechanism which initially displaces the stable air (the mountain) is stationary, the lee waves also tend to be stationary in spite of the fact that the air is moving rapidly through them. Therefore, they are also referred to as **standing waves**. The waves are warm in the troughs where the stable air has descended, and cold in the crests where the stable air has risen.

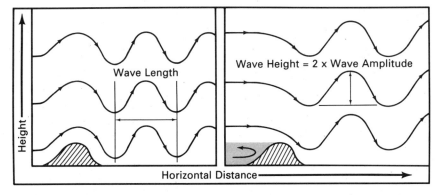

Figure 5-2. Cross-section showing the formation of lee waves downwind of a ridge. On the left, stable air flowing from left to right is lifted by the ridge. On the right, the airstream is blocked at low levels (shaded) and stable air from aloft descends in the lee. In both cases, the vertical displacement of the stable air from its equilibrium level causes lee waves.

Before proceeding with a description of the characteristics of lee waves, two important points must be emphasized. First, as with all atmospheric gravity waves, mountain waves require a stable environment. Such waves are not possible in atmospheric layers that are neutral or unstable.

Second, the scale of the mountain lee wave problem must be kept in mind throughout the chapter in order to develop useful models of lee waves and MWT. A good place to start is with the dimension of the "mountain" that we refer to in the term, "mountain lee wave." This usually indicates a single ridge in a mountain range. In some cases, it refers to a single, isolated peak. Typically, individual ridges vary in width from a mile to more than 30 miles, and in height (above the surrounding area) from a few hundred feet to a several thousand feet. Therefore, a broad mountain range, such as the Rocky Mountains, will have many ridge lines capable of producing lee waves and MWT.

WAVELENGTH

Under typical mountain wave conditions, lee wavelengths average about 5 n.m. However, they can vary widely from a few miles to more than 30 n.m., depending on stability and wind speed.

The stability influence operates as follows. In general, when an air parcel in a stable environment is given a push upward or downward, it will accelerate back toward its original altitude. The resulting motion is similar to that of a weight suspended from a spring. If the weight is pulled down, then released, it will oscillate up and down around its initial position. The rate (frequency) of the parcel oscillation is determined by the stability (comparable to the strength of the spring). Weak stability produces slow oscillations; strong stability produces rapid oscillations.

If the air parcel is also moving horizontally as it fluctuates above and below the equilibrium level, then the parcel trajectory will have a wave shape downwind of the point where it was initially displaced. For a given frequency of oscillation (determined by stability), an air parcel moving rapidly downwind will have a longer wavelength than a slowly moving parcel. These effects of the stability and wind speed of the airstream on the lee wavelengths are illustrated in figure 5-3.

As used here, the term "wind speed" refers only to that portion of the total wind that is at right angles to the ridge line. It is also known as the **perpendicular wind component**. If the wind direction is within 30 degrees of being perpendicular to the ridge, then the total wind speed can be used as the perpendicular component with only a small error. However, if the angle is larger, then the perpendicular component may be much different than the total wind speed. Some examples are shown in figure 5-4.

In some lee wave situations, winds at low levels blow directly across a ridge line; while at high levels, wind directions are significantly different. This dramatically alters the lee wave. For example, if the winds at high level become parallel to the ridge line so that the perpendicular wind component is zero, lee waves will be present only at low levels.

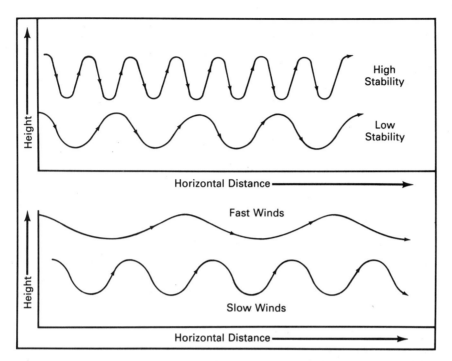

Figure 5-3. Top: Two cases of lee wave flow with identical wind speeds but different stabilities. The short waves occur with stronger stability and the long waves with weaker stability. Bottom: Two cases of lee wave flow with identical stabilities but different wind speeds. The short waves occur with low wind speeds and the long waves with high wind speeds.

In another situation, stability conditions may be favorable for lee waves, while winds at all levels are parallel to the ridge line. Well-defined lee waves will not occur. However, there still may be significant LLT due to the strong winds over rugged terrain.

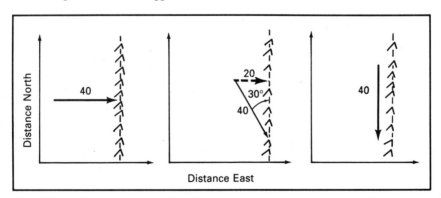

Figure 5-4. Three examples showing the relationship of the total wind (solid arrow) and the perpendicular wind component (dashed arrow) for a ridge line oriented north-south. On the left, a 40-knot westerly wind is perpendicular to the ridge. The perpendicular wind component is equal to the total wind speed (40 knots). In the center, the angle between the direction of the total wind and the ridge line is 30°. From simple trigonometry, the perpendicular wind component (heavy dashed) is .50 x 40 knots = 20 knots. On the right, the total wind is parallel to the ridge, so the perpendicular wind component is zero.

Because atmospheric stability usually varies over a rather narrow range of values when lee waves occur, it is possible to make reasonable estimates of lee wavelength on the basis of the perpendicular wind component alone. If the average wind speed in the layer in which the lee waves occur is U (knots), then the wavelength, L (nautical miles) is given approximately by the following formula (Corby, 1957).

$$L=(U/6)-1.6.$$

This simple equation can be used in two different ways. For example, say that you know from surface reports or PIREPs that there is mountain wave activity in a particular area. If you also know that the wind speed at flight level (U) is 30 knots, then from the equation given above, L is about 3.4 n.m. Flying at a groundspeed of 180 knots, it would take a little more than a minute to fly through one lee wave.

If you can estimate the wavelength from the spacing of the wave clouds (for example, from visual observations or from a satellite image), then the above formula can be used to estimate the perpendicular wind component at the level of the clouds. For example, a spacing of 7 n.m. would correspond with a wind speed (perpendicular wind component) of about 52 knots.

WAVE HEIGHT

Lee wave height (vertical distance a parcel of air will travel from lee wave trough to lee wave crest) is influenced primarily by stability and by mountain shape and size. Large wave heights are favored by a layer of strong stability just above the top of the ridge.

The dependence of wave height on the height of the mountain seems obvious. The greater the vertical push, the greater the height of the wave. However, this is only true up to a point. Wave heights tend to be greater where the width of the ridge "matches" the lee wavelength (ridge width equivalent to a half wavelength). Since the lee wavelength depends on atmospheric stability and wind speed, there will be some situations when the wavelength matches the width of a particular ridge and cases when it does not.

In general, ridges that are less than a mile or two wide do not match typical lee wavelengths. Therefore, they are not usually effective in producing waves with heights that have a significant impact on flight (although such barriers are always capable of producing strong LLT when winds are strong).

For very wide ridges, the shape of the lee slope, rather than the overall width of the ridge line is important in determining lee wave height. High, broad ridges with steep lee slopes often produce large amplitudes. This is especially true when the height of the terrain decreases 3,000 feet or more within a few miles downwind of the ridge line. (Figure 5-5)

The strengths of the vertical gusts in the lee waves depend not only on lee wave height, but also on windspeed and wavelength. In general, wave

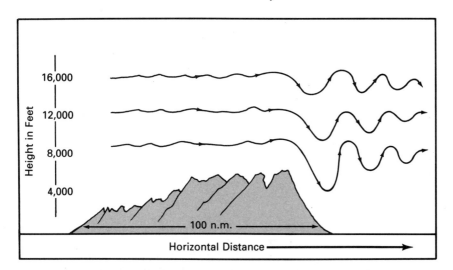

Figure 5-5. Cross-section showing lee waves over a broad mountain range with a steep lee slope. Note, lee waves may occur elsewhere across the mountains, but the response is typically much larger over the lee slope. Both the Sierra Nevada near Owens Valley and the Rocky Mountains near Boulder, Colorado, which are known for strong lee waves have this type of terrain profile.

action significant for aviation should be expected with mountain top wind speeds of 20 knots or more and wavelengths of 5 n.m. or more.

Section
B

THE LEE WAVE SYSTEM

The simple picture of lee waves presented in the last section should help you understand the basic causes of lee waves and the reasons for certain wave characteristics. In this section, we will examine a model that shows typical mesoscale flow conditions when lee waves are present. The model not only includes lee waves, but also the associated turbulent layers. Once you are familiar with it, it will help you locate regions of lee wave action and MWT from cloud observations and other visible indicators. The model will also help you deduce lee wave and MWT conditions from macroscale airflow patterns shown on weather maps.

OVERVIEW

Our model of choice is one that has been developed from observation and theory over the last 40 years. It appears in various forms in many flight manuals and is shown in figure 5-6. The model is represented by a cross-section through an idealized lee wave event at the peak of its development. We will refer to this model as the **lee wave system**.

The lee wave system is divided into two layers, an upper **lee wave region** where smooth wave flow dominates and microscale turbulence occurs occasionally, and a **lower turbulent zone** from the ground to just above mountain top level.

Soundings taken during lee wave conditions show a number of common features. (Figure 5-6) Temperature soundings typically have a stable layer near mountain top level with less stable layers above and below, while wind soundings display increasing wind speed with height. For significant

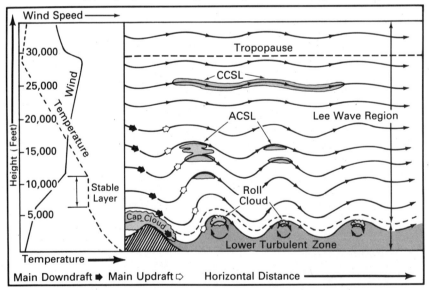

Figure 5-6. The Lee Wave System. Airflow through the lee waves is indicated by thin solid lines with arrows. Lower turbulent zone is indicated by the darker shading at the bottom of the diagram. Characteristic lenticular ACSL, CCSL, cap, and roll clouds are labeled. Temperature and wind speed soundings taken just upstream of the ridge are shown on the left. Note stable layer just above the mountain top.

wave activity, the wind speed (perpendicular component) at mountain top level should be about 20 knots (less for short mountains, more for tall mountains).

LEE WAVE REGION

In the lee wave portion of figure 5-6, the lee waves have their greatest amplitudes within a few thousand feet above the mountains, decreasing above and below. Lee wavelengths are longer in the upper troposphere and lower stratosphere than they are in the lowest levels. This structure is common in most (but not all) actual mountain wave events.

Mountain waves may extend to very high levels in the atmosphere. Evidence of significant mountain wave and MWT activity has been reported by aircraft in the 60,000- to 80,000-foot altitude range, and have been detected at much higher levels in studies of the transmission of radio signals.

Two other important characteristics of the lee wave region are shown in figure 5-6. One is the presence of several wave cycles with decreasing wave heights downwind of the ridge. The second feature is the upwind tilt of the lee waves; that is, the crests and troughs of the lee waves are located farther upstream at higher levels. Glider pilots flying in mountain waves commonly report that they must "work upwind" as they gain altitude. This is necessary for them to stay in that part of the wave that has upward motions. For example, it is not unusual for a glider pilot to start a climb near mountain top level, well downwind of the ridge, and after an altitude gain of 10,000 feet or so, to be directly over the ridge.

LOWER TURBULENT ZONE

In figure 5-6, the lower turbulent zone extends from the ground to a wave-shaped upper boundary at the base of the smooth lee wave region. A major feature of the lower turbulent zone is the **rotor** circulation found under one or more of the lee wave crests. Note that the center of the rotor circulation is about ridge top level. The rotor under the first wave crest is the most intense and is usually the major source of significant turbulence in the lower turbulent zone if not in the entire lee wave system.

Other properties of the lower turbulence zone are the generally low stability, gusty winds, and the tendency for the strongest surface winds to occur along the lee slopes of the mountain. All of these features contribute to the dominance of turbulence in this layer and will be examined closely later in the section on mountain wave turbulence.

CLOUDS

A number of unique clouds form in the lee wave system. When present, they offer a visual connection between the model described above and the reality that you encounter in flight. The clouds of the lee wave system are usually variations on three basic types as presented schematically in figure 5-6 and shown photographically in figure 5-7. They are the **cap cloud** immediately over the mountain tops, the cumuliform rotor- or **roll cloud** associated with the rotor circulation, and the smooth, lens-shaped

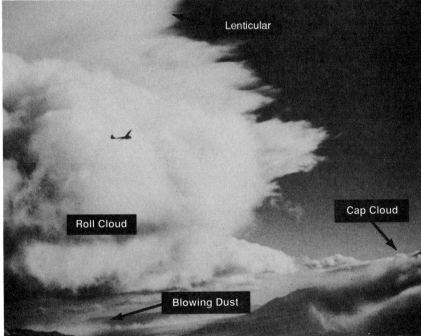

Figure 5-7. Mountain wave clouds in the lee of the Sierra Nevada. Airflow is from right to left in both pictures. Only lenticular clouds appear in the top figure. Sailplane in the bottom figure was experiencing 4,000 f.p.m. updrafts at the time of the photograph and subsequently reached an altitude of 40,000 feet. (Top photo by Betsy Woodward, Bottom Photo by Harold Klieforth)

"altocumulus standing lenticular" (ACSL) or **lenticular clouds** in the crests of the lee waves.

The identification of lenticular clouds of the cirrus variety (CCSL or CISL) is not always easy. Cirrus clouds consist of ice crystals. Compared to water droplet clouds, more heat is necessary to dissipate ice clouds. Therefore, cirrus clouds tend to persist longer in downdrafts than water droplet clouds. This can result in a cirrus lenticular extending downwind in a continuous sheet through wave crests and troughs. (Figure 5-6) The undulations in the cirrus may be visible at flight level, but they are often difficult to see from the ground. Often, the only evidence of lee wave activity at high levels is a broad cirrus cloud with a sharp upwind edge parallel to the ridge line.

The importance of clouds as indicators of the presence of lee waves cannot be stressed enough. In lieu of PIREPs or high resolution satellite imagery, the only source of information about the presence of lee waves are your own visual observations of clouds. In addition, evidence of wave activity is also found in the remarks of surface weather reports. Some examples are:

CCSL N-W   (Cirrocumulus standing lenticular north through west)

ACSL ALQDS   (Altocumulus standing lenticular all quadrants)

ROLL CLD W   (Roll cloud west).

Although observations of wave and roll clouds are invaluable, there are some cautions. While the clouds indicate the positions of the wave crests and the rotor, they don't give much information about the intensity of the lee waves or associated turbulence. This is true because clouds depend on both lifting (for adiabatic cooling) and moisture. For example, a well-defined lenticular cloud may form in weak lee wave updrafts when there is an adequate supply of moisture. In contrast, an intense lee wave system can be present without any of the characteristic clouds because the air is dry. Therefore, you must have some independent methods to judge the intensity of lee waves and to determine their presence in a cloud-free atmosphere. Some alternatives will be presented later in the chapter.

VARIATIONS

In order to make the best use of the lee wave system model, likely deviations from that "average" structure should also be known. There are two types of these: variations in space (vertical and horizontal) and variations in time.

VERTICAL VARIATIONS

The lee wave configuration shown in figure 5-6 represents a structure that lies between two extremes. These are shown in figure 5-8. In one extreme, wave activity is confined to the lower part of the troposphere. This occurs when the stability above the mountain-top stable layer is very low and/or because wind speed increases very rapidly with height above the mountains. In this case, the waves show little tilt and weaken rapidly above the

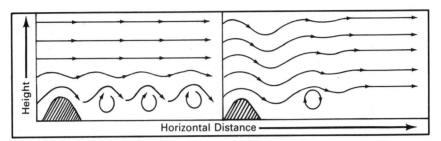

Figure 5-8. Two extreme variations of lee wave structure. On the left, waves are completely trapped at and below the stable layer just above the mountain top. Note the great downwind extent of the wave activity. On the right, untrapped waves reach great altitudes, but the wave activity does not extend very far downwind of the mountains.

mountain top stable layer. Because the wave energy remains in the lowest layers, these mountain waves are often called **trapped** or "resonance" waves. The wave activity often extends hundreds of miles downwind of the ridge.

The right of figure 5-8 shows the other extreme of wave structures found in the lee wave region. There is no trapping. The waves tilt upwind and the wave energy reaches high levels above the mountain. These mountain waves are called "vertically propagating" or **untrapped**. In this case, neither the decrease in stability above the mountain top stable layer nor the increase in wind with height are sufficient to trap the lee waves. Note the characteristic tilt of the waves with height is present in this case. Although the maximum height attained by untrapped waves is much greater than in the trapped case, the horizontal extent of significant wave activity is greatly reduced in the untrapped case. As also shown in figure 5-8, the lengths of untrapped waves tend to be longer than trapped waves.

The model lee wave system presented in figure 5-6 may be classified as a case of "partially trapped" lee waves, since it shows properties of both extremes. Shorter waves are trapped at low levels, while longer lee waves reach the stratosphere.

Evidence of the presence of trapped and untapped waves can sometimes be seen in satellite images of lee wave clouds. For example, figure 5-9 shows an area of trapped lee waves indicated by the extensive bands of lenticular clouds at low levels. In comparison, figure 5-10 shows a single, high-level cloud band associated with untrapped lee waves. A "mixed" situation, where many, short, trapped waves at lower levels coexist with a single, long, untrapped wave at higher levels is shown in figure 5-11.

HORIZONTAL VARIATIONS

Our model of the lee wave system (figure 5-6) is based on airflow across an idealized ridge. Real mountain ridges are complicated by rugged peaks of different sizes and separations. Also, a typical mountainous area is more likely to be made up of several ridges which are not quite parallel and are irregularly spaced. This means that when wind and stability conditions are generally favorable for lee waves over a wide area, wave characteristics will

Figure 5-9. Trapped mountain waves in the lee of the northern Sierra and the Cascades are revealed by extensive areas of lenticular clouds. State boundaries are indicated by dotted lines. Airflow is approximately left to right.

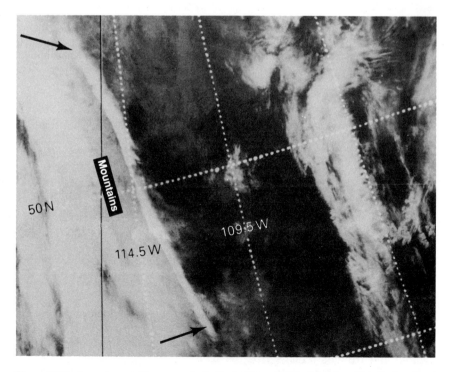

Figure 5-10. An untrapped lee wave is indicated by a single, high-level lenticular cloud (arrows) in the lee of the Rockies in southwestern Alberta. Airflow is from left to right.

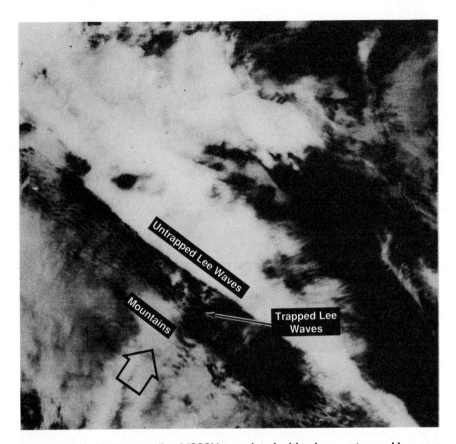

Figure 5-11. A single wave cloud (CCSL) associated with a long, untrapped lee wave near the tropopause appears over a series of shorter, trapped lee waves at low levels. Because this is an infrared satellite image, the high, cold cloud appears white, and the lower, warmer clouds appear gray. The airflow is indicated by the arrow in the lower left of the photo.

vary due to local differences in stability, wind speed, and the various orientations, shapes, and sizes of the terrain features. Some examples are shown in the following figures.

Figures 5-12 and 5-13 are helpful in locating some regions where significant variations in lee waves occur across two large mountainous areas. Unfortunately, such information is not available for every potential lee wave region. Also, it is impossible to provide general rules of thumb to cover the effect of every possible terrain configuration. However, it is possible to isolate a few of the more common deviations from our idealized ridge line. These include effects of ridge orientation, multiple ridges, and isolated peaks.

RIDGE LINE ORIENTATION

As can be seen in the wave clouds in figure 5-9, lee wave crests (cloud bands) and troughs (clear strips between the bands) tend to parallel the bends in upwind ridges. Although the clouds may look similar along the ridge, the strength of the lee waves will vary, depending on the angle of the

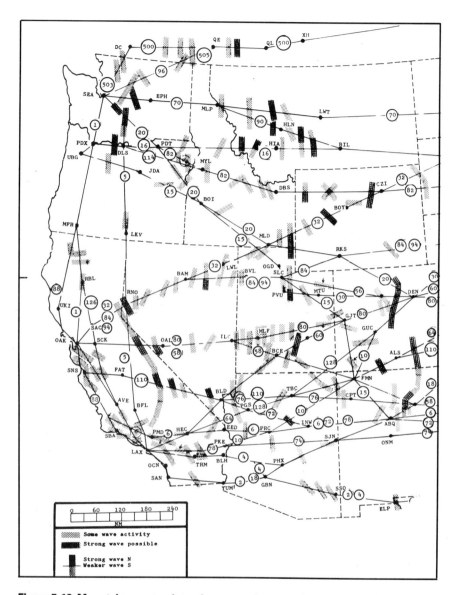

Figure 5-12. Mountain wave regions along some jet routes in the western U.S. Shading indicates wave strength. Wave areas were evaluated on the basis of pilot reports, surface observations, and lee wave theory (Harrison and Sowa, 1966).

wind to the ridge line. The lee waves (and rotor) are stronger in those areas where the flow is perpendicular to the ridge line. Also, as illustrated in figure 5-14, lee waves (and rotor) are stronger where the ridge line is concave upwind.

Occasionally, the roll and/or lenticular clouds will form very straight lines, generally paralleling the ridge; that is, not reflecting the detailed bends in the ridge line. In these cases (usually associated with large mountains such the Sierra), the roll cloud may be very deep, extending well above

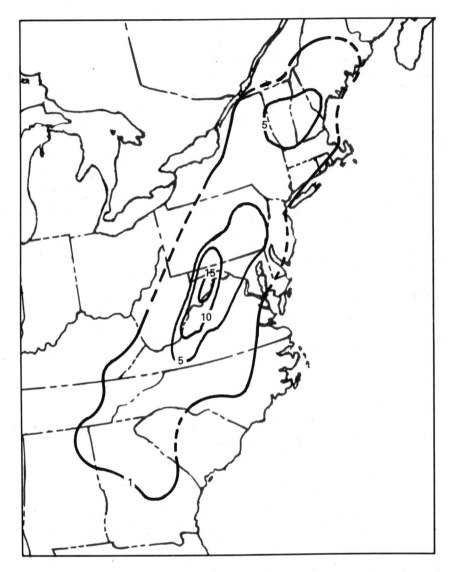

Figure 5-13. Number of times mountain wave clouds were observed from satellites over the Appalachians during a three-year period. The frequency of occurrence is uncertain where the lines are dashed. The analysis is based on a study by Lindsay and Lacy (1972). Note, actual frequencies of lee waves are probably greater than shown here because clouds are not necessary for lee wave occurrence.

mountain top level. This situation indicates very strong lee waves and intense turbulence. It is usually accompanied by strong cross mountain winds and long lee wavelengths.

MULTIPLE RIDGES

Where the air flows across several parallel ridges, wave activity from an upwind ridge will affect the lee waves generated by a downwind ridge. This is illustrated in figure 5-15. The effect depends on the lee wavelength and the spacing of the ridges. The wave action from the downwind ridge

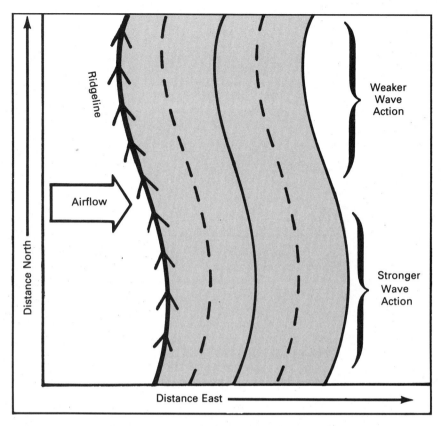

Figure 5-14. Lee wave crests (thin solid lines) and lee wave troughs (dashed lines) parallel to a ridge line. The wind is blowing from left to right. The lee wave system is stronger where the wind direction is perpendicular to the ridge line, especially where the ridge line is concave upwind.

will be reinforced if the two ridges are exactly one wavelength apart (or 2.0, 3.0, 4.0, etc.). If the ridges are exactly one-half wavelength apart (or 1.5, 2.5, etc.), the waves set up by the ridges will interfere and eliminate the lee wave action downwind of the second ridge.

ISOLATED PEAK

If a ridge is not very long, the flow of air around the sides of the mountain becomes important in the formation of lee waves, eddies, and turbulence. If the barrier is an isolated peak, there are a number of well-known wake patterns that may evolve. These were discussed briefly in Chapters 2 and 3.

When wind and stability conditions for lee waves are satisfied, airflow over an isolated peak will cause a "V-shaped" wave pattern similar to a **ship's wake**. An example is given in figure 5-16. The angle (A) between the wave crest depends on the stability. It will only be a few degrees wide with weak stability and increase to perhaps 40° if the stability is strong. Compared to lee waves caused by a long ridge, waves from an isolated peak weaken much more rapidly with distance downwind.

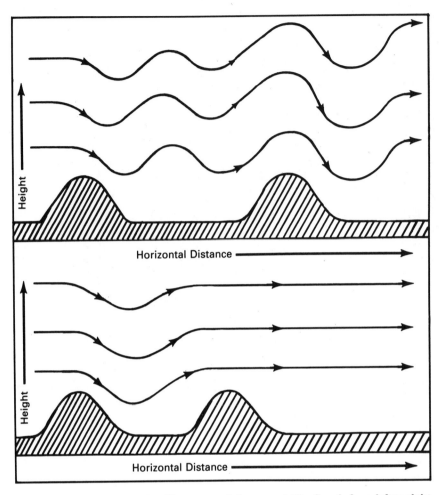

Figure 5-15. Top: An example of lee wave reinforcement. The flow is from left to right. The ridge on the right is about two wavelengths downwind from the ridge on the left. Lee wave effects from both ridges are added, producing a larger wave height in the lee of the second ridge. Bottom: Example of lee wave interference. The ridge on the right is about 1.5 wavelengths downwind from the ridge on the left. The two patterns cancel the wave action in the lee of the second ridge.

The lower turbulent zone will be greatly modified in the case of airflow past an isolated peak. Because of the wide range of mountain shapes and sizes, it is not possible to give a general description. However, horizontal wind shears can be very large, producing unsteady vortexes with a variety of shapes, intensities, and orientations. The potential for severe turbulence in the lee of an isolated peak should not be underestimated.

TIME VARIATIONS

Lee wave activity in any mountainous location is only present part of the time. Furthermore, when lee wave systems do occur, their characteristics (wavelength, wave height, vertical and horizontal extent, turbulence intensity, etc.) will often vary from occurrence to occurrence. In addition, during a single lee wave event, the same characteristics will undergo short term changes. For a given mountain, all of these variations are related to

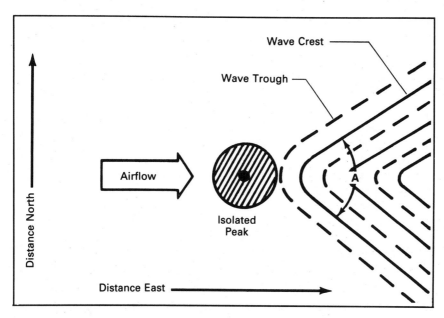

Figure 5-16. Top view of ship's wake lee wave pattern formed by the flow of stable air over an isolated peak. Airflow is from left to right. Note, cirrus clouds forming with this type of flow often appear as a long plume downwind of the peak.

fluctuations in stability and/or wind speed and direction. The causes of some of the more important time fluctuations in lee wave occurrence and intensity are listed with the periods over which they occur in figure 5-17.

Causes	Periods
Seasonal changes in position of the sun	Months
Change in position of the storm track	3 to 30 days
Cycle of solar heating and cooling	Daily
Passage of fronts and macroscale waves	1 to 24 hours
Microscale eddy shedding, wave breaking	Minutes to hours

Figure 5-17. Typical causes of variations in lee wave activity and the periods over which they occur.

The influence of the macroscale waves and fronts on the production of lee waves will be discussed in the last section of the chapter. The others are considered below.

SEASONAL VARIATIONS

Mountain waves may form any time of year, but they occur most often during the cooler months when mountain-top winds are stronger and stability is greater. In middle latitude regions, there appears to be a single winter month, December or January, when lee wave activity is at a maximum. At higher latitudes, there are often two cool season peaks in the frequency of lee waves, one in Fall and another in late Winter. The double maximum is evidently caused by the seasonal movement of the storm track to lower latitudes in the Fall and its retreat to higher latitudes in late Winter.

DAILY VARIATIONS

As you saw in Chapter 3, the lower layers of the atmosphere are subjected to daily changes in stability due to radiational heating and cooling of the earth's surface. With decreasing stability during the daytime, mountain waves in the lowest layers tend to lengthen and weaken. If surface heating is sufficient, the lower atmosphere will become neutral or unstable and lee waves at lower levels may completely disappear during the day. In contrast, lee waves will shorten and strengthen at night as the low-level stability increases. For this reason, they are sometimes called "evening" waves.

EDDY SHEDDING

Lee wavelengths undergo fluctuations caused by the development of local flow patterns along the lee slope. Eddy shedding refers to a process where

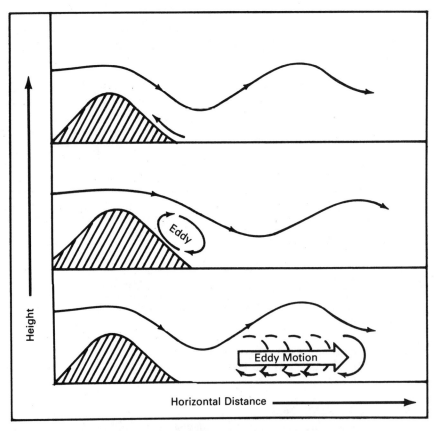

Figure 5-18. An example of eddy shedding. Top: The general flow is from left to right with lee waves at low levels. Middle: A lee eddy forms when the lee slope is heated during the day and the air immediately next to the lee side of the mountain moves upslope. As this occurs, the first lee wave trough moves downwind. Bottom: The eddy breaks away from the lee slope, dissipating as it is swept downstream. During this process, the lee wave trough moves back upwind to its initial position.

an eddy periodically detaches and moves downwind from the lee slopes where it first formed. Some aspects of this topic were examined briefly in Chapter 2 in the discussion of terrain effects in the boundary layer. An example is shown in figure 5-18. This process often repeats, contributing to unsteadiness in the position of waves in the lowest portion of the lee wave regions.

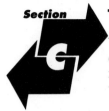

Section

TURBULENCE

With the lee wave system model as background, we now examine the causes and characteristics of MWT. Our discussion focuses on the two main layers of the lee waves system: the lee wave region and the lower turbulent zone.

LEE WAVE REGION

Probably the most impressive characteristic of flight in lee waves is the exceptional smoothness of the wave motions, especially in the updrafts. However, this smoothness is occasionally interrupted by significant turbulence. For example, the following incident took place in a lee wave over the mountains of eastern Turkey (Chambers,1973).

> At FL310, with winds 080° at 80 knots, turbulence was suddenly encountered. It persisted for 96 seconds producing incremental accelerations as large as -0.9g and +0.5g. Air speed fluctuated between 277 and 310 knots. A meal was being served and "all trays were thrown about the cabin and every glass on the aircraft was broken." As a crew member looked aft for a moment during the incident he saw the rear galley disappear from view as the fuselage flexed.

It was also noted in the previous chapter that significant CAT occurs more frequently over mountains than over plains or oceanic areas. Given the stable conditions of the upper troposphere and lower stratosphere and the smooth airflow characteristic of lee waves, the question is, how can such turbulence occur?

MWT CAUSES

As discussed in earlier chapters, atmospheric gravity waves may actually produce turbulence for aircraft under certain circumstances. It will be helpful to review those circumstances, especially as they apply to turbulence in the lee wave region.

WAVE ACTION

The existence of a mountain wave implies the presence of vertical gusts. Even though the flow in the waves is smooth, if the wavelength is short and/or the wave amplitude is large, then the vertical motions associated with the wave may be perceived as turbulence. This effect, of course, increases with the speed of the aircraft.

WAVE BREAKING

Turbulence is also produced when atmospheric gravity waves grow and "break" producing truly chaotic flow. These waves are often of the shearing-gravity wave type and are embedded in the longer lee waves when vertical shears are strong enough. Shearing-gravity wave production is most likely in lee wave troughs and crests where the curvature of the airflow contributes to strengthening of the vertical shear. These waves can sometimes be seen as billow clouds superimposed on a larger lenticular clouds. (Figure 5-19) A related rule of thumb for pilots is

avoid high-level lenticular clouds with ragged edges.

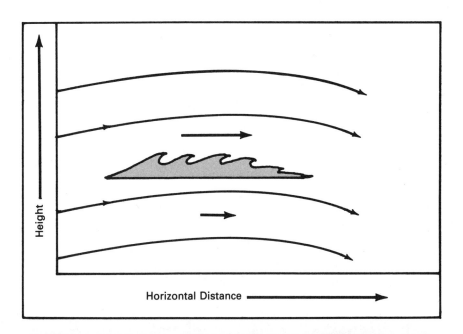

Figure 5-19. Top: Cross-section through a lenticular cloud (shaded) in a lee wave crest. The airflow is indicated by thin solid lines with arrowheads. Wind speeds are indicated by the length of the thick, horizontal arrows. Presence of shearing-gravity waves are indicated by the sawtooth edge of an otherwise smooth cloud. Bottom: Photo of several lenticular clouds. Rough cloud edges indicate the presence of shearing-gravity waves. Compare with the lenticular clouds in figure 5-1.

In addition to the influence of shearing-gravity waves, some studies suggest that amplitudes of the mountain waves may become so large that they also overturn. An example is shown in figure 5-20. In this case, very strong up- and downdrafts and extensive layers of MWT are found in the primary wave cycle. This situation is also accompanied by exceptionally strong surface winds along the lee slopes of the mountains. Details are given in the next section.

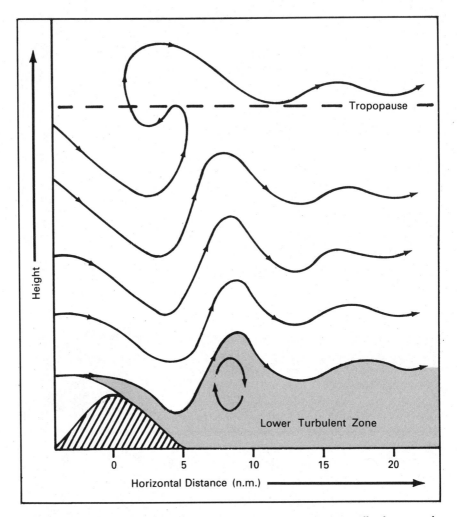

Figure 5-20. Cross-section showing the overturning of a very large amplitude mountain wave near the tropopause. Airflow is from left to right. Note the region where the airflow lines reverse direction.

The turbulence-producing processes discussed above make it clear why MWT in the lee wave region occurs more frequently near the tropopause. The wind and stability patterns that favor strong lee waves often include the jet stream with its associated fronts (which favor CAT). When such conditions are present, mountain wave activity near the tropopause strengthens vertical shears already present in the vicinity of the jet stream. Therefore, the more frequent MWT/CAT activity is primarily due to a combination of lee wave motions and enhanced shearing-gravity wave activity.

MWT CHARACTERISTICS

The difference in the dimensions of the usually smooth lee waves and gusts related to shearing-gravity waves often allows the pilot to distinguish between "wave action" and "turbulence" in the lee wave region. With lee waves, the pilot usually has time to adjust to smoothly changing updrafts and downdrafts. However, the picture becomes obscured when lee waves are so strong that the vertical drafts overwhelm the ability of the pilot to compensate, or when the embedded turbulence dominates the wave motion. The following are typical pilot descriptions of turbulence and wave action. They are taken from PIREPs given by light aircraft flying in the lower part of the lee wave region.

/TB LGT OVR E SLOPES MTNS/RM UDDF 1000-2100 FPM

/TB LGT TURBC/RM MDT-SVR UDDF

/TB MDT-SVR 110-150/RM UDDF 1000-2500 FPM CLIMB AND DESCEND 1500-3000 FEET

/TB MDT/RM SUSTAINED UDDF 1200 FPM

/TB SVR/RM UDDF 500-1000 FPM

/TB LGT/RM WAVE ACTION DOWNDRAFTS 2000 FPM

Note that the turbulence estimations in the above reports do not necessarily correspond with the strength of the updrafts as defined in Chapter 1 (moderate or greater turbulence: vertical gusts 1200 f.p.m or greater). Obviously, caution is required in the interpretation of such reports.

Three more examples of PIREPs are given below, but these are taken from tropopause level. They again indicate MWT as a mix of turbulence and strong lee wave action. These reports are from a mountain wave event near Cimarron (CIM), New Mexico.

LSV UA /OV CIM 270050/TM 1500/FL390/TP CL60/TB HEAVY/RM SEVERE UP AND DOWNDRAFTS 40 KTS CHANGE IN WIND

LSV UUA /OV CIM-CIM 270040/TM 1545/FL390/TP CL60/TB SVR/RM RAPID CHG OF WIND DIRECTION PLUS 500 FPM UDDFS

LSV UUA /OV CIM 270005/TM 1625/ FL 330/TP B767/TB SVR/RM ACFT ROLLED 30 DEGREES

Lee waves systems are often described as "weak," "moderate," or "strong." These strength classifications are related to the magnitude of the wave action and/or the intensity of the shorter period turbulence. In figure 5-21, lee wave strength is shown in terms of wave action only (speeds of the vertical drafts and wave heights).

Extreme vertical drafts of over 5,000 f.p.m. have been observed in the lee wave region. One of the most extreme cases ever reported involved an updraft encountered during the Sierra Wave Project in the 1950's. A twin engine WWII fighter (P-38) actually gained significant altitude in a lee wave with both engines shut down. Estimated updrafts were 8,000 f.p.m.

Wave Strength	Vertical Speed (±f.p.m.)	Wave Height (feet)
Weak	300 to 900	500 to 2,000
Moderate	900 to 1,800	2,000 to 4,000
Strong	1,800 to 3,600	4,000 to 8,000

Figure 5-21. Classification of lee wave strength (MWT potential) in terms of observed up- and downdrafts and wave height (Holmboe and Klieforth, 1957).

Because the strength of the waves is not the same throughout the lee wave region (the primary wave is the most intense), an aircraft approaching a ridge from the lee will often receive a gentle warning of impending MWT. This is due to the gradual increase in wave activity along the flight path. Wave indicators include periodic variations in altitude, vertical gusts, airspeed, and temperature (cold lee wave crests and warm lee wave troughs). Here are two rules of thumb that apply to flight on the lee side of a ridge.

1. In potential mountain wave areas, watch your altimeter, especially at night.

2. When there is a sustained loss of altitude while flying parallel to a ridge, rising air will often be found a few miles to the left or right of track. The exception is a downdraft close to the ridge. In that case, fly downwind.

The impact of the wave action is much different when the wave area is approached from the upwind side of a ridge. The preliminary indications listed above will not be present. Unless the wave activity can be anticipated from PIREPs, SAs, or forecasts, there will be a large element of surprise as the aircraft crosses the ridge and penetrates the most intense (primary) wave. Safe turbulence penetration speeds must be maintained in areas of potentially large gusts.

This problem is illustrated by the following description of an incident during an eastward (downwind) flight at 21,000 feet across the Continental Divide in the Canadian Rockies (Buckler, 1965).

Two severe jolts were experienced. "The pilot estimates that the aircraft descended 800 feet in 3 to 5 seconds, followed by a choppy interval, then a second violent descent. Three seats were pulled loose in the cabin. Passengers with unfastened seat belts were injured. Roof panels were bent and displaced when passengers were thrown upwards. Some seat mountings were broken . . ."

Postflight analysis suggested that the encounter was made worse because of reinforcement of the wave action by downstream ridges. Near the location of the incident, the mountains average about

10,000 feet MSL near the Continental Divide; terrain heights fall off rapidly in the lee where there are a series of parallel ridges. The wind speed at flight level was probably in excess of 100 knots.

The effect of MWT on flight near the tropopause can be especially dramatic when the aircraft is near its design or weight limit. Changes in temperature, airspeed, and Mach number may occur so quickly that a significant departure from assigned altitude due to stall or upset becomes a distinct possibility (Stack, 1991).

Three examples of mountain wave turbulence are given below. In the first, the aircraft was influenced by turbulence and a downdraft associated with an exceptionally long lee wave.

At FL350, an airliner was flying westward (upwind) toward the Continental Divide near Pincher Creek, Alberta during a mountain wave situation. At 63 n.m. east of the major ridge line, the aircraft encountered a brief period of moderate turbulence with a variation of total temperature from -17°C to -30°C. Beginning at 37 n.m. east (downwind), the aircraft experienced a smooth downdraft until it crossed the main ridge line.

In the next case, the aircraft was also flying upwind toward a major mountain ridge at tropopause level. Figure 5-22 is the record of the aircraft altitude during the turbulence event (Lester and Bach, 1986).

The altitude fluctuations were the result of the influences of lee waves and control inputs made to counter the wave effects. As the aircraft approached the mountains, it experienced lee waves of increasing amplitudes and periodic bursts of light to moderate turbulence until the last cycle (closest to the mountains) where severe turbulence was experienced. The aircraft finally descended in an attempt to exit the turbulence region. Further analysis of available data revealed that the severe turbulence was actually due to microscale shearing-gravity waves superimposed on the lee waves.

The influence of shearing-gravity waves is clearer in the final example. In this case, an aircraft was flying downwind near the tropopause when it crossed a ridge line and entered a train of lee waves.

Severe turbulence was experienced with passenger injuries. Post flight analysis gave very strong evidence that the aircraft encountered the turbulence in a vortex about 1,200 feet in diameter. The axis of the microscale eddy was oriented horizontally across the flight path. (Figure 5-23) The eddy was the result of a shearing-gravity wave as it overturned just downwind of the crest of a lee wave. The aircraft passed through the vortex in less than two seconds. Maximum vertical gusts were estimated to be ±4,000 to 5,000 f.p.m.

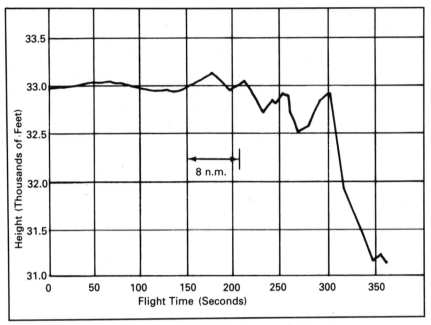

Figure 5-22. Altitude record of DC-10 during a flight upwind into lee waves.

Some rules of thumb for anticipating and avoiding MWT in high-level flight through lee waves include the following (Sorenson, 1976; FAA, 1985; Stack, 1991).

1. When mountain top wind speeds (perpendicular to the ridge) are between 25 and 50 knots, moderate turbulence is expected in the lee wave region within 5,000 feet of the tropopause and at the base of relatively stable layers. Turbulence can extend 150 to 300 miles downwind of the ridge.

2. When mountain top wind speeds exceed 50 knots, severe turbulence is expected within 5,000 feet of the tropopause and from 50 to 150 miles downwind of the ridge.

3. To avoid the most hazardous mountain wave activity, change your route. If this is not possible, change your altitude away from tropopause level.

4. Significant MWT is more likely when the tropopause is colder than standard. If the tropopause temperature decreases below -68°C, the probability of severe turbulence increases.

LOWER TURBULENT ZONE

In this section, we examine the lowest part of the lee wave system where the wave activity is still important, but turbulence plays the dominant role. For reference, a cross-section of the lower turbulent zone is presented in figure 5-24.

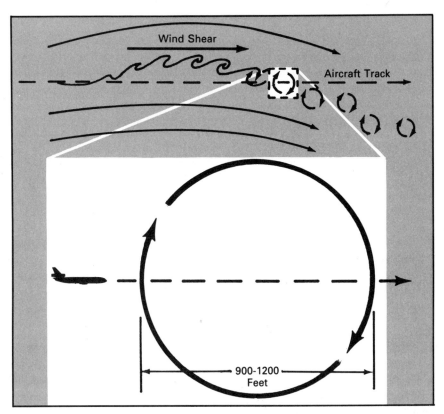

Figure 5-23. Schematic cross-section showing flight path through a vortex that formed when a shearing-gravity wave overturned. The top diagram shows a train of shearing-gravity waves developing in strong vertical shear at the crest of a lee wave. The exploded view shows a vortex formed by a single overturning wave (Parks, et al, 1985).

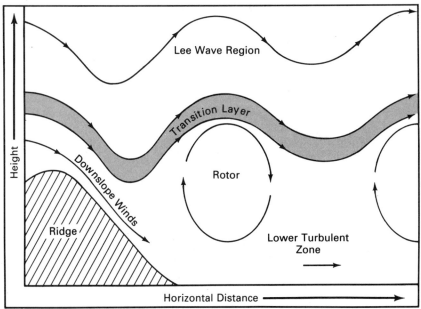

Figure 5-24. Cross-section through lower turbulent zone. Airflow is from left to right.

TURBULENCE CAUSES

The lower turbulent zone is the boundary layer of the lee wave system. The interaction of the lee wave flow at the top of the layer and the rough ground at the bottom can cause intense turbulence to develop in a number of different ways.

THE ROTOR

Typically, the most turbulent regions of the entire lee wave system are the rotor circulations that develop in the lower turbulent zone under the lee wave crests. The rotor motion results in a complete overturning of the air. This produces extremely unstable and turbulent conditions. A rotor is most likely to be found below the crest of the primary lee wave; however, if the lee waves are trapped, rotors may exist in succession under several wave crests.

DOWNSLOPE WINDS

Another important turbulence hazard in the lower turbulent zone is strong, gusty **downslope winds** which develop along the lee slopes of the mountain. They are a result of the upwind tilt of the lee waves shown in figure 5-24. Because of the tilt, winds tend to be stronger in the downdraft portions of the lee waves. Since the downdraft of the first (strongest) wave cycle is close to the lee slope, the surface winds are stronger in that location than elsewhere in the lower turbulent zone. Extreme gustiness is caused by the rough terrain. Downwind, the influence of the lee waves is reduced. The strength and the gustiness of surface winds typically decreases away from the mountains.

Downslope winds caused by lee waves are warm due to the descent of stable air on the lee slopes. On a larger scale, the general movement of a warm airmass across a major mountain range often results in warm, dry winds that descend the lee slopes of the mountain and move well out into the plains. This phenomenon occurs in the lee of many large mountain ranges throughout the world. It is known variously as Foehn, Chinook, Santa Ana, and several other local names. When a Chinook-like wind occurs, smaller scale lee wave activity is often present near the mountains. That activity (especially in the downslope wind area) causes the Chinook winds to be warmer and stronger on the lee slopes than elsewhere.

TRANSITION LAYER

Another turbulent hazard is found at the top of the lower turbulent zone. This is a sharp transition layer between the smooth lee wave flow aloft and the turbulent zone below. (Figure 5-24) The altitude of this layer undulates with the lee waves. It is lower in the troughs and higher in the crests. A band of stronger winds (similar to a low-level jet) is often found just above the base of the transition layer with vertical wind shear above and below. Similar to the capping stable layer above a convective boundary layer, there are two flight problems created by the transition layer. The first is the sudden onset of significant turbulence when an aircraft crosses the layer from the smooth lee wave region to the lower turbulent zone. Because of the wave shape of the transition layer, this problem can be encountered while either descending or while in horizontal flight.

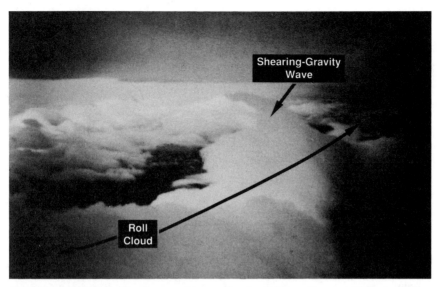

Figure 5-25. Cloud pattern shows evidence of a shearing-gravity wave in the transition layer on the top of a roll cloud. Photo courtesy of R. Mamini.

The second problem encountered in the transition layer is the sporadic outbreak of turbulence due to shearing-gravity wave activity. Evidence of this process is shown in figure 5-25.

Turbulence may also occur near the trough of the primary lee wave (just upwind of the rotor circulation in figure 5-24). This turbulence is generated by sharp flow curvature and strong wind shear.

HYDRAULIC JUMP
The lower turbulent zone described above is a product of the lee wave activity. Put another way, the lee waves generate the rotor and the other turbulent phenomena near the ground. However, it is important to realize that a similar lower turbulent zone may exist in the lee of a ridge under conditions that do not produce a well-defined lee wave region.

When a cold airmass upstream of a ridge is just deep enough to spill over the ridge top, two important flow features can develop in the lee of the barrier. As shown in figure 5-26, a shallow layer of cold (dense) air flows rapidly down the lee slope in what is called "shooting flow." This corresponds to the downslope wind region. Near the base of the barrier the airstream undergoes a turbulent transition (similar to a rotor) to a deeper and more tranquil flow downwind.

This process is very much like water flowing over a dam. The "turbulent transition" is similar to a hydraulic jump that occurs when water reaches the base of the dam. The actual location of the jump downwind of the ridge depends on the height of the hill, and the depth and temperature of the cold air, among other things. If the cold air becomes too deep, the shooting flow and the jump will not form.

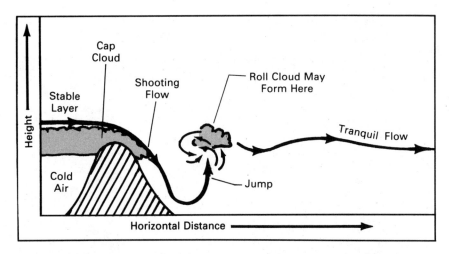

Figure 5-26. Cross-section showing a shallow layer of cold air flowing rapidly down a mountain side to the base of the slope where a turbulent jump forms. Flow is from left to right.

These lower turbulent zones often occur on small scales over unimpressive terrain with weak large flow; however, the turbulence may be significant. An example is found along the California coast during the warmer months of the year. In that area, cool, moist air from the Pacific is frequently confined west of the coastal mountain range and below the elevated marine inversion. Phenomena resembling hydraulic jumps develop on the east side of the mountains when the cool marine air (below the elevated inversion) deepens until it is just above ridge top. The air that flows over the mountains is made visible by the presence of a stratus cloud layer. Evidence of the shooting flow and the turbulent "jump" appears in the photograph of the associated cloud patterns in figure 5-27. There is usually no strong "lee wave region" coupled with the lower turbulent zone in this case.

Cold downslope winds occur in many areas of the world. For example, strong winds and turbulent jumps are common along the coast of Antarctica when extremely cold air flows down the mountain slopes from the interior. Another, perhaps better known, example of cold downslope winds is the famous Bora of Yugoslavia. Bora winds at the coast of the Adriatic Sea may reach hurricane strength with an extremely turbulent jump (rotor) just offshore.

The downdrafts (shooting flow) and turbulence (jump) at low levels in the atmospheric version of a hydraulic jump must be treated with the same caution given to downslope flow and rotors in full blown lee wave systems. The intensity of the turbulence depends on the wind speed at ridge top, the temperature difference between the warm and cold air, and the height of the ridge, among other things.

TURBULENCE CHARACTERISTICS

The main turbulence features of the lower turbulent zone are the rotor and the downslope wind area. This section focuses on the nature of turbulence associated with those two features.

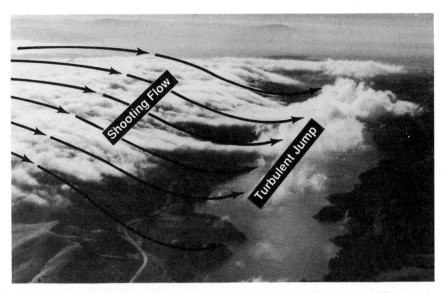

Figure 5-27. Photograph of stratus clouds along the central California coast. The clouds indicate airflow from the left dips downward in the lee of the coastal hills in shooting flow and then passes through a turbulent jump.

ROTOR

The center of the rotor circulation is about mountain top level. (Figure 5-28) If present, the roll cloud is normally located in the upper part of the rotor. When fully developed, a rotor is a closed circulation, producing a reversal of the winds in the lower levels. In many cases, there is a great unsteadiness in surface wind speeds and directions below strong rotors.

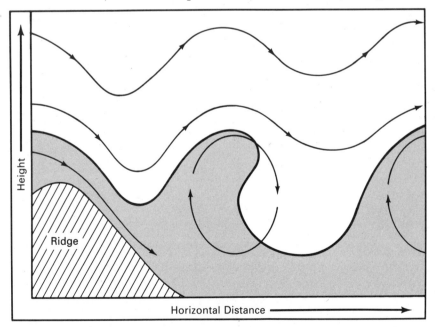

Figure 5-28. Cross-section through the lower turbulent zone. Airflow is from left to right. Although the entire lower turbulent zone is prone to turbulence, that turbulence tends to be more intense and more frequent in some regions (shaded).

The strength of the rotor is proportional to the strength of the lee waves. In particular, the rotor will be stronger where the lee slope of the mountain is steep and high, and where the mountain top wind speed is strong.

If the strength of the lee wave is stronger along one portion of a ridge line compared to another, the rotor intensity will similarly vary. If the roll cloud is present, these differences are often indicated in cloud appearance. A large roll cloud usually indicates a strong rotor.

The turbulence intensity is not the same throughout the rotor. The strongest turbulence is located in the updraft of the rotor. As shown in figure 5-28, this is on the upwind side of the rotor circulation. Not only is turbulence stronger there, but the turbulent eddies are also larger.

Figure 5-29 shows the true airspeed record from a twin engine research aircraft (Queen Air) that flew downwind through the top of a rotor in the lee of the Rocky Mountains near Boulder, Colorado. Severe turbulence was experienced. Note that the airspeed varied between 135 and 195 knots over a period of only a few minutes, with variations of ±10 knots or more over much shorter time periods.

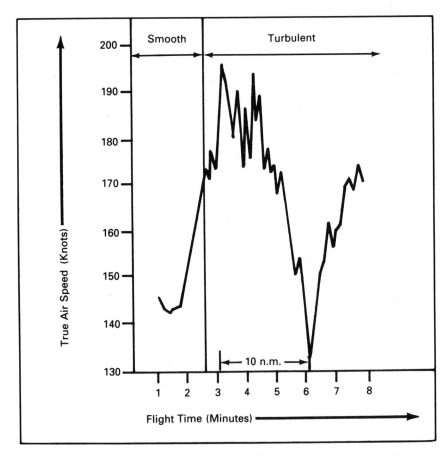

Figure 5-29. True airspeed record for an aircraft flying downwind through the top of a rotor.

There are few eye witness descriptions of the violence of rotors that compare to Larry Edgar's account of the destruction of his Pratt-Read Glider in the Sierra Wave Project (Edgar, 1955; Holmboe and Klieforth, 1957). His report is given below.

"The flight path went to the very top of the little cloud puff. It seemed to swell up before the nose at the last moment. Suddenly and instantaneously the needle went off center. I followed with correction, but it swung violently the other way. The shearing action was terrific. I was forced sideways in my seat, first to the left, then to the right. At the same time, when this shearing force shoved me to the right, a fantastic positive g-load shoved me down into the seat. This positive load continued. Just as I was passing out, it felt like a violent roll to the left with a loud explosion followed instantaneously with a violent negative g-load.

"I was unable to see after blacking out from the positive g load. However, I was conscious and I felt my head hit the canopy with the negative load. There was a lot of noise and I felt like I was taking quite a beating at this time. I was too stunned to make any attempt to bail out . . . Just as suddenly as all this violence started, it became quiet except for the sound of wind whistling by. I felt I was falling free of all wreckage except something holding my feet."

Edgar's parachute trajectory carried him around the rotor circulation first to the east, then westward, back toward the Sierra. During that time he saw the wreckage of his glider carried past him, upward into the roll cloud.

Turbulent (hydraulic) jumps, caused when cold air streams down the lee slopes of mountains, can also be catastrophic as illustrated by the following example.

Several years ago an F-27 crashed during an approach to an airport on the mountainous coast of Alaska. It was wintertime and surface temperatures inland of the coastal mountain range were very cold (-50°F) while temperatures near the airport were near 30°F. As the aircraft descended, it apparently penetrated a turbulent jump (rotor) caused by the flow of the cold air the over the mountains toward the coast. The aircraft suffered structural failure and all aboard were lost.

DOWNSLOPE WINDS

Winds that occur along the lee slopes offer a serious hazard for low-level flight because they are both turbulent and directed downward. The following accident reports emphasize the potential danger.

Cessna 150. One fatality, one serious injury. Substantial damage. Aircraft caught in downdraft. Stalled and crashed in trees. Exceeded capabilities to cross mountain.

Fairchild FH227B. 13 fatalities. Aircraft destroyed. Aircraft flew into a downdraft in the lee of a mountain at an altitude insufficient for recovery. Wind 61 knots at 3,000 feet.

If reported surface winds from a station on the lee slopes of a ridge are directed away from the ridge and exceed 20 knots, downslope winds should be suspected and verification from other indicators should be sought.

Visual evidence of gusty winds and turbulence in the lee slope area is sometimes seen in blowing snow or in dust that is carried up into the rotor. Vortices similar to dust devils and snow devils have been observed at low levels on the upwind side of the rotor. They develop where the updraft leaves the ground. Horizontal shear in that area generates the eddies which are stretched (spun up) in the updraft. Convection is not required for these whirlwinds but it may enhance their development.

A few times during the cool season in the lee of large mountains, downslope winds caused by lee waves exceed hurricane force (64 knots or greater). These **strong downslope windstorms** may last several hours and extend over large areas on the lee slopes of the mountains, causing significant property damage. The large amplitude lee waves which produce these windstorms can cause the wind speeds on the slopes to exceed the speeds at the top of the ridge.

Turbulence during strong downslope windstorms is widespread, often severe, and occasionally extreme. In the vicinity of the primary wave, the lower turbulent zone may actually extend from the surface through the tropopause and more than 50 n.m. downwind of the largest mountains (for example, the Front Range of the Rockies).

Figure 5-30 shows a cross-section from a strong downslope windstorm that occurred near Boulder, Colorado (Lilly, 1978). In this case, the lee wave system was dominated by a single (untrapped), long lee wave with a very large wave height. Note that some of the flow lines descend more than 10,000 feet in a horizontal distance of only 10 n.m. Aircraft crossing the lee wave at altitudes of 20,000 and 30,000 feet experienced very large wind decreases from the downdraft of the wave (strong winds) into the center of the lee wave trough (weak winds). A 94 knot change in 3 n.m. was observed during one flight leg. Severe or greater turbulence was encountered from the surface into the lower stratosphere.

The following PIREPs were received during a similar strong downslope windstorm in the lee of the Canadian Rockies in Alberta. The first report describes two low-level flights between Calgary (YYC) and Edmonton (YXD), well downwind of the mountains but well exposed to strong downslope winds. In the second PIREP, the aircraft crossed the mountains near tropopause level.

> YYC PIREP C210 YYC TO YXD 40 TO 50 ASL. ABORTED OLDS AREA DUE SEVERE TURBULENCE. SECOND FLT C310 YXD TO YYC 85 ASL MDT TURBC THRUT

> YYC PIREP B707 FROM 50 S YYC TO 10 MIN E YXC AT FL 330 EXTREME SEVERE TURBULENCE EXPERIENCED UPSET WITH PASSENGER INJURIES ABOARD.

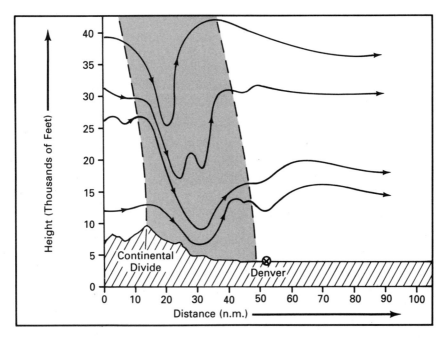

Figure 5-30. Cross-section through a strong downslope wind storm near Boulder, Colorado. Airflow is from left to right. This analysis is based on data gathered by instrumented research aircraft. It has been simplified to show the major features. The primary turbulent region is shaded.

ISOLATED PEAK

In the case of strong winds past an isolated peak, the horizontal extent of the lower turbulent zone may be limited compared to a long ridge. However, the turbulence can be locally severe due to the added effect of strong horizontal shears as part of the airflow goes around the peak. The formation of unsteady vortexes about nearly vertical axes (similar to "snow devils") should be expected. Lee vortexes (made visible by clouds) with diameters of more than a mile have been reported (Musaelyan, 1962). A notable example of turbulence in the lee of an isolated peak is given below (Chambers, 1973; Nicholls, 1973; Harrison, 1976).

In 1966, a B-707 broke up at 16,000 feet MSL 10.5 miles ESE of Mt. Fuji (peak at 12,600 feet MSL) in "extreme mountain wave turbulence." The g-load on the 707 was in excess of 8g. An A-4C descending to 5,000 feet AGL to inspect the crash site experienced g-loads in excess of +9g and -3g, but managed to depart the area safely. There were no clouds to alert the pilots to lee wave activity.

LOW-LEVEL COLD AIR

On some occasions when significant lee waves activity is present above the mountain peaks, surface winds may be calm or even directed upslope. This condition can occur when the boundary layer stabilizes at night; when a shallow cold airmass is located in the lee of the mountains; or when cold air is trapped in mountain valleys. A climbout from the calm air near the surface into the lee wave system aloft may cause difficulties for the unwary pilot. In addition to the typical flight effects of the lee wave system, turbulence and shear are found in the stable layer at the top of the cold air. The following rules for mountain flying are appropriate during such conditions.

1. If taking off from a valley, climb above the mountain top level before leaving the valley. Maintain lateral clearance from the mountains sufficient to recover if caught in a downdraft (FAA, 1975).

2. When mountain waves are present, difficulties await any pilot who chooses to fly across the lee slopes of a ridge at low levels even when the downslope winds do not reach the ground.

UNSTEADINESS
The lower turbulent zone can be much less organized than shown in previous figures. Unsteady conditions (rapid variations in the intensity and location of the main turbulent regions) should be expected when wind and stability change quickly. This can happen, for example, during a frontal passage.

RULES OF THUMB
While flight anywhere in the lower turbulent zone is likely to be turbulent, the turbulence hazard is particularly bad in the vicinity of the rotor and the downslope winds.

Several useful guidelines and rules of thumb address flight problems in, and just above the lower turbulent zone. These are listed below. (Alaka, 1960; FAA, 1975; Lindsay, 1978; Stack, 1991).

1. The worst circumstances are flight in a light aircraft across a substantial ridge against strong headwinds when vigorous waves are operating.

2. Flying mountain passes and valleys is not a safe procedure during high winds. If winds at mountain top level are strong, go high, or go around.

3. Avoid the cap cloud area with its strong downdrafts.

4. Except for the highest mountains, the following procedure is recommended: When approaching a mountain wave area from the lee side during strong winds, start the climb at least 100 n.m. away from the mountains. Ascend 3,000 to 5,000 feet above the mountain tops before beginning to cross. The best procedure is to approach the ridge at a 45° angle to enable a rapid retreat in case turbulence is encountered. If unable to make good on the first attempt, and if your aircraft has higher altitude capabilities, you may want to make another attempt at a higher altitude. Sometimes you have to choose between turning back and detouring.

5. In upwind flights, the updrafts of secondary lee waves just above the lower turbulent zone can often be used to gain sufficient altitude to fly through the downdraft in the primary wave.

6. In order to avoid rotors during arrivals and departures across rugged terrain in strong low-level wind conditions, delay descent until clear of the area. If necessary, pass over the airport and make descent from the other side.

9. Local knowledge is particularly helpful for determining where the worst rotor problems are most likely to be located.

10. Mid-level lenticulars are valuable in diagnosing the rotor situation.

MACROSCALE INDICATORS

In the previous sections, several meso- and microscale "indicators" of the presence and strength of MWT were examined. They included:

1. Terrain shape, size, and orientation

2. Mountain wave cloud types and locations

3. Direction and magnitudes of mountain top winds

4. MWT PIREPs

When some or all of this information is available, it can be used with the model of the lee wave system to answer important questions related to flight planning and turbulence avoidance. In relation to your area of interest, these questions are:

1. Do lee waves exist?

2. If so, where?

3. To what altitude do they extend?

4. Where are the turbulent regions?

5. What is the intensity of the waves and turbulence?

The task of answering these questions can be made easier if you are familiar with the macroscale weather patterns favorable for lee waves. This broader view of the lee wave environment will allow you to identify areas of probable lee wave activity even when the meso- and microscale indicators listed previously are not available. Knowledge of the macroscale patterns associated with lee waves will also aid you in the interpretation of forecast material.

MACROSCALE WEATHER PATTERNS

Any airmass that is conducive to the development of significant lee wave activity must satisfy two important requirements: there must be a stable layer just above the mountain and the wind speeds at, and above, the mountain top must be at least 20 knots. These conditions are commonly met when jet streams and cyclones move across mountainous areas, bringing strong cross-mountain flow and widespread stable layers associated with fronts.

Because the occurrence of lee waves also depends on the orientation of the terrain relative to the airflow, there are many macroscale flow patterns that will produce lee waves depending on the geographical area. Some typical examples are given in the following sections.

SIERRA WAVE

The famous lee wave system known as the "Sierra Wave" develops on the east side of the Sierra Nevada mountain range when a macroscale wave trough approaches the California coast. (Figure 5-31) The 500 mb chart in

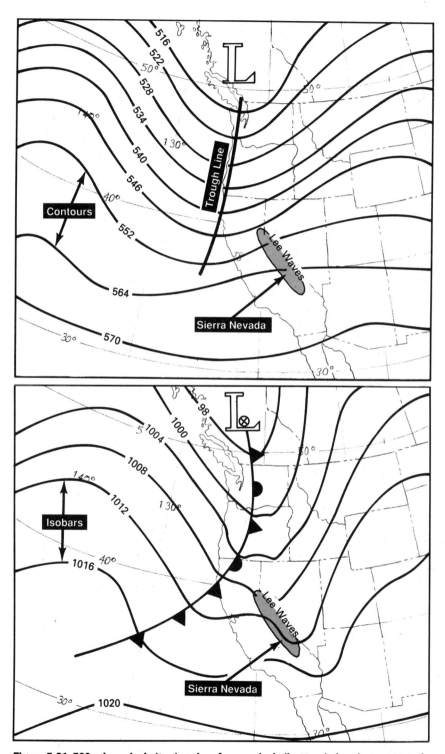

Figure 5-31. 500 mb analysis (top) and surface analysis (bottom) showing patterns for a developing Sierra Wave. Note the macroscale wave trough at 500 mb and the front at the surface. Although the attention is on the Sierra Wave in this case, lee wave activity also occurs in the lee of the coast ranges and the Cascades under these macroscale conditions.

that figure shows the macroscale wave trough just off the California coast. This large scale feature has moved in from the northwest and caused the winds across the Sierra Nevada to increase in speed and gradually shift from northwest to west or southwest (nearly perpendicular to the mountain range). A rule of thumb is that

> lee wave activity begins when the axis of the approaching macroscale trough is less than 300 n.m. upwind of the mountains.

The surface weather analysis chart in figure 5-31 shows an occluded front approaching the coast from the northwest. This "prefrontal" pattern is typical of significant wave activity across the western U.S. and southwestern Canada. The stable layer above the mountain tops is caused by a warm frontal zone or a jet stream front. The surface analysis chart is notable by the absence of the warm front. Typically, a warm front is too diffuse to be located easily at the surface along the west coast of the U.S.

A lee wave "event" has a typical lifetime of several hours. This period corresponds to the time it takes a macroscale wave of average dimensions to pass a given location. Sometimes a series of macroscale waves and surface cyclones will pass over a given mountain range (such as the Sierra) over a few days. In this case, lee wave activity will strengthen and weaken as the macroscale disturbances pass at intervals of 18 hours or so.

SANTA ANA

Mountain lee waves and a warm, dry, gusty winds known as a "Santa Ana" develop along the southern slopes of the mountains that are located on the north and northeastern side of the Los Angeles Basin when the upper air flow over the intermountain region of the western U.S. becomes northerly. (Figure 5-32) A large surface high pressure is typically located in the Nevada desert. This MWT hazard is not usually indicated by lee wave clouds because the air is dry.

ROCKY MOUNTAIN LEE WAVE

Surface and upper air charts are shown in figure 5-33 for a case of mountain waves and MWT over the slopes of the Northern Rockies in Alberta and Montana. Note that this lee wave area is on the northern periphery of a surface high pressure region. A jet stream is present over northern Alberta.

This pattern produced an exceptionally strong lee wave and a strong downslope windstorm over southern Alberta and Northern Montana. Two of the many turbulence reports received during the storm were presented in the previous section on strong downslope windstorms.

Close inspections of the surface analyses in figures 5-31 and 5-33 reveal a common feature of surface pressure patterns over mountainous areas during lee wave events. In each case, the sea level pressure is higher upwind of the mountain and lower on the lee side when mountain waves are present. In general, if you know that the wind speed at mountain top is 20 knots or more when this type of sea level pressure pattern is present, then you can be confident that lee waves are also present. The stronger the winds at

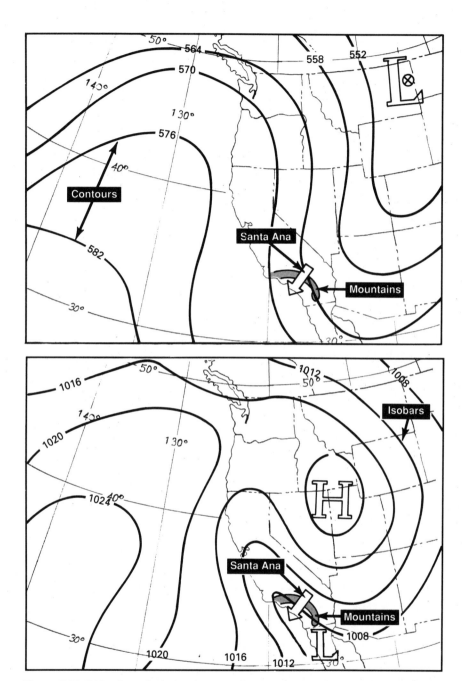

Figure 5-32. 500 mb analysis (top) and surface analysis (bottom) showing weather patterns during lee wave/Santa Ana condition over the Los Angeles Basin. Note the large difference in sea level pressure between southern Nevada (high) to the Southern California coast (low).

ridge top and the greater the sea level pressure difference between the upwind and downwind sides of the mountain, the stronger the lee waves and MWT.

Figure 5-34 shows the surface and 500 mb conditions favorable for lee wave activity along the east slopes of the central Rockies. Note the

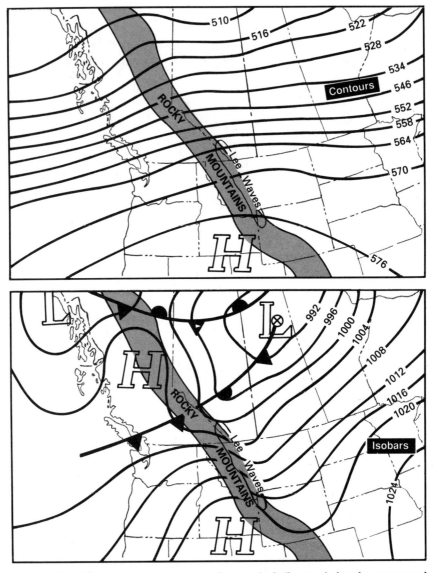

Figure 5-33. 500 mb analysis (top) and surface analysis (bottom) showing macroscale airflow patterns for lee waves and MWT over Montana and southwestern Alberta. On the bottom, note the trough of low sea level pressure in the lee wave area and the ridge of high pressure upwind of the mountains.

approach of both a macroscale short wave and a surface front northwest of the lee wave area.

APPALACHIAN WAVE

For the Sierra and the Rocky Mountains, the passage of the surface front and the macroscale trough aloft usually signals an end to the lee wave activity. This happens because of the orientation of those mountain ranges. In contrast, lee waves east of the Appalachian Mountains (southwest-northeast orientation) occur with northwest winds after a cold front has passed. An example is shown in figure 5-35.

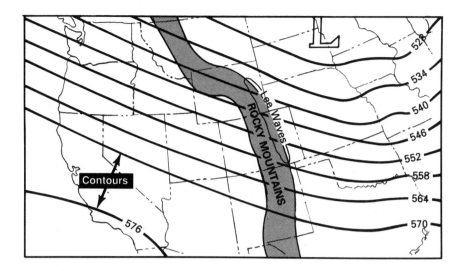

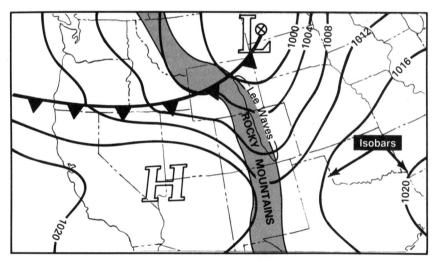

Figure 5-34. 500 mb analysis (top) and surface analysis (bottom) showing macroscale patterns conducive to lee waves over the lee slopes of the Rocky Mountains in Wyoming and Colorado.

MWT NEAR THE JET STREAM

When lee waves occur over a large region, the position of the jet stream axis is useful for identifying the area of the most intense lee wave activity and MWT. The key location is where the jet axis intersects a major mountain ridge. (Figure 5-36)

In this case, the primary lee wave activity extends from the surface to the lower stratosphere over and downwind of the ridge on the right side of the jet axis (looking downwind). The affected area may be 300 n.m. wide and extend 100 n.m. or more downwind. Additionally, an area of significant high-level MWT extends about 100 n.m. to the left of the jet axis in a layer from about 5,000 feet below to about 5,000 feet above the tropopause.

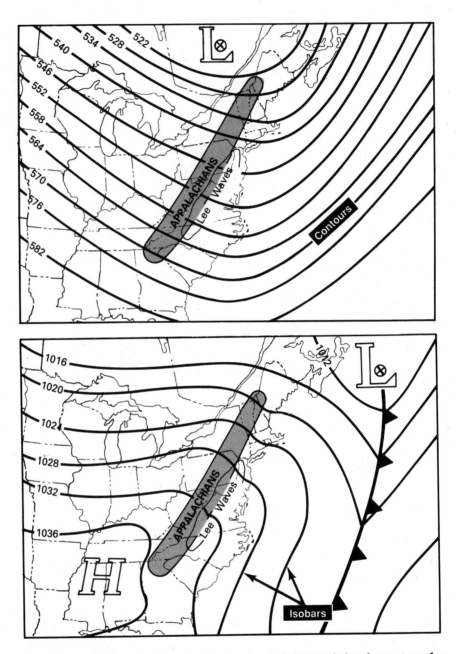

Figure 5-35. 500 mb analysis (top) and surface analysis (bottom) showing patterns for lee waves and MWT east of the Appalachians. The lee wave area is shaded. Note the cold front is well to the east of the mountains over the Atlantic Ocean. Similarly, the axis of the trough aloft has passed the lee wave region.

In applying figure 5-36, keep in mind that a mountainous region may have many nearly parallel ridges, and that a jet stream may be oriented perpendicular to those ridges over several hundred miles. Therefore, the lee wave area actually "activated" by a jet stream and accompanying stable layers may be much larger than shown in the figure.

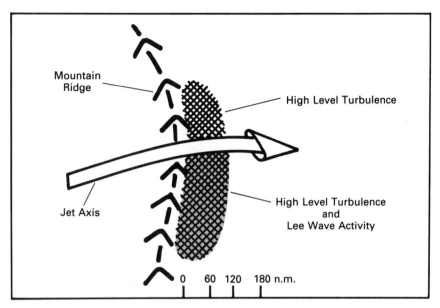

Figure 5-36. MWT area near the location of the intersection of a jet stream axis with a major mountain ridge. The light cross-hatched area indicates lee wave activity and the possibility of significant MWT from the surface through the tropopause. The dark cross-hatched area indicates significant MWT only near the tropopause.

When lee wave activity ceases in a particular area, moderate or greater turbulence will continue near and below the peaks as long as the winds near the mountain tops exceed 25 knots. Similarly, if the jet stream remains in the area, even though it is parallel to the ridges, CAT is still a distinct possibility.

SUMMARY

In this chapter, we have outlined the basic causes and characteristics of mountain waves and mountain wave turbulence. A practical model of the lee wave system has been developed to help you visualize the lee waves and turbulence regions relative to the mountain. The model can be used with both small scale indicators (visual observations, PIREPs, etc.) and with macroscale weather patterns to help you deduce the structure of the lee waves and the location and strength of MWT.

As with other turbulence types, your study of MWT should not be limited to this text. Much of our practical knowledge of lee waves has been acquired by glider pilots and the gliding community has published extensive literature on the subject.

Mountain waves occur in many other areas and with a wider variety of flow patterns than were covered here. Further knowledge of the large scale conditions that favor lee wave activity in your area of interest can be acquired with a little research. Some simple procedures for carrying out this task are presented in Chapter 6.

The general subject of gravity wave development and behavior was not taken very far in the nonmathematical treatment used in this and other chapters. Topics such as wave interaction, trapping, propagation, reflection, resonance, and interference have only been described with great simplification. The purpose was to make you aware of the occurrence and importance of gravity wave characteristics and processes. Further study is encouraged.

KEY TERMS

Bora
Cap Cloud
Chinook
Criteria for Lee Waves
Downslope Winds
Eddy Shedding
Evening Wave
Hydraulic Jump
Lee Wave Amplitude
Lee Wave Climatology
Lee Wave Height
Lee Wave Region
Lee Wave System
Lee Wavelength
Lee Waves
Lenticular Cloud
Lower Turbulent Zone
Macroscale Patterns
Mountain Lee Waves
Mountain Top Stable Layer
Mountain Wave Turbulence
Mountain Waves
Partially Trapped Lee Waves
Perpendicular Wind Component
Primary Cycle
Roll Cloud
Rotor
Ship's Wake
Shooting Flow
Standing Waves
Strong Downslope Windstorm
Trapped Lee Waves
Tropopause Temperature
Untrapped Lee Waves
Wave Breaking

CHAPTER QUESTIONS

1. Describe the hazards of flying upwind and downwind through a lee wave system.

2. Two lee wave cycles extend downwind from a particular mountain ridge. The wind at their level is blowing across the ridge at 30 knots. About how long will it take an aircraft to fly from a lenticular cloud in the second cycle to the ridge line? The airspeed is 120 knots. Draw a diagram to explain your computations.

3. Soaring flight in lee waves is possible over the island of Oahu, Hawaii about 40 days per year. At first glance, this seems odd because Oahu is in the tropics. What causes the lee waves?

4. Obtain a detailed topographical chart of the Sierra Nevada mountain range. Use it to explain the likely reasons for the variation of lee wave intensity in that region (see figure 5-12).

5. List all of the specific "indicators" of lee wave activity referred to at the beginning of Section D. What is the relationship between MWT and each item that you have listed?

6. Does figure 1-16 provide a comprehensive visual representation of all of the hazards of mountain wave turbulence? If not, redraw the MWT portion of the diagram to include any missing parts.

7. Can you determine the wind direction relative to the wave clouds in figure 5-1? Do you see any evidence of rotor activity in that photograph? Discuss.

8. Document the "lee wave climatology" in your local flying area. Where do the waves occur? What time of year do they occur? What are the common macroscale weather patterns that occur with lee waves? Where is the MWT the strongest? Can variations be explained on the basis of the local terrain? If there are no mountain wave problems in your area, select another location with your instructor's guidance.

9. (True, False) Any "lee wave climatology" based on cloud observations alone will underestimate the frequency of lee waves. Explain.

TURBULENCE AND
FLIGHT PLANNING

INTRODUCTION

In this chapter, the descriptions and explanations of LLT, TNT, CAT, and MWT are systematically combined with available meteorological information to assess the turbulence threat. In practice, this is only one part of the entire flight planning process which includes the assessment of all weather hazards. However, for instructional purposes, we will temporarily strip away those other hazards and concentrate on the turbulence problem.

The chapter begins by describing additional practical information that will enhance pilot's turbulence awareness. Next, common meteorological information relevant to the observation and prediction of turbulence is reviewed. In the final section, a procedure for the evaluation of the turbulence threat is presented.

TURBULENCE AWARENESS

An important result of the study of the material in this text is your development of a higher level of **turbulence awareness**. Turbulence awareness helps you to interpret forecasts and make accurate and timely estimates of turbulent conditions. As you might expect, turbulence awareness depends on your knowledge of turbulence causes, characteristics, and consequences (as discussed in the previous chapters). However, it also depends on how well you are informed about the types and favored locations of turbulence near your airport and along commonly travelled routes. Therefore, you will reach an adequate level of turbulence awareness when you are able to combine a solid background of models of turbulence types with a practical knowledge of both the local terrain and a local turbulence climatology. This mix will permit you to quickly evaluate turbulence potential from available weather data.

MODELS

Models act as essential connections between turbulence causes and characteristics and available weather information. Models help you to interpret relevant observations and forecasts and allow you to visualize the turbulence and its mesoscale environment. They also focus your attention on critical turbulence indexes such as mountain-top wind speed, vertical shear, and tropopause temperatures. A summary of the more common

TURBULENCE MODELS		
Turbulence	**Primary Models**	**Secondary Models**
LLT	Stable boundary layer Convective boundary layer	Gust, eddy, thermal, mechanical turbulence, dust devil, wake, frontal zone, sheared stable layer, low-level jet, shearing-gravity wave, thermal waves, convergence zone, sea breeze front, elevated stable layer, sea/land breeze, mountain/valley breeze, cloud streets.
TNT	Thunderstorm	Single cell, updraft, downdraft, multicell, supercell, downburst, gust front, gustnado, tornado, wakes, squall line, mesoscale convective complex.
CAT	Jet stream cross section	Tropopause, tropopause break, jet stream front, sheared stable layers, shearing-gravity waves
MWT	Lee wave system	Mountain lee waves, rotor, hydraulic jump, shearing-gravity waves, downslope windstorms.

Figure 6-1. Summary of turbulence models.

turbulence models discussed in the preceding chapters is given in figure 6-1. In that figure, "primary models" are comprehensive. They contain most of the important mesoscale characteristics of the turbulence-producing mechanisms. "Secondary models" help describe the details of individual components of the primary models.

In order to make a quantitative evaluation of the turbulence threat, it is important to keep in mind the primary quantitative indicators for the diagnosis and prediction of turbulence intensity. These were described in the previous chapters and are summarized in the figure 6-2.

TURBULENCE	
Type	**Intensity Indicator**
LLT	Surface wind speeds and gusts, wind shear (LLWS), airspeed fluctuations, frontal speed and strength
TNT	VIP level, heights of thunderstorm tops, wind shear, tropopause winds, stability index
CAT	Maximum wind speed at the jet axis, vertical wind shear, horizontal wind shear
MWT	Mountain top wind speed, tropopause temperature

Figure 6-2. Primary quantitative indicators of turbulence intensities.

TERRAIN

The essential question when evaluating the terrain is what are the important turbulence-producing features of the area over which you will fly? The answer focuses on the terrain characteristics near frequently used airports as well as along common flight routes.

You should be familiar with the general roughness of the area of interest. This includes the determination of the location, absolute and relative heights, and orientation of terrain features that are potential lee wave and/or turbulent eddy generators. Surface cover (for example, snow, forest, bare soil, water) and the orientation of coastlines and hillsides are also important to help identify sources of thermals and to locate local circulations such as upslope flows and sea breezes.

The slope and orientation of valleys is important for the identification of areas with significant mountain/valley breezes. Also valleys are always suspect for the existence of elevated, sheared inversion layers when the air at the ground is very cold.

TURBULENCE CLIMATOLOGY

In the previous chapters, typical meteorological conditions were given for the various turbulence types. For example, you saw that low-level turbulence due to dry convection is favored during the day and is particularly strong in the summer over desert regions. In contrast, mountain wave turbulence is more frequent in the cooler months when winds aloft are stronger and atmospheric stability is greater. Similarly, CAT is favored in the wintertime when jet streams are strong, while TNT is a common problem in spring, summer, and early fall when stability conditions favor moist convection.

If time and information are available, the development of an expanded **turbulence climatology** will prove useful. This is a more detailed version of the climatology of macro- and mesoscale conditions favorable for turbulence in your flying area.

The development of the expanded turbulence climatology should proceed along two lines:

1. The collection of relevant climatic summaries

2. The documentation of turbulence cases

CLIMATIC SUMMARIES

Standard climatic summaries for the various states have narratives which describe the significant weather problems for the state. Tabular and/or graphic climatic summaries are available for individual weather stations. These are monthly and annual summaries which give useful information about such things as the mean and extreme winds and their usual directions, local breezes, number of thunderstorm days, typical time of occurrence of thunderstorms, mean and extreme temperatures, and the number of clear or partly cloudy days per month. These data are based on surface observations (NOAA, 1968, 1991). In combination with your knowledge of the terrain, they will allow you to make certain deductions about the likelihood of LLT, TNT, CAT, and MWT. Such climatological information is often available at your local airport or library or it can be obtained for a nominal fee from the National Climatic Data Center (NCDC). You can contact NCDC by writing: NCDC, Federal Building, Asheville, NC 28801-2696.

If there are upper air sounding stations in the local area, annual and monthly averages of soundings may also be available from NCDC or local pollution control agencies. These summaries include such information as the frequencies and strengths of low-level inversions, winds, and vertical wind shears.

There is a wide variety of questions that a comprehensive climatology can answer. These include:

1. During what periods are thunderstorms most frequent? Seasonally? Monthly? Daily?

2. During what months are strong winds present? What is their prevailing direction? What are the extreme winds of record?

3. What months do lows with their associated fronts, LLWS, jet streams, and upper fronts occur?

4. Is a low-level jet common over your flight region? Day? Night? Both?

5. During what months are land/sea breezes most common? mountain/valley breeze? Where do they occur most frequently? What is their typical depth? Are they associated with a well-defined sea breeze front? When and where does the front occur?

TURBULENCE CASES

Although climatic summaries are fairly easy to acquire, they only permit you to infer general turbulence conditions in your local flying area. More detailed information about specific turbulence problems may be found in reports and eye-witness descriptions of turbulence incidents and accidents. Occasionally, nearby military airfields already have a compiled turbulence climatology in the form of maps and/or formal written descriptions of the hazards. Some research will be required to locate copies of the desired information, usually in the form of a "Terminal Forecast Manual." These are often available through the National Technical Information Service (NTIS). Information may be requested by writing: NTIS, Marketing and Customer Service, USDC, Springfield, VA 22161.

In the absence of a comprehensive local turbulence climatology, the task of developing one falls to the concerned pilot. Under these circumstances, a **case study** approach is especially useful for the documentation of details of LLT and MWT hazards. This may be done by acquiring official records of turbulence-related incidents and accidents. Most aircraft accidents have related NTSB reports. If turbulence was involved, these often provide useful case studies. NTSB reports are typically quite complete, including descriptions and illustrations of relevant weather conditions, and an analysis of their contribution to the accidents.

In addition to formal accident reports, other details about local turbulence hazards can often be obtained from "local experts"; that is, from experienced pilots and meteorologists. Although such anecdotal material is subjective and extra effort is usually required to obtain it, it can be extremely valuable. This is especially true when the information is systematically gathered and summarized.

Turbulence case studies should be organized on the basis of season, meteorological conditions, turbulence type, time of day, and incident location. It is useful to gather the weather maps (surface and constant pressure analysis) and, where applicable, weather radar charts, soundings, and surface observations (also available from NCDC). These help to illustrate the conditions around the time of incidents.

The development of turbulence awareness is an ongoing process. This is especially important when new or better information about local turbulence hazards becomes available or if the area of flight operations changes. Additionally, the turbulence climatology should be reviewed at the beginning of each season.

USEFUL WEATHER INFORMATION

Although the development of turbulence awareness goes far in preparing you to deal with the turbulence threat, it is your ability to integrate that awareness with meteorological observations and forecasts that has the greatest practical benefit. Obviously, an important requirement for the success of this process is familiarity with the available information. In this section, we summarize the weather products useful in the evaluation of the turbulence threat. It is assumed that you know how to read the various reports and forecasts. If not, you may first want to review that material (for example, *Aviation Weather Services*, (AC 0045C). Also, with ongoing improvements in weather products and changes in their formats, schedules, and sources, it is always a good idea to take regular refresher training.

KEY INFORMATION

Current and forecast weather conditions are in a constant state of flux and require preflight review and inflight monitoring for every flight. When you consider the task at hand; that is, the evaluation of the turbulence threat on the basis of current and forecast meteorological information, there often appears to be an overwhelming amount of information to assimilate in a short time. The pilot must be able to discriminate among the various pieces of available information because valuable flight planning time can be wasted in attempting to interpret irrelevant data. Fortunately, not all weather information is necessary for the evaluation of turbulence conditions.

Key information is defined as those weather products that are relevant in the evaluation of the turbulence threat. Those data, together with their sources and schedules of availability are the basis of a successful evaluation system. There are three basic types of key information: observations, forecasts, and advisories/warnings.

OBSERVATIONS

Some of the more useful turbulence-related observations which can be used by pilots over the continental U.S. are shown in figure 6-3.

In figure 6-3, turbulence types that are "shown" refer to those products which specifically indicate areas where turbulence is expected and the turbulence intensity. The turbulence type will not necessarily be stated, but the geographical area, altitude, topography, and the presence or absence of thunderstorms should be sufficient for the pilot to deduce the turbulence type.

In contrast, turbulence types that are "implied" in figure 6-3 refer to those weather products which don't show turbulence explicitly. In these cases, the pilot must deduce the potential for turbulence from the information provided. An example is a surface analysis chart. The presence of a fast-moving cold front in the flight area should translate to a possibility of LLT.

Some of the information types listed in figure 6-3 (for example, soundings) may also be produced in other formats. These do not appear in the figure

OBSERVATIONS AND ANALYSES		
Type	**Format**	**Turbulence (shown or implied)**
Surface	Coded surface aviation weather reports (SA, ASOS, AWOS) Surface analysis chart Weather depiction chart	LLT, TNT, MWT
Soundings	Constant pressure charts Tropopause data chart Composite moisture and stability chart Winds aloft chart	LLT, TNT, CAT, MWT
Radar	Coded radar weather reports (RAREPs) Radar summary chart	LLT, TNT
Satellite	Visible and infrared images	LLT, TNT, CAT, MWT
Pilot reports	PIREPs (UA)	LLT, TNT, CAT, MWT

Figure 6-3. Observational data and analyses useful for the evaluation of the threat of various types of turbulence.

because they require further data processing and/or interpretation and are not readily available to pilots. The formats of the listed information are discussed thoroughly in government publications such as *Aviation Weather Services* (AC 0045C) and in the Jeppesen Sanderson pilot training materials.

FORECASTS

Common forecast information that can be accessed for the continental U.S. is listed in figure 6-4.

Most aviation forecasts concentrate on periods of up to 24 hours beyond the present time. Forecasts with less detail than those listed are available for periods up to a week or more. Although these extended range forecasts do not include specific forecasts for turbulence, the positions of features such as macroscale waves, jet streams, and surface fronts help identify potential turbulence problems.

ADVISORIES AND WARNINGS

Commonly available inflight advisories and weather warnings relevant to turbulence are listed in figure 6-5. Currently, all are plain language bulletins.

FORECAST MATERIALS		
Type	**Format**	**Turbulence (shown or implied)**
Area (FA)	Plain language	LLT, TNT, CAT, MWT
Terminal (FT, TAF)	Coded data	LLT, TNT, CAT, MWT
Observed winds aloft	Observed winds aloft charts	LLT, TNT, CAT, MWT
Winds and temperatures aloft (FS)	Upper level wind prog chart	LLT, TNT, CAT, MWT
Low-level significant weather prog	Significant weather prog charts Surface prog charts	LLT, TNT, CAT, MWT
High-level significant weather prog	Significant weather prog charts Tropopause data chart package. Includes tropopause forecast maps for tropopause height, winds, and wind shears.	TNT, CAT, MWT
Convective out-look (AC)	Plain language	TNT
Severe weather outlook	Severe weather outlook chart	TNT

Figure 6-4. Forecast materials useful for the evaluation of the threat of various types of turbulence.

The key information listed in figures 6-3, 6-4, and 6-5 may not completely suit your needs. Also, the information may change, due to FAA and NWS improvements in observations, forecasts, and communications. These are discussed in Chapter 7. In any event, the lists given in the figures should be considered as a starting point. You are expected to modify them for your specific applications.

AVAILABILITY

Meteorological information only becomes a practical aid in the evaluation of the turbulence threat when you know when and where it can be acquired. Currently, the most common sources are the FAA Flight Service Stations (FSS and AFSS), National Weather Service Offices (WSO), and National Weather Service Forecast Offices (WSFO), Transcribed Weather Broadcasts (TWEB), Pilot's Automatic Telephone Answering Service (PATWAS), Voice

ADVISORY AND WARNING MATERIALS	
Type	**Turbulence**
Convective SIGMET (WST)	TNT
SIGMET (WS)	LLT, TNT, MWT
AIRMET (WA)	LLT, TNT, CAT, MWT
Severe weather watch alert (AWW) and bulletin (WW)	TNT
Meteorological impact statement (MIS)	LLT, TNT, CAT, MWT
Center weather advisory (CWA)	LLT, TNT, CAT, MWT

Figure 6-5. Advisory and warning materials useful for the evaluation of various types of turbulence.

Response System (VRS), Telephone Information Briefing Service (TIBS), Direct User Access Terminal (DUAT), Enroute Flight Advisory Service (EFAS), and Hazardous Inflight Weather Advisory Service (HIWAS). The availability of these services varies depending on location. Also, the information menu, broadcast schedules, and times of updates of transcribed information varies with the source and purpose of the information.

An important rule for flight planning is "always use the latest meteorological information." This isn't always as easy as it sounds. The time that turbulence-related surface observations become available depends on observation time and on your mode of acquisition.

For example, although large airports report weather conditions twenty-four hours a day, many smaller airports do not take late night and early morning observations. This lack of information causes the first FTs of the day for the smaller stations to be delayed until after the station opens.

The nighttime closing of stations can also be a serious problem over mountainous areas. In rugged terrain, critical changes in weather conditions often occur over short distances. A particular critical condition observable in daytime will go unobserved when a station ceases operations at night. Obviously, knowledge of the hours of operation for part-time weather stations is useful information. Also, full attention should be paid to reported observation times. Old reports often remain in the current data base until the latest report is received. The establishment of a national network of automated observing stations will help overcome this problem. This development is discussed in the next chapter.

Your efficient use of forecasts requires that you know the time the forecast was issued, the forecast period, and the "valid time" (VT) of the forecast. For example, if you are planning a flight for this afternoon, is the information that you are using a 24-hour forecast from yesterday afternoon? or a 12-hour forecast based on this morning's data? The more recent forecast provides the more accurate prediction. Often, a short wait for an updated forecast will be worthwhile.

Another consideration is whether the forecast is valid for a period of time (such as an FT) or for a point in time (such as the low-level significant weather prog). In the latter case, you usually assume that the forecast applies to a period of a few hours before the valid time to a few hours after. The accuracy of this assumption depends on how fast the turbulence-generating system is changing. The time the forecast was issued, the forecast period, and the valid time are usually printed clearly on the forecast product.

For preliminary planning purposes, commercial radio and television provide broad weather coverage. Although these sources do not usually address aviation turbulence problems directly, your knowledge of the relationship of turbulence to fronts, jet streams, and other macroscale patterns should alert you to turbulence potential. More on this is discussed in the next section.

Specialized sources of information include cable television's "The Weather Channel" and public television's "A.M. Weather." Caution is advised for users of information from a late morning broadcast of A.M. Weather, especially in the western U.S. That program originates early on the east coast, and may be several hours old when aired in the west. More recent observations and forecasts may be available.

In the last several years, turbulence-related weather information has become available via personal computer and facsimile for a fee through private vendors. The basic data include NWS coded and plain language observations, forecasts, advisories, and warnings. Some specialized businesses such as Jeppesen Data Plan offer both alphanumeric and graphic products tailored for aviation purposes.

Depending on your location, there may also be a number of turbulence-related observations that are taken by other government agencies and private groups. These may provide you with a useful indication of turbulence in areas where standard weather observations are not available. For example, surface wind and thunderstorm observations may be available from U.S. Forest Service (USFS) fire towers, Bureau of Land Management (BLM) remote sites, and lightning detection networks. These data are often available through the local NWS office.

Additional turbulence information for local flight planning may be found through private groups. For example, soaring pilots, hang glider enthusiasts, wind surfers, and other outdoor enthusiasts often find it useful to install remote weather stations with telephone access for the acquisition of wind and temperature data. The availability of such information can usually be determined by contacting local clubs and other interest groups.

EVALUATION OF THE TURBULENCE THREAT

The relevant question at this point is: "Given all of the available information, how should it be combined and interpreted to avoid or minimize the impact of turbulence?" In the next several paragraphs, a practical procedure to accomplish the evaluation of the turbulence threat is outlined.

The approach is based on the philosophy that, in order to properly evaluate the turbulence threat, you must "look over the shoulder of the forecaster." This means that the evaluation process goes beyond a simple glance at the prognostic charts; that is, it considers the "why?" as well as the "what?" of the forecast.

Although most pilots rarely come face-to-face with the forecaster in these days of centralized forecasts, the concept of "looking over the shoulder of the forecaster" can still be applied. It simply requires an effort to understand the forecast reasoning. This approach primarily aids in forecast interpretation, but it also prepares you to make those inflight decisions that are always necessary to adjust for the small scale vagaries of aviation turbulence. Finally, this more thoughtful approach will also prepare you to interpret weather information when a forecast is not available.

OBSERVATION AND FORECAST LIMITATIONS

Before examining the details of the suggested evaluation procedure, it is useful to review the impact of the microscale dimensions of turbulence on the task at hand. Certain recurring problems characterize all turbulence observations and forecasts. These are significant factors that must be kept in mind when evaluating the turbulence threat and when making the decision to fly. They are as follows:

1. The forecaster (or the pilot) must always "infer" current or predicted turbulent conditions from macroscale weather patterns and a few small scale observations (PIREPS).

2. The sizes of the predicted turbulence areas are often much larger than the areas where the turbulence actually occurs.

3. Turbulence forecasts are often not issued until turbulence is actually reported. Even in areas where there is a high degree of confidence in the turbulence forecast, the precise location of regions of severe and extreme turbulence usually cannot be pinpointed until a PIREP has identified the location.

4. As the time since a forecast was issued becomes longer, the forecast becomes less reliable. This problem is worse for forecasts of small scale, fast-moving, and/or rapidly developing systems.

5. Every turbulence occurrence cannot be predicted; the only way to avoid all turbulence is to stay in the hanger.

In addition to the scale-related problems listed above, you should be aware that current forecast procedures give priority to "significant" turbulence (moderate or greater). Recall that light turbulence occurs far more frequently than moderate or greater turbulence and, although it is usually only a nuisance, it does contribute to pilot fatigue. Furthermore, if light turbulence occurs abruptly or in combination with other flight hazards, it may compound flight difficulties, especially near the ground.

EVALUATION PROCEDURE

An outline of the flow of information relative to the flight planning process is shown in figure 6-6. The diagram is rather general; that is, it could (and should) be applied to a variety of aviation weather hazards in addition to turbulence. We will focus on the turbulence application.

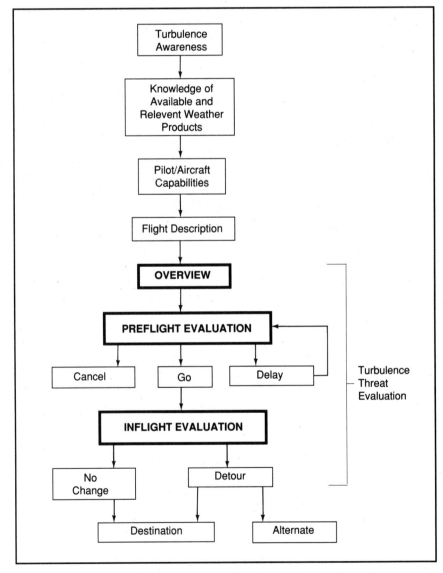

Figure 6-6 The flow of information in the evaluation of the turbulence threat.

The four items at the top of the flow diagram are "given"; it is assumed that you have acquired an adequate degree of turbulence awareness and that you know about available weather products. Furthermore, you know your limitations as a pilot and the limitations of your aircraft with regard to flight in turbulence. It is also assumed that you know your approximate departure time, route, altitude, and destination.

The remainder of the diagram in figure 6-6 focuses on the turbulence threat evaluation. It requires three steps:

1. Overview

2. Preflight evaluation

3. Inflight evaluation

The time that you allot to carry out these steps determines to a great extent the amount of key information that you can use. For example, if your flight-planning period is longer than the lifetime of the turbulence-producing phenomenon (for example, a thunderstorm), that phenomenon may not be in existence at the time you start your threat evaluation. On the other hand, if the flight planning period is too short, there may not be enough time to absorb all the important information available.

It is advisable to begin assessing the turbulence threat early (at least a day ahead of time), as is done in the procedure outlined below. Since this is not always possible, it is a good idea to identify and prioritize key information according to the length of the preparation time.

OVERVIEW

The **overview** is an examination of the weather in the planned flight area for the purpose of identifying large scale weather patterns related to significant turbulence. Many meteorologists and pilots refer to this step as acquiring "the big picture." As discussed here, it is assumed that the overview step is initiated more than 24 hours before the planned takeoff. If this is not true, then the overview and the preflight evaluation are combined.

The overview should proceed fairly rapidly since only large scale weather patterns are the concern. Your knowledge of macroscale patterns (for example, lows, fronts, jet streams) and their relationship to turbulence is the key to the successful estimation of turbulence conditions.

The overview should answer four questions:

1. Where are the potential turbulence areas now?

2. How have those areas been moving/developing in the past?

3. Where will they be at the time of your flight?

4. What is the turbulence type (LLT, TNT, CAT, MWT)?

Since a primary goal of the threat evaluation process is to understand the forecast reasoning, the clear identification of all turbulent types is particularly important. This will not only help to isolate turbulence causes, but it will also reduce the list of intensity indicators, rules of thumb, and models that must be considered.

The overview can be acquired by examining only a few pieces of graphical information. These are selected to represent the macroscale flow patterns near the surface and near the tropopause. The primary tools are the surface chart, a jet stream chart (for example, 300 mb), and a satellite image.

SURFACE CONDITIONS (LLT, TNT, MWT)

The surface analysis chart allows a quick preliminary estimate of the turbulence threat in the lower atmosphere. The key features are lows, highs, fronts, and strong pressure gradients. Once you have identified these, the process of deducing the turbulent threat is simple. Here are a few examples.

Aside from an occasional hurricane, most cyclones of importance in midlatitudes are those low pressure areas that move from west to east and are associated with airmasses and fronts. These should be considered potential sources of significant LLT, TNT, and wind shear.

Areas with strong pressure gradients and fast-moving fronts are suspect for strong winds and LLT. Slow-moving but strong fronts are concerns for wind shear. Any front traversing rough terrain should be considered a good source of LLT.

In areas where there is a significant pressure gradient across a mountain range, the possibility of MWT over the mountain and on the low pressure side should be considered. Since the flow above mountain top level is also critical in this assessment of MWT, the upper airflow pattern (discussed in the next section) must also be considered.

Although areas dominated by high pressure are typically characterized by stable air and weak winds, light and moderate LLT are possible. For example, during the warmer months of the year, in the daytime, this situation favors the presence of a well-defined capping inversion above a convectively active boundary layer. In the colder part of the year, a strongly sheared inversion can exist when moderate winds are found at the top of the boundary layer with cold, calm air near the surface. Supplementary information such as the winds aloft chart or the 850 mb analysis (5,000 feet MSL) may be used to estimate winds near the top of the boundary layer.

Regions where macroscale pressure gradients are weak are conducive to the development of mesoscale circulations such as sea breezes and land breezes, especially during the warmer times of the year. Recall that these circulations may be sources of light and occasionally moderate turbulence and wind shear.

TNT is favored with cold fronts and squall lines, but thunderstorms may also occur in other areas due to less obvious mesoscale causes. For this reason, the radar chart is a useful supplement to the surface chart for determining the location and movement of areas of moist convective activity.

Since instability plays such an important role in thunderstorm production, the stability chart showing the distribution of lifted and K indices is often a useful supplementary tool for the overview. This is especially true if the thunderstorms have not yet developed. Unstable regions that are (or will be) disturbed by fronts and low pressure areas are especially prone to thunderstorm activity. In the absence of macroscale circulations, surface heating and/or some other mesoscale phenomenon (a sea breeze front) can set off thunderstorm activity. This is a good example of where climatological knowledge of thunderstorm behavior in the area of interest is of use.

TROPOPAUSE CONDITIONS (TNT, CAT, MWT)

The 300 mb constant pressure analysis is examined for evidence of jet streams and macroscale waves. These features have far-reaching influences on turbulence production at both low and high levels. Macroscale waves and jet streams reach their greatest intensity near 300 mb and can be easily identified at that level. In the later preflight evaluation a lower level chart may be more appropriate, depending on your intended flight altitude. The following are examples of the turbulence overview for a wide variety of flight levels.

If an upper trough is just upstream (usually to the west) of a surface low, development of the surface low should be suspected. In this case, LLT production will be enhanced due to stronger winds and stronger fronts. Also, CAT should be expected at high levels, north and east of the developing surface cyclone. The threat of TNT is noted where upper level troughs approach unstable areas (as indicated by the stability chart). This may not necessarily occur in the vicinity of a low pressure area or a well-defined front.

Where substantial flow across a mountain range is indicated by the winds and/or the packing and orientation of the 300 mb height contours, lee wave activity and MWT should be suspected. This is especially true where cross mountain pressure gradients (with low pressure downwind of the mountain) were identified previously on the surface analysis. The mountain wave activity is often tied to the approach or passage of an upper level trough. Lee waves and MWT develop as the upper winds become more perpendicular to the major mountain ridges. Therefore, movements of macroscale troughs over mountainous areas should be monitored closely. For mountain heights of only a few thousand feet, a lower level chart (for example, 700 mb) is more appropriate for determining MWT potential.

The 300 mb analysis also gives other indications of possibly turbulent regions. CAT should be generally expected with the strong jet streams in the region of strong horizontal wind shear on the left side of the jet axis (the jet stream front). Jet streaks and macroscale waves with sharply curved flows have a high potential for CAT.

The combination of conditions favorable for both CAT and MWT are particularly important for the identification of significant turbulence regions over mountainous areas. Furthermore, if the jet stream is located over areas with thunderstorm activity, special attention should be given to the possibility of significant TNT around, over, and downwind of the thunderstorm cells.

SATELLITE IMAGES

Weather satellite images of the region of interest are often particularly useful sources of information for the overview. As seen in previous chapters, unique cloud patterns are associated with cyclones, fronts, jet streams, thunderstorms, and lee waves. When available, single satellite images or loops should be used to identify these features. Satellite images are particularly useful when combined with the surface and 300 mb analyses described previously.

Satellite images and loops are usually available during the weather portion of TV news programs together with a simplified surface weather analysis. If you are alert for the location and movement of important cloud patterns, even these simple presentations will prove helpful in your initial efforts to evaluate the turbulence threat.

PREFLIGHT EVALUATION

The quantitative evaluation of the turbulence threat adds numerical detail to the patterns examined in the overview, and helps to identify regions of significant turbulence. This process usually takes place within a few hours of the flight. It uses the latest graphical and alphanumeric forecast products as well as the latest observations.

The key information to be examined in the quantitative evaluation are:

1. Significant Weather Prognostic Charts

2. Forecasts, Advisories, and Warnings

3. Current Observations

LOW-LEVEL SIGNIFICANT WEATHER PROG

Significant weather prognostic ("prog") charts are flight planning tools which represent 12- and 24-hour forecasts of flight conditions below 24,000 feet (low level) and from 24,000 to 63,000 feet (high level). Although specific turbulence types are not identified on these charts (LLT, TNT, CAT, MWT), there is usually enough information to identify the type. This task is easier if the preflight step has been preceded by a careful overview.

In the present application, the important features on the significant weather prog charts are forecasts of moderate or greater turbulence. Those layers are explicitly marked with heights and turbulence intensity symbols. Thunderstorm (CB) activity (implied moderate or greater turbulence) is also indicated. A low-level significant weather prog is shown in figure 6-7. Note that the low-level prog also includes 12- and 24-hour forecast surface weather maps.

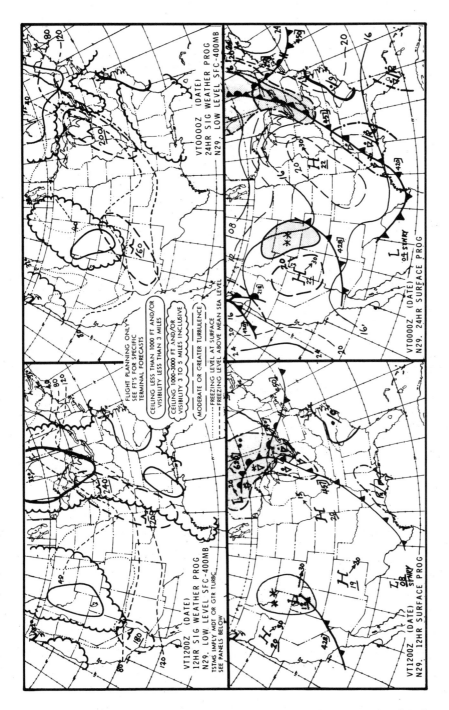

Figure 6-7. The two lower panels of the low-level prog chart are 12- and 24-hour forecasts of surface weather conditions, while the two upper panels are 12- and 24-hour forecasts of flight conditions between the surface and 24,000 feet.

High-level significant weather charts give similar turbulence information as well as useful information about the position and height of the jet

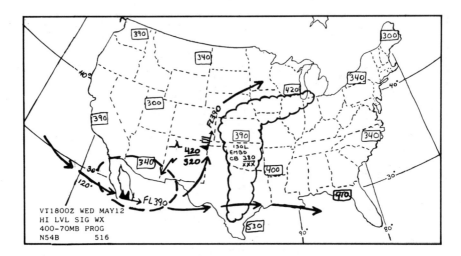

Figure 6-8. The high-level significant prog chart covers the altitude range of 400 millibars (24,000 feet) to 70 millibars (63,000 feet). The three-digit numbers contained in boxes represent the forecast height of the tropopause in hundreds of feet MSL. A dashed line is used to enclose areas of forecast turbulence.

stream axis, and tropopause heights. Both domestic and international (FL250 to FL600) versions of this chart are available. (Figure 6-8)

Other useful information for this step are the severe weather outlook chart, the forecast winds and temperatures aloft charts, and the tropopause data chart.

Severe weather outlook charts give information about the likely areas of thunderstorm activity, especially severe, over the next 24 hours. Obviously they are useful tools for anticipating TNT over or near your planned flight path.

The forecast winds and temperatures aloft charts show winds and temperatures at flight levels from 6,000 to 39,000 feet MSL. They are useful in locating and evaluating the strength of fronts and jet streams (LLT and CAT) and cross mountain airflow (MWT).

The tropopause data chart provides high-level flight information that goes far in explaining why certain areas are suspect for significant turbulence (TNT, MWT, CAT). It gives not only forecast conditions (the high-level significant weather prog), but also observed jet stream patterns and numerical turbulence criteria (tropopause height, wind speed, and wind shear).

FORECASTS, ADVISORIES, AND WARNINGS

As the flight departure time approaches, the quantitative evaluation of the turbulence threat increases in detail. The turbulence threat evaluation now includes the examination of plain language information such as area and route forecasts, terminal forecasts, advisories, and warnings. The best advice at this point is to be sure to use the most recent information and continue to keep in mind the inherent forecast problems caused by the small scale of turbulence. The overview step plus the examination of the turbulence forecast maps described in the preceding paragraphs should provide adequate background for the interpretation of the plain language forecasts, advisories, and warnings.

CURRENT OBSERVATIONS

Close to departure time, current observations in the vicinity of your planned route of flight should be examined. The most important of these are surface weather observations, weather radar observations, and PIREPs. These data serve as "nowcasts" of turbulent conditions, at least during the first part of your flight.

A common error in the use of weather data is the misinterpretation of the time that the observation was taken. This error becomes more serious as you approach the time of takeoff. An old report is not very helpful and may even be misleading, especially when it is used to describe a short-lived and potentially dangerous phenomenon such as turbulence.

PREFLIGHT BRIEFING

Your preparation to this point provides background for posing specific questions to the briefer and for interpreting answers. In particular, you want to be sure that your understanding of potential turbulence problems is correct and that you have the latest information (for example, via DUAT or a personal visit to a FSS). You also want to be sure that you are aware of any complicating weather factors such as IFR conditions, precipitation, and icing.

INFLIGHT EVALUATION

If the decision is made to "go," the third step in the turbulence threat evaluation assumes major importance.(Figure 6-6) With the background information derived from the previous evaluation phases, you have a good idea where, when, and what kind of turbulence can be expected. Based on that information, the inflight evaluation of the turbulence threat may be summarized in two words: "eyes" and "updates."

EYES

Eyes refers to the constant visual scanning of the instruments and the sky for turbulence indications. From the time preflight begins until the aircraft is parked at your destination, your eyes are a primary sensor of the presence of turbulence. Many of the more visible turbulence indicators presented in Chapters 2 through 5 and are summarized in figure 6-9.

Instrument indications of turbulence types and causes include fluctuations of rate of climb and outside air temperature (LLT, MWT), airspeed variations (wind shear) and, if available, radar returns (TNT). Although CAT has few visible indicators, aircraft flying near jet stream level and/or near the tropopause, usually have onboard instrumentation to determine winds along the flight track. This information can be combined with outside air temperature measurements to deduce the whereabouts of the location of the jet stream core, the tropopause, and the jet stream front in relation to the aircraft. These estimates require a good understanding of the

| TURBULENCE ||
Type	Visible Indicator
LLT	Blowing dust, blowing snow, dust devils, snow devils, cold air funnels, whitecaps, pollution gradients, cloud streets, sheared (tilted) cumulus clouds, sea breeze front, billow clouds
TNT	Cumulus and cumulonimbus clouds, anvil tops, rainshafts, overshooting tops, shelf cloud, rain-free base, tornadoes, gustnadoes, roll cloud, blowing dust, squall line
CAT	Billow clouds, cirrus uncinus
MWT	SCSL, ACSL, CISL, rotor cloud, cap cloud, billow clouds, blowing dust

Figure 6-9. Useful visible indicators of the presence of turbulence.

distribution of winds and temperatures near the jet stream (Chapter 4). Also good preflight preparation is required so that the approximate position of the jet stream relative to the flight track is known.

Another "eyes" application is the evaluation of the potential for wake turbulence. Whether on the ground or in the air, your proximity to the wakes of large aircraft should be constantly monitored.

UPDATES

Updates refer to the inflight acquisition of current surface observations, PIREPs, forecasts, advisories, warnings, and other relevant advice from ATC. The need for turbulence updates will vary in proportion to the flight time and the rate at which conditions are changing. Recalling the special observation and forecast problems that are associated with turbulence, it is always wise to extend the inflight monitoring of turbulence conditions beyond your visual range by requesting inflight updates.

SUMMARY

The scheme described in this chapter is one of many possible approaches to the evaluation of the turbulence threat. It is designed to encourage modification on the basis of your own needs and resources. The development of a checklist approach is appropriate once an adequate level of turbulence awareness and a good knowledge of available weather products has been developed. Other approaches may simply be the integration of the new knowledge gained here into an already "tried and true" scheme for preflight preparation. Whatever procedure is finally used, there are three essential characteristics that all turbulence evaluation schemes must contain.

First, the evaluation must take the "scale" of the problem into account. That is, meteorological information must be examined sequentially from the macro- to the microscale. This "mind set" recognizes the important connection between turbulence and larger scale weather patterns and the difficulty in observing turbulence. It is the key to understanding turbulence forecasts and using turbulence information to your best advantage.

Second, there must be an ongoing effort to stay abreast of FAA and NWS modernization initiatives. Meteorological observations (including turbulence) and methods of information transfer will improve rapidly in the near future. Changes must be carefully monitored to benefit from the improvements. More on this subject will be discussed in the next chapter.

Finally, the evaluation of the turbulence threat must be completely integrated with the pre- and inflight considerations of all other weather hazards.

The knowledge of turbulence that you have gained from the preceding chapters can only be enhanced by applying it in the evaluation of the turbulence threat. The development of a systematic approach to the accomplishment of this task will go a long way towards your goal of minimizing the impact of turbulence.

KEY TERMS

Advisories
Climatic Summaries
Forecasts
Inflight Evaluation
Information Schedules
Information Sources
Key Information
Observations
Overview
Preflight Evaluation
Terrain
Turbulence Awareness
Turbulence Case Studies
Turbulence Climatology
Turbulence Indicators
Turbulence Models
Turbulence Threat Evaluation
Warnings

CHAPTER QUESTIONS

1. Develop a turbulence climatology for your local flying area.

2. Prepare a list of all turbulence observation and forecast sources for your local flying area. Include the time the information is available, the mode of information acquisition (for example, television, radio, telephone, computer, walk-in), as well as pertinent numbers such as channels and telephone numbers. If available through a private vendor, include the costs.

3. Several turbulence indicators are listed in figure 6-2. Prepare a table listing those items versus numerical thresholds or critical numerical ranges for the various turbulent types.

4. Figure 6-9 gives a list of visible indicators of the various types of turbulence. Explain the physical relationship between each indicator and turbulence type. List and explain any other visible indicators with which you are familiar.

5. Develop a checklist for evaluating the turbulence threat. The checklist should cover a 36-hour period and include the overview and preflight evaluation steps.

THE FUTURE

INTRODUCTION

Many of the current difficulties with the detection and prediction of turbulence are captured by the following description of an incident during a flight across the Rockies. The aircraft was at 37,000 feet, 30 n.m. west of Denver. The pilot's comment:

> Encountered severe turbulence in mountain wave. There was no warning or visual cue such as lenticular clouds. Had airspeed fluctuations in excess of 100 knots and loss of 1,000 feet altitude. No injuries, but could have (had some) as seatbelt sign was off. Need some kind of detection and warning for this severe turbulence before it causes an accident!

This chapter briefly examines significant developments in turbulence measurement and prediction, and in communication systems. It also describes the integration of these improvements into the aviation weather system of the future.

SOLVING THE TURBULENCE PROBLEM

Currently, turbulence is poorly measured and areas of expected turbulence are often over-predicted. In addition, enroute information concerning turbulence and other related weather conditions is inadequate, often not timely, and not clearly depicted. It is clear that there is room for improvement in the current state of the art of turbulence observation and forecasting (Stack, 1991; Sumwalt, 1991).

In the last several years, FAA and NWS have taken the lead in finding solutions to a variety of aviation weather problems through a comprehensive modernization and restructuring process. The results of this process will be a better understanding of all weather hazards, including turbulence. Significant improvements are also expected in the quality, format, and communication of observations, forecasts, advisories, and warnings of weather hazards for the pilot on the ground, in the terminal area, and enroute.

IMPROVED OBSERVATIONS

Future measurements of turbulence and its environment must be more frequent, more detailed, and more quantitative. These goals are being realized through efforts to develop techniques for both remote and direct detection of turbulence. Promising systems now operate from the ground, from space, and from aircraft (Ray, 1986; Camp and Frost, 1987; Atlas, 1990; AMS, 1991).

GROUND-BASED MEASUREMENTS

Ground-based measurements include a variety of new or vastly improved observations from fixed points on the earth's surface. They include automated surface weather stations, improved weather radar, and new atmospheric sounding systems.

AUTOMATED SURFACE OBSERVATIONS

For many years, the rising costs of manning weather stations resulted in a decrease of the total number of those installations. The number of remaining stations that operate 24 hours per day also decreased. This loss has had an adverse effect on the ability of both meteorologist and the pilot to diagnose meso- and microscale weather conditions, especially those related to the presence of turbulence in the boundary layer.

This situation is changing. Significant expansion of the number of conventional surface weather stations is now possible through the automation of observations and the use of high speed data links. The FAA **Automated Weather Observing System (AWOS)** and a similar system being developed by NWS called the **Automated Surface Observing System** or **(ASOS)** are being installed at approximately 1,000 small and medium airports across the U.S. (Goff and Gramzow, 1989). The combined network, which will be completed in the next several years, is shown in figure 7-1.

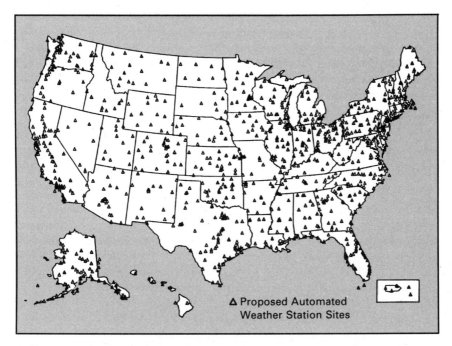

Figure 7-1. Tentative locations of FAA and NWS automated weather stations (AWOS, ASOS).

LLWAS

Low-Level Wind Shear Alert System (LLWAS) networks are designed to provide detection and warning of microbursts, gust fronts, wake vortices, and general wind conditions around selected airports. Each LLWAS is an array of conventional surface wind instruments. They have been, or soon will be, installed at terminals which have a combination of heavy air traffic and a high frequency of thunderstorms. At each airport, wind data are transmitted from the measurement sites to a central computer that alerts tower operators when certain wind shear thresholds are exceeded.

LLWAS was originally meant to be an interim observational system to deal with the wind shear problem until the installation of the terminal doppler weather radar systems. However, experience has shown LLWAS to be an important complement to the doppler radar. Therefore, LLWAS sites are now being improved by relocating and adding more wind instruments for better coverage, improving computation and display, identifying shear type, and by integrating LLWAS and the terminal doppler weather radar system to fully utilize their complementary warning capabilities.

WEATHER RADAR

One of the major advancements in weather radar in the last 20 years has been the development of operational doppler weather radar. Doppler systems not only sense target reflectivity, as conventional weather radars, but they also can also determine the speed of targets moving toward or away from the antenna. This ability to sense the wind at various heights and distances makes the doppler valuable for determining certain mesoscale circulations and wind shear.

Another capability of the doppler radar is the direct measurement of small scale motions. High-powered, ground-based doppler radars with small beam widths and large antennas are able to resolve downbursts, tornado cyclones, gust fronts, and even some disturbances in clear air. Doppler radar also provides a measurement of the intensity of turbulence. Small scale turbulence causes the reflected radar energy to spread over a broader frequency range. The measurement of the amount of this "smearing" gives a direct estimate of turbulence intensity.

The process of replacing the nationwide network of conventional NWS weather radars with the **next generation doppler radar (NEXRAD)** network is under way. The modernization should be completed in the near future. (Figure 7-2)

In addition to the new network dopplers, special **Terminal Doppler Weather Radar (TDWRs)** are being installed at more than 40 major airports where air traffic is heavy and thunderstorms and downbursts are frequent. The TDWR is better able to resolve microburst-induced wind shears in the vicinity of the terminal area than is the network doppler radar.

An additional improvement in the weather radar coverage in the U.S. will occur as the FAA replaces its airport surveillance radars (ASRs). The new models (ASR-9s) will have a doppler weather radar channel that will further enhance weather radar coverage.

WIND PROFILER

For decades, twice-daily balloon (rawinsonde) soundings have been the primary source of information about the vertical distribution of pressure,

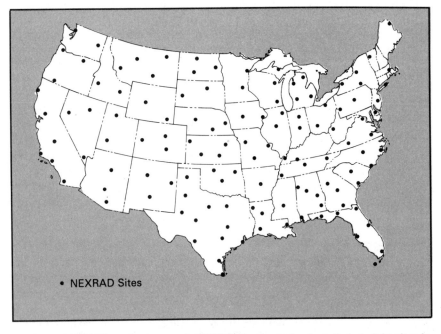

Figure 7-2. NEXRAD station network. NEXRAD is also being installed at eight sites in Alaska and at three sites in Hawaii (NWS, 1992).

temperature, humidity, winds, and wind shear. These are now being supplemented with a variety of remote sensing devices.

One of the most powerful new sounding systems is the **wind profiler**. It is a vertically pointing microwave radar that measures horizontal wind speed and direction information between about 1,500 feet AGL and 53,000 feet. A demonstration profiler network has been established in the central U.S. to provide experience for planning a national network. (Figure 7-3)

A major advantage of the wind profiler over the old balloon sounding system is its nearly continuous operation. Operational wind profilers make wind soundings every six minutes. These are then used to generate hourly average soundings.

The profiler depends on reflections (technically, backscattering) of the radar beam caused by very small scale fluctuations in temperature and humidity that are almost always present in the free atmosphere. When the scattering layers are swept along by the wind, there is a change in the frequency of the returned energy. The measured change (doppler shift) is then used to calculate wind speed and direction at various altitudes. The same principle applies to the doppler weather radars described in the last section, except NEXRAD and TDWR primarily look at the motions of precipitation particles and, in some cases, other small targets such as insects.

Profilers also have the potential to measure turbulence directly using the frequency spreading technique described above for NEXRAD. The operational applications of this technique are being investigated (Foss and Hinkellman, 1991).

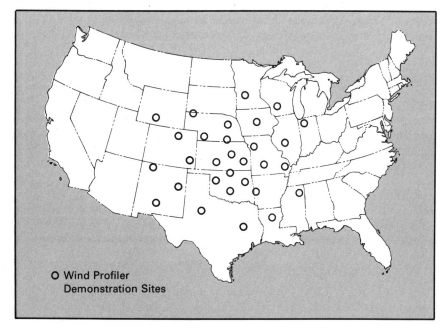

Figure 7-3 Demonstration wind profiler network.

The continuous monitoring of the vertical distribution of winds and sheared layers by the profiler is extremely useful for aviation forecasting purposes. Research efforts are being directed toward the systematic integration of the profiler information with other data bases to develop better turbulence forecasts.

OTHER SOUNDING SYSTEMS

In addition to the wind profiler, there are several other ground-based remote sounding systems that are being applied to the operational turbulence problem. For example, vertically pointing radiometers are being used to extract temperature and moisture data from radio waves emitted by water and oxygen molecules in different layers of the atmosphere. Such **thermodynamic profilers** are very useful for the evaluation and monitoring of short term (one hour) variations in atmospheric stability. When these systems become operational, they will permit a much more detailed assessment of the potential for turbulence due to convection, fronts, and other meso- and microscale phenomena.

Another promising sensor is the **radio acoustic sounding system (RASS)**. It operates on the principle that the speed of sound depends on temperature. Temperature measurements are made by generating a strong audible sound pulse at the ground and monitoring vertical speed as it moves upward. The monitoring is accomplished by sensing the time of the return of electromagnetic (radio) waves transmitted from the ground and reflected from the upward-moving sound pulse.

Laser systems have been widely used in atmospheric science for remote soundings of the atmosphere. Also known as optical radar or **lidar (light detection and ranging)**, these systems use the scattering of light from particulates or air molecules to determine the structure of convection and stable layers in the atmosphere. Lidars which are sensitive to the absorption of light by various atmospheric gases also have been developed for temperature and moisture soundings. Additionally, doppler lidars have wind sounding capabilities similar to the profiler.

Acoustic sounders have been especially useful in boundary layer research and in a number of operational applications. In its simplest form, this device, which is called a **sodar (sound detection and ranging)** consists of a loudspeaker, a microphone, and electronics to time sound pulses during their trip from antenna to the target and back. Primarily a boundary layer instrument, the sodar detects sound reflected from temperature structures related to thermals, stable layers, gravity waves, and shear layers in the lowest few thousand feet of the atmosphere. Displays show a continuous record of the height of these features above the transmitting/receiving antenna.

The sodar may also be configured to take advantage of the doppler principle to obtain wind information. A three-axis antenna design allows the determination of the vertical wind and the horizontal windspeed and direction at various heights.

In general, none of the individual remote sensing systems discussed above can provide complete and unambiguous details of turbulence, wind, and wind shear. However, when used in combination, they offer a powerful new way to detect structures and circulations that play important roles in turbulence production.

SPACE-BASED MEASUREMENTS

There are several developments in the use of satellites as platforms for atmospheric measurements useful in the diagnosis and prediction of turbulence. For many years satellite observations of clouds have been used to imply mesoscale circulations and turbulence using visible, infrared, and water vapor imagery. This is done by identifying unique cloud, temperature, and water vapor patterns which are related to the location and intensity of sea and land breezes, weak convection, thunderstorm outflow, squall lines, CAT, mountain waves, and overshooting thunderstorm tops.

Cloud-tracking by satellites has provided wind information at the level of the clouds for many years. These wind observations are used regularly in weather prediction models. Satellite observations also have been combined with conventional surface observations, upper air data, and pilot reports to infer the turbulence patterns.

Vertical soundings are made by some weather satellites using downward-pointing radiometers. These soundings do not yet have the vertical resolution of ground-based sounding systems, but they give meteorologists information on temperatures and lapse rates over areas which previously had little or no coverage.

In the future, better radar and radiometric sensors on satellites will yield more detailed observations of winds, temperatures, and other variables related to turbulence and its production. In addition, these data will be acquired at five minute intervals rather than the current 30 minutes (McCarthy, 1991).

AIRCRAFT MEASUREMENTS

The expansion and improvement of ground-based arrays of instruments to sense meso- and microscale atmospheric motions go far in improving our ability to detect and forecast turbulence. However, the coverage afforded by those systems is limited by cost. Therefore, the priority for placement of many of the most sophisticated surface-based instruments will continue to be busy terminal areas. Large, remote land areas and oceanic regions will be covered primarily by instruments at fixed locations (for example, ASOS, AWOS, and profilers) and by lower resolution, space-based sensors. Although the overall coverage will be better in the future, there still will be many obvious "holes" in this observational network; aircraft will continue to be a primary observing platform for turbulence measurement.

As discussed in Chapter 2, current turbulence observations from aircraft are subjective, qualitative, and not easily transferable between aircraft types. Research and development of onboard measurement systems to overcome these problems has been under way for some time and offers significant improvements in the near future. Advancements in onboard turbulence sensors are developing along two lines: direct measurements and remote measurements.

DIRECT MEASUREMENTS

Ongoing improvements in direct measurements of turbulence take advantage of the standard instrumentation aboard modern jet passenger aircraft. These instruments measure not only heading, altitude, airspeed, and air temperature, but also control positions and horizontal and vertical accelerations. In addition, accurate aircraft positioning is possible via ATC radar, an inertial navigation system (INS) and/or the global positioning system (GPS). From these measurements and knowledge of the aircraft design and performance, a wide variety of quantitative indexes of turbulence intensity can be derived. For example, airspeed fluctuations, vertical accelerations, vertical air velocity, and derived gust velocity can be computed automatically. This situation presents an excellent opportunity to increase the number and quality of objective aircraft reports (including turbulence) at prescribed intervals along aircraft tracks.

REMOTE MEASUREMENTS

Even if there are significant improvements in turbulence reporting, rarely will there be enough PIREPs to give the pilot a complete and detailed picture of the turbulent conditions everywhere along the flight track.

It has been recognized for many years that the development of a dependable airborne device that could detect turbulence ahead of the aircraft would be a major breakthrough in the aviation turbulence problem. The ideal instrument would be a forward-looking sensor that would identify turbulence far enough ahead of the aircraft to give the pilot enough time to avoid the turbulence region. Of course, airborne radar already does this for most TNT. What is needed is an additional instrument that will go beyond the ability of conventional radar to detect turbulence in clear air and in nonprecipitating clouds. MWT, CAT, and dry downbursts are of particular interest.

Currently, the most promising turbulence detection systems are doppler microwave radar, doppler lidar, and radiometers. Radiometers are used to detect vertical temperature soundings ahead of aircraft by measuring radiation from various atmospheric gases such as water vapor and carbon dioxide. Such soundings can be used to identify and locate stable layers, fronts, tropopauses, and atmospheric gravity waves; that is, in places where turbulence is often (but not always) found. Airborne radiometers also have been tested to detect temperature changes associated with microbursts at distances of a few miles.

It appears that the most promising application of remote sensing devices will be to use them in combination with other direct or remote sensors. For example, there has been a proposal to combine a forward-pointing microwave radar with the onboard wind measurements to produce warnings of impending CAT. The radar, scanning vertically above and below the flight path ahead of the aircraft, would sense the radiation emanating from oxygen molecules to determine the vertical distribution of temperature. This information would then be combined with the measurements of horizontal winds along the flight track to produce an index of turbulence probability (Gary, 1992).

Although efforts to develop a remote turbulence detector for an aircraft have been going on for over 20 years, an acceptable system has not yet been found. Most techniques work only part of the time. They frequently suffer from problems of inferring the presence of turbulence in a situation where none exists, and/or not identifying turbulence when it does exist. Since pilots will be making critical decisions based on these onboard remote sensors, these problems cannot be ignored. Further research and testing continues.

IMPROVED PREDICTION

Objective methods to evaluate the turbulence threat on the basis of forecast model output have been used by NWS, the Navy, and the Air Force for many years, but with a only a limited degree of success. This situation has begun to change in the last few years as forecast models increase rapidly in detail and reliability.

Advancements in observations and communications will result in greatly improved "nowcasts" (very short range forecasts) of turbulent areas. Computer forecast models that give extremely detailed 1 to 3 hour predictions in and around the terminal area are already being tested. These models use all of the local observational systems described earlier. In addition to obvious turbulence applications, their output of forecast winds and temperatures will feed directly into the automated air traffic control systems of the future.

For forecasts over longer periods and larger areas (the continental U.S.), improved PIREP and profiler data, and better communications are being used to improve the detail and frequency of operational computer forecast models for the continental U.S. Rather than producing forecasts every 12 hours, the new models will provide detailed six hour forecasts, updated every three hours.

These and other mesoscale forecast models are being developed and tested to deal specifically with the prediction of aviation weather hazards (including turbulence) and great improvements are expected over the next 10 years.

IMPROVED COMMUNICATIONS

Improved weather observations and forecasts really benefit the pilot only if those products can be transmitted in a timely fashion. This requirement for rapid communication is especially important in dealing with aviation turbulence.

Recent developments in communications include the efforts of several major air carriers and Aeronautical Radio, Inc. (ARINC) to put into operation a data communications system to acquire PIREPs automatically from aircraft equipped with the **ARINC communications, addressing, and**

reporting system (ACARS). ACARS will rapidly expand from the 1991 level of 12,500 reports per day to 150,000 in the near future. (Taylor, et al, 1991). An international ACARS program is also under development.

FAA is expanding the ACARS type VHF data link to allow pilots of properly equipped light aircraft very rapid, direct, and inflight access to weather information (Klein, 1989; McLaurin, 1992). Weather graphics information will be displayed in the cockpit either relative to the aircraft location or relative to the aircraft route. Turbulence information will, of course, be part of that package. In the future, the VHF data link will be enhanced by mode select (Mode S) secondary radar system and satellite links.

THE AVIATION WEATHER SYSTEM OF THE FUTURE

The FAA has initiated a process that will lead to the automation of ATC by early in the next century. The impetus for this modernization comes from the rapid growth of commercial air traffic in the U.S., the complexity of the airspace environment, and human limitations that constrain system operating capacity (Foss and Hinkleman, 1991). Weather (including turbulence) and weather information is recognized as a critical part in the automation.

In order to deal with the weather component of the automation, the FAA is executing a plan that will integrate present and pending technological developments (discussed above) to significantly improve aviation weather services over the next 10 to 15 years. The goal of the system is to "provide better aviation weather information, to increase the safety and efficiency of flight, and to improve the airspace system capacity" (Hansen, 1991).

An important characteristic of the overall FAA/NWS modernization initiative is the development of comprehensive analysis and forecast computer programs. The programs will integrate multisensor surface, radar, sounding data, and satellite information to produce mesoscale analyses and short range forecasts tailored for aviation applications. Two crucial components of the planned system are the **Aviation Weather Products Generator (AWPG)** and the **Integrated Terminal Weather System (ITWS)**.

The AWPG will produce a number of new analysis and forecast products intended for use by pilots, controllers, and air traffic managers. The products will deal with all weather hazards and will include graphic tools such as:

Convection Initiation — Regions where thunderstorms are expected in the next 30 minutes.

Convection Hazard — Composite avoidance region for turbulence, hail, heavy rain, wind shear, and lightning.

Vertical Wind Shear — Doppler radar and profiler product for wind shear detection and warning.

Inflight Turbulence — Product based on doppler radar and ACARS information. Includes short term forecast (0 to 3 hours).

An important feature of AWPG is that it will produce graphics and text designed for use by the pilot without the need for the interpretive skills of the meteorologist. They will reflect the detail of the new observational tools and forecast models, and will also be available enroute via the data link described previously (McCarthy, 1991). In short, they will be better, simpler, and faster.

It is expected that the amount of new information available from AWOS, ASOS, profilers, TDWRs, ACARS, and LLWAS will greatly increase the current data base. In order to use these data fully for the timely issuance of accurate advisories and warnings, special efforts will be made to integrate them, then blend them with information available from other systems such as AWPG and CWU. This task will be accomplished by ITWS. Its purpose will be to provide an integrated set of graphical and textual information, alarms, alerts, and products for use in the terminal area by pilots, controllers, terminal area traffic managers, and terminal automation systems.

CONCLUSION

The future bodes well for solutions to the turbulence problem. Future observation and forecast systems, as well as those just coming on line will bring more and better turbulence-related information to the pilot. These improvements will be enhanced by faster delivery systems and the development of easily interpreted products.

Better pilot education is a critical component of the advancements in technology described here. Specifically, better formal training should be required of general aviation pilots in the area of turbulence. This includes formal training in the use of new system products as they apply to the turbulence problem. To that end, follow-on-training is extremely important as the technology continues to rapidly change.

Better observations, better forecasts, better graphics, and better delivery systems do not replace the need to understand turbulence. If anything, these improvements emphasize the need for you, the pilot, to know more about turbulence, its causes, its measurement, and its prediction.

It is well to keep in mind that when you are finally in the air, it is you who will have completed the preflight examination of the weather data, and it is you who must now look at that instrument output, or at those clouds, or at that dust, or at those mountains, and make the decision that will result in turbulence being avoided or minimized . . . or not.

KEY TERMS _____

ARINC Communications, Addressing, and Reporting System (ACARS)
Automated Surface Observing System (ASOS)
Automated Weather Observing System (AWOS)
Aviation Weather Products Generator (AWPG)
Integrated Terminal Weather System (ITWS)
Light Detection and Ranging (LIDAR)
Low-Level Wind Shear Alert System (LLWAS)
Next Generation Doppler Radar (NEXRAD)
Profiler
Radio Acoustic Sounding System (RASS)
Sound Detection and Ranging (SODAR)
Terminal Doppler Weather Radar (TDWR)

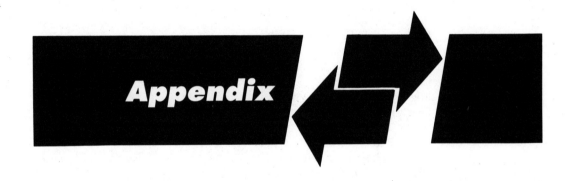

TERMS AND CONCEPTS FOR REVIEW

A list of important meteorological concepts and terminology is given below. The reader is expected to be familiar with these on an elementary level. Note the list is organized by topic. It generally follows the order of presentation of topics in most elementary meteorology texts.

Atmospheric Structure
   Composition
   Temperature, Pressure, Density
   Troposphere, Tropopause, Stratosphere
   Standard Atmosphere
Moisture
   Water Vapor
   Condensation, Evaporation
   Sublimation
   Freezing, Melting
   Dewpoint, Relative Humidity
   Adiabatic Process
   Cloud Formation, Cloud Types
   Condensation Level
   Fog Formation, Fog Types
   Precipitation Formation, Precipitation Types
Stability
   Lapse Rate
     Dry Adiabatic Lapse Rate
     Moist Adiabatic Lapse Rate
   Stable Layer, Inversion
   Stability Criteria
Winds
   Pressure Gradient Force
   Coriolis Force
   Frictional Effects
   Gusts
   Wind Shear
   Jet Stream
   Local Winds
Cyclones
   Winds
   Airmasses
   Fronts, Frontal Types, Frontal Structure
   Weather Distribution
   Stages, Life Cycle
Anticyclones
   Winds
   Weather Distribution
Thunderstorms
   Causes
   Stages, Life Cycle
   Weather
Surface Weather Reports
Surface Weather Map

Constant Pressure Chart
Weather Depiction Chart
Radar Summary Chart
PIREPs, AIREPs
FA, FT, SIGMET, AIRMET

There are many elementary manuals and textbooks in which some or all of the above topics are discussed at a level appropriate to the material in this text. A few of these are listed below:

Ahrens, C.D., 1992: *Meteorology Today*. 4th Edition. West Publishing Company. St. Paul, MN.

FAA, 1975: *Aviation Weather AC 00-6A*. U.S. Department of Transportation, Federal Aviation Administration and National Oceanic and Atmospheric Administration. Washington, D.C. 219pp.

FAA, 1985: *Aviation Weather Services AC 00-45C*. U.S. Department of Transportation, Federal Aviation Administration and National Oceanic and Atmospheric Administration. 122pp. (Note this publication is currently being updated.)

Jeppesen Sanderson, 1993: *Private Pilot Manual*. Jeppesen Sanderson, Inc., Englewood, CO. 462pp.

Jeppesen Sanderson, 1993: *Instrument Rating Manual*. Jeppesen Sanderson, Inc., Englewood, CO. 512pp.

USAF, 1990: *Weather for Aircrews AFM 51-12*. Department of the Air Force. Available from U.S. Government Printing Office, Washington, D.C., 20402. 146pp.

PILOT REPORTS (PIREPs)

Pilot reports of current weather conditions often provide such information as the height of bases and tops of cloud layers, in-flight visibility, icing conditions, and turbulence, which are not routinely available from other observation sources. When you encounter unexpected weather conditions, you are encouraged to make a pilot report. If the ceiling is at or below 5,000 feet, or visibility is at or below five miles, ATC facilities are required to solicit PIREPs. If you make a PIREP, the ATC facility or the FSS can add your report to the distribution system, and it can be used to brief other pilots or to provide in-flight advisories. [Figure A-1.] You are encouraged to obtain pilot reports and practice decoding them. This will help you get the most information from each PIREP, and it will help you give better PIREPs.

PIREP CODE	
PIREP Elements	**Explanations**
UA or UUA	Type of report — UA is routine PIREP; UUA is urgent PIREP
/OV	Location — In relation to VOR or route segment (station identifier, radial, DME
/TM	Time — Coordinated Universal Time (UTC)
/FL	Altitude — Above mean sea level (MSL)
/TP	Type of aircraft — Example, Cessna 172
/SK	Sky cover — Cloud bases and tops (both MSL), amount of coverage (scattered, broken, overcast)
/WX	Weather — Precipitation, visibility, restrictions to vision
/TA	Temperature — Degrees Celsius
/WV	Wind — Direction in degrees magnetic, speed in knots
/TB	Turbulence — Light, moderate, severe, as appropriate
/IC	Icing — Trace, light, moderate, severe, as appropriate
/RM	Remarks — To clarify the report or for additional information

Coded PIREP: UA/OV OKC 063064/TM 1522/FL 080/TP C172/TA
–04/WV 245040/TB LGT/RM IN CLR

Decoded PIREP: Routine pilot report . . . 64 n.m. on the 63° radial from Oklahoma City VOR . . . at 1522 UTC . . . flight altitude 8,000 feet . . . type of aircraft is a Cessna 172 . . . outside air temperature is minus four degrees Celsius . . . wind is from 245° magnetic at 40 kts . . . light turbulence and clear skies.

Figure A-1. PIREPs are made up of several elements, as indicated in the upper portion of this figure. The lower part provides a sample PIREP and its plain-language interpretation. Notice that MSL altitudes are used unless otherwise indicated.

GLOSSARY

Adiabatic layer — An atmospheric layer where the observed lapse rate is equal to the adiabatic lapse rate (3°C/1,000 feet or 5.4°F/1,000 feet). In the convective boundary layer, the adiabatic layer is usually found between the top of the superadiabatic layer and the base of the capping stable layer.

Airmass thunderstorm — A short-lived thunderstorm cell characterized by a generally vertical updraft. May occur as a single cell or in clusters. Occasionally associated with severe convective weather. See **thunderstorm, severe thunderstorm, supercell thunderstorm.**

Airmass wind shear — Vertical wind shear that occurs in the boundary layer at night under fair weather conditions (no fronts present). The strongest airmass wind shears are usually found at the top of the nocturnal inversion. See **nocturnal inversion.**

Airspeed fluctuation — An index of turbulence and wind shear intensity. It is the variation of airspeed from a sustained value.

Anticyclonic side of the jet stream — Right side of the jet axis looking downwind (Northern Hemisphere).

ASOS — Automated surface observing system. A network of remote surface weather observation stations maintained by NWS.

Atmospheric gravity waves — Periodic vertical motions that arise in a stable layer when it is displaced vertically. Gravity is the primary restoring force acting on the displaced air.

Attenuation — As used here, the decrease in the strength of a radar signal with distance from its source. Caused by absorption, reflection, and scattering of the signal by the atmosphere.

Average wind — See **sustained wind.**

Aviation Turbulence — Bumpiness in flight.

AWOS — Automated weather observing system. A network of remote surface weather observation stations maintained by FAA.

AWPG — Aviation weather products generator. Part of an automated system designed to improve future weather observations, forecasts, and communications. Will produce weather products for use by the pilot without the need for the interpretive skills of the meteorologist.

Billow clouds — Parallel cloud bands which often form at the base of a stable layer. Cloud bands are typically spaced a few hundred feet to a few miles apart. Billow clouds often occur in the crests of shearing-gravity waves in which case the cloud bands are perpendicular to the wind shear vector. See **shearing-gravity wave.**

Bora — Cold downslope wind that occurs along the coast of Yugoslavia in the winter. Often used to describe any cold, downslope wind. See **downslope winds**.

Boundary layer — The transition layer between the earth's surface where frictional effects are important and the free atmosphere.

Cap cloud — A generally stratiform cloud that is often found at the summit of a mountain under lee wave conditions. When viewed from the lee side, the cap cloud often resembles a water fall with cloud filaments descending the lee slopes and evaporating.

Capping stable layer — The stable layer (sometimes an inversion) found at the top of the convective boundary layer under fair weather conditions.

CAT — Clear air turbulence. Turbulence which occurs in the free atmosphere away from visible convective activity.

Chinook — A warm, dry, gusty, downslope wind in the lee of the Rocky Mountains. See **downslope winds**.

Clear air turbulence — See **CAT**

Cloudy convection — Convection in saturated air; produces cumuliform clouds.

Coastal front — A strong mesoscale airmass boundary that occurs in the late fall and winter between the Atlantic coast and the Appalachian Mountains.

Confluence — The meeting of two adjacent air streams. For example, if two jet streams approach each other, they are said to be "confluent." See **difluence**.

Contours — Lines of constant height on a constant pressure chart.

Contrail — A contraction of "condensation trail." Refers to cloud lines that form in the wakes of aircraft due to the addition of combustion products (including water vapor) to very cold air and/or cooling caused by pressure decreases in wake vortexes.

Convection — The transfer of heat through vertical air motions. Usually used in the sense of "free convection"; that is, the vertical movement of unstable air. See **forced convection**.

Critical range — Refers to the dimensions of only those atmospheric circulations that cause bumpiness in flight.

Cyclonic side of the jet stream — Left side of the jet axis looking downwind (Northern Hemisphere).

Derived gust velocity — An index of turbulence intensity. A theoretically determined, nearly aircraft independent, estimate of the vertical gust velocity.

Difluence — The splitting or spreading out of a flow field. See **confluence**.

Downburst — A concentrated, severe downdraft that induces an outward burst of damaging winds at the ground.

Downslope winds — In general, a wind directed toward lower elevations along a mountainside. For example, this term describes the surface wind direction in the lee of a mountain during a Chinook, Santa Ana, and a Bora. See **strong downslope windstorm**.

Drainage flow — Downslope wind driven by cold (dense) air. See **downslope winds**.

Dry line — Boundary between a warm, moist airmass and a warm, dry airmass. Under certain macroscale conditions, severe thunderstorm activity is initiated along a dry line.

Dust devil — A microscale vortex or whirlwind that occasionally forms in the superadiabatic layer over hot, dry areas in light wind conditions.

Eddy — An organized wind circulation. As applied to the study of turbulence, an eddy is often interpreted as a microscale vortex embedded in the general airflow.

Elevated stable layer — A stable layer (sometimes an inversion) with its base above ground level.

Entrainment — In general, the process where surrounding air is mixed into an embedded circulation. An example is the turbulent mixing of cooler, drier, outside air into a thermal or larger convective circulation such as a thunderstorm.

Equilibrium level — The level at which the temperature of a convective updraft becomes equal to the temperature of its surroundings.

Foehn — A warm, dry downslope wind that occurs along the northern slopes of the Alps. Often used to describe any warm, dry downslope wind. See **downslope winds**.

Forced convection — The vertical movement of stable air caused by some external mechanism such as a front or a mountain. See **convection**.

Frontal wind shear — Horizontal and/or vertical wind shears across frontal transition zones. See **frontal zone**.

Frontal zone — The region of transition between the cold side and the warm side of a front. See **frontal wind shear**.

Funnel cloud — A tornado that does not reach the ground.

G-load — Gust load. As used here, an index of turbulence intensity. Usually expressed as the incremental deviation of the aircraft vertical acceleration from normal gravity (1.0g). The combined effect on the aircraft structure of an atmospheric gust and the pilot's effort to counteract that gust.

Gust front — The leading edge of the cool air that moves out (horizontally) from the downdraft region of a thunderstorm. Sometimes described as a mesoscale cold front. It may move several miles away from the thunderstorm bringing abrupt changes in the wind direction, strong gusty winds, and turbulence.

Gust — In general, the difference between the instantaneous wind and the sustained wind. A surface wind gust is reported when the wind speed varies at least 10 knots between peaks and lulls. Also used generally to describe motions due to turbulent eddies in the free atmosphere. See **derived gust velocity, vertical gust velocity, G-load.**

Gustnado — A tornado-like vortex that sometimes occurs in strong shears and updrafts near gust fronts and downbursts.

Initial lift — The vertical displacement required to destabilize potentially unstable air.

Isotachs — Lines of constant wind speed.

Isotherms — Lines of constant temperature.

ITWS — Integrated terminal weather system. Part of an automated system designed to improve future weather observations, forecasts, and communications. Provides an integrated set of weather products to facilitate traffic management and the issuance of nowcasts, forecasts, and warnings in the terminal area.

Jet stream axis — Also "jet axis." The intersection of the core of maximum winds in a jet stream with a constant pressure chart. The jet axis is often represented as a line of maximum winds on a constant pressure chart. See **jet stream charts.**

Jet streak — A region of relatively strong winds along the jet axis. See **jet stream axis**.

Jet stream — A narrow band of high speed winds found near the tropopause. Minimum wind speeds are usually taken to be 60 knots. A well-defined jet stream is typically thousands of miles long, hundreds of miles wide, and five or six miles thick. See **low-level jet stream**.

Jet stream charts — Constant pressure charts in the vicinity of the tropopause. Specifically, the 200 mb, 250 mb, and 300 mb analyses.

Jet stream core — The three-dimensional zone of maximum winds in a jet stream. See **jet stream axis**.

Jet stream front — Also "jet front." An upper tropospheric frontal zone associated with a jet stream. The jet stream front is located below the jet core. It slopes downward from the tropopause on the cyclonic side of the jet axis, to the mid-troposphere on the anticyclonic side.

Land breeze circulation — A mesoscale circulation that develops along coastlines during the night under fair weather conditions. The circulation consists of an offshore branch at low levels (the "land breeze"), and an onshore branch aloft (a "return flow").

Lee wave system — An idealized model of the characteristic mesoscale disturbances that form in the lee of a topographical barrier when a stable air stream crosses the mountain. It includes an upper lee wave region and a lower turbulent zone. See **mountain lee wave, rotor**.

Lee wave — See **mountain lee wave**.

Lenticular clouds — Generally smooth, lens-shaped clouds that form in the crests of lee waves when adequate moisture is available.

Lidar — Light detection and ranging. A laser system designed for probing the distribution of temperature, moisture, and wind in the atmosphere.

LLT — Low-level turbulence. Turbulence in the layer within a few thousand feet of the ground where surface influences are significant.

Low-level jet stream — A narrow band of relatively strong winds located within about 5,000 feet of the ground. Characterized by strong horizontal and vertical shears. The low-level jet has no minimum wind speed but speeds of 25-50 knots are not unusual. See **jet stream**.

Low-level turbulence — See **LLT**

Low-level wind shear (LLWS) — Wind shear below 2,000 feet AGL along the final approach path or along the takeoff and initial climbout path. See **wind shear**.

Low-level wind shear alert system (LLWAS) — A network of surface wind instruments placed in the vicinity of an airport for the purpose of detecting critical shears and alerting tower personnel and aircrews of potential wind shear hazards.

Macroscale — Term commonly used to describe the sizes and lifetimes of the largest and most persistent atmospheric circulations. Refers generally to atmospheric circulations with horizontal dimensions of 1,000 n.m. or more and time periods greater than about one day. See **mesoscale, microscale**.

Macroscale waves — Refers to the wave-like disturbances in the contours of constant pressure charts. Wavelengths are in the "macroscale" range of horizontal dimensions. The trough of the macroscale wave is more commonly referred to as a "trough aloft" or an "upper level disturbance." See **macroscale**.

Maneuvering — The introduction of aircraft accelerations by pilot input.

Mechanical turbulence — Bumpiness in flight through turbulent eddies caused by strong winds blowing across the earth's surface.

Mesoscale — Term commonly used to describe the sizes and lifetimes of "middle-sized" atmospheric circulations. Refers generally to atmospheric circulations that have horizontal dimensions between about one n.m. and 1,000 n.m. Mesoscale circulations have lifetimes which range from a few hours to about one day. See **macroscale, microscale.**

Mesoscale convective complex — See **mesoscale convective system**.

Mesoscale convective system. An organized group of multicell thunderstorms. Typical patterns are linear, such as squall lines, and nearly circular, such as mesoscale convective complexes.

Microburst — A downburst with horizontal dimensions of 2.2 n.m. or less. See **downburst.**

Microscale — Term commonly used to describe the sizes and lifetimes of the smallest atmospheric circulations. Refers generally to atmospheric circulations with horizontal dimensions less than one n.m. and lifetimes of an hour or less. See **macroscale, mesoscale.**

Mixed layer — That portion of the convective boundary layer that includes the superadiabatic and adiabatic layers.

Mountain breeze circulation — A mesoscale circulation that develops in mountainous areas during the night under fair weather conditions. The circulation consists of a "mountain breeze" directed down the valley center line at low levels, and a "return flow" directed up the valley center line aloft. Along the sides of the valley, a similar, but smaller scale, "downslope wind" will move down the mountain sides.

Mountain lee wave — A region of periodic up and down motions found downwind of a ridge when the cross mountain airflow is stable. Also called "lee wave," "mountain wave," and "standing wave."

Mountain wave turbulence — See **MWT**

Mountain wave — See **Mountain lee wave**.

Multicell thunderstorm — A cluster of several thunderstorm cells in different stages of development. The cells are mutually supportive; that is, they contribute to the continued regeneration of new cells. The clusters may be made up of either airmass or supercell thunderstorms, or both.

MWT — Mountain wave turbulence. Turbulence produced in connection with mountain lee waves. It includes bumpiness caused by surface winds, rotors, lee waves, and wind shear.

NEXRAD — Next generation (doppler) weather radar.

Nocturnal inversion — A very stable layer (temperature increases with height) that forms next to the ground at night caused by radiational cooling of the earth's surface. Occurrence favored with clear skies and light winds. See **airmass wind shear.**

Outflow boundary — An old gust front that continues to exist after the parent thunderstorm has dissipated.

Perpendicular wind component — With reference to mountain lee waves, that portion of the total wind that crosses the ridge line at a 90° angle.

Polar front jet stream — The westerly jet stream that generally parallels the polar front. Typically found close to 30,000 feet MSL.

Potential instability — A condition that describes stable air that can become unstable if it is given sufficient lifting.

Profiler — A vertically pointing microwave doppler radar that measures wind speed and direction between altitudes of about 1,500 feet and 53,000 feet.

Rainshaft — Region of precipitation below the thunderstorm base.

RASS — Radio acoustic sounding system.

Return flow — The upper branch of a thermally driven circulation. See **sea breeze circulation, land breeze circulation, mountain breeze circulation.**

Roll cloud — This term is used to describe a cloud form that develops under two distinctly different situations. One is a cumuliform cloud band which is occasionally seen parallel to the thunderstorm gust front. The cloud band has a distinct rolling motion. See **gust front.**

The second use of the term is to describe a cumuliform cloud (often a band) that forms in a rotor circulation associated with lee wave activity. See **rotor, lee wave system.**

Rotor — An extremely turbulent closed circulation that forms near mountain top level below one or more lee wave crests in the lower turbulent zone of the lee wave system. Sometimes described as a "horizontal vortex" or a "horizontal tornado." May be identified by the presence of a roll cloud when there is adequate moisture for cloud formation. See **lee wave system, roll cloud.**

Santa Ana — Warm, dry, gusty, downslope, northeasterly wind that occurs in the Los Angeles Basin. See **downslope winds.**

Sea breeze circulation — A mesoscale circulation that develops along coastlines during the daytime under fair weather conditions. The circulation consists of an onshore branch at low levels (the "sea breeze"), and an offshore branch aloft (a "return flow").

Sea breeze front — Mesoscale transition zone between cool oceanic air and warm inland air. Found at the leading edge of a sea breeze as it penetrates inland during the day.

Severe thunderstorm — A thunderstorm capable of producing wind gusts of 50 knots or more, hailstones with diameters 3/4" or more, and/or strong tornadoes.

Shear line — An elongated zone where surface winds converge. Also called a "convergence zone."

Shearing-gravity waves — Small scale waves which occur in stable layers subjected to strong vertical shear. Waves are typically a few hundred feet to a few miles in length. May be made visible by the presence of "billow clouds" in the wave crests. Waves may overturn when the wind shear is strong enough, producing turbulence.

Shelf cloud — Smooth, rain-free cloud layer located near the base of a cumulonimbus cloud where the updraft is entering the thunderstorm.

Ship's wake — Term used to describe the characteristic shape of mountain waves in the lee of an isolated peak. Has also been used to describe disturbances produced in the lee of a thunderstorm top which penetrates a region of strong winds.

Single cell thunderstorm — A short-lived airmass thunderstorm cell.

Sodar — Sound detection and ranging. A system which uses audible sound pulses to determine the vertical temperature and wind structure of the lower atmosphere.

Squall line — A continuous or broken line of nonfrontal thunderstorms. Also called an instability line. See **mesoscale convective system**.

Standing wave — See **mountain lee wave**.

Strong downslope windstorm — A downslope wind event where wind speeds reach hurricane strength (64 knots or greater). See **downslope winds**.

Subtropical jet stream — A low latitude westerly jet stream that occurs in winter. Over the continental U.S., it is usually found between latitudes 25° and 35° at an altitude of about 40,000 feet. Not associated with any surface fronts.

Superadiabatic layer — An atmospheric layer where the observed lapse rate exceeds the adiabatic lapse rate. Commonly found immediately above the ground (at the base of the convective boundary layer) on warm days.

Supercell — A very large thunderstorm cell. It is characterized by a long life time and a very strong, tilted, and nearly steady state updraft. It always produces a severe thunderstorm.

Sustained wind — The average of the instantaneous wind over a period of time. Also known as the "average" wind. In surface weather observations, the averaging period is usually one minute.

TDWR — Terminal doppler weather radar.

Thermal — Rising bubble of warm air in the convective boundary layer; often cloud-free. See **vortex ring**.

Thermal turbulence — Bumpiness in flight caused by rising bubbles of warm air in the convective boundary layer. See **thermal**.

Thermodynamic profiler — Vertically pointing multichannel radiometer designed to make vertical soundings of temperature and humidity.

Thunderstorm — A mesoscale convective storm produced by a cumulonimbus cloud and accompanied by lightning, thunder, significant turbulence, and icing. It usually produces strong wind gusts, sometimes hail and, occasionally, tornadoes.

Thunderstorm cell — The updraft region of a thunderstorm.

TNT — Turbulence in and near thunderstorms. Includes turbulence and wind shear within thunderstorms, in thunderstorm wakes, above thunderstorm tops, and in downbursts and gust fronts.

Tornado — A violently rotating column of air found below some cumulonimbus clouds. Capable of causing extreme damage.

Transverse bands — Lines of clouds embedded within a broader cirriform cloud band on the anticyclonic side of the jet stream.

Trapped lee waves — Lee waves that are confined in and below a stable layer that is typically found just above the mountain tops. Trapped lee waves often extend hundreds of miles downwind of the mountain. See **untrapped lee waves**.

Tropopause — Boundary between the troposphere and overlying stratosphere.

Tropopause break — Discontinuity in the height of the tropopause. Tropopause breaks are found near jet streams. The tropopause is distinctly higher on the anticyclonic side of a jet stream and lower on the cyclonic side. See **tropopause**.

Turbulence awareness — The background knowledge a pilot acquires for the purpose of dealing with turbulence. Ideally, it combines knowledge of turbulence causes, characteristics, consequences, and a detailed turbulence climatology.

Turbulence climatology — A description of the average seasonal and daily occurrences of turbulence in the local flying area and along frequently traveled routes. This information is usually combined with a documentation of specific turbulence hazards related to passing storms and local terrain.

Untrapped lee waves — Lee waves that are not confined to the lower layers of the atmosphere. Untrapped lee waves typically reach into the stratosphere and do not extend more than a few wave lengths downwind of the mountains. Also referred to as "vertically propagating" lee waves. See **trapped lee waves.**

Upslope wind — Wind directed toward higher elevations along a mountainside. See **valley breeze circulation.**

Valley breeze circulation — A mesoscale circulation that develops in mountainous areas during the day under fair weather conditions. The circulation consists of a "valley breeze" directed up the valley center line at low levels, and a "return flow" directed down the valley center line at high levels. Along the sunlit sides of the valley a smaller scale "upslope wind" will be directed toward the ridges.

Vertical acceleration — The rate of change of the vertical velocity of the aircraft. Commonly measured at the aircraft center of gravity. See **G-load.**

Vertical gust velocity — An index of turbulence intensity. The instantaneous upward or downward velocity of the air. See **derived gust velocity**.

Vortex ring — As applied here, it is a donut-shaped circulation which may be either rising or sinking. It is often used to describe the structures of thermals and downbursts. In a thermal (entire circulation generally rising), air is moving rapidly upward in the center and downward on the edges. In a downburst (entire circulation generally sinking), air is moving rapidly downward in the center and upward on the edges. See **thermal, downburst.**

Wake turbulence — Bumpiness that occurs when an aircraft intersects the wake generated by an aircraft in flight.

Waterspout — A tornado over water. Usually not as intense as tornadoes over land areas.

Wave amplitude — In airflow through a wave, this is the maximum distance a parcel of air is displaced from its average position. See **wave height**.

Wave height — Distance from the wave trough to the wave crest; equal to twice the wave amplitude. For example, with a water wave, the wave height is the difference between the height of the water surface in the wave crest and the height in the wave trough.

Wavelength — Distance between two successive wave crests (or troughs).

Wind profiler — See **profiler**.

Wind shadow — Refers to an area sheltered from the prevailing winds, usually by a stand of trees or a hill. During the daytime, stronger "shadow thermals" may form in the wind shadow. See **thermal**.

Wind shear — The change in wind speed and/or direction over a distance. If the change occurs over a vertical distance, it is referred to as "vertical wind shear." If the change occurs over a horizontal distance, it is called "horizontal wind shear." See **LLWS, airmass wind shear, frontal wind shear.**

REFERENCES AND RECOMMENDED READING

Alaka, M. (Ed.), 1960: "The Airflow over Mountains." WMO TN No.34. World Meteorological Organization. 135pp.

AMS, 1989: _Preprints, Third International Conference on Aviation Weather Systems._ Anaheim. American Meteorological Society, Boston. 492pp.

AMS, 1991: _Preprints, Fourth International Conference on Aviation Weather Systems._ Paris. American Meteorological Society, Boston. 484pp.

Atkinson, B.W., 1981: _Mesoscale Atmospheric Circulations._ Academic Press. 495pp.

Atlas, D. (Ed.), 1990: _Radar in Meteorology._ American Meteorological Society, Boston. 806pp.

Bradbury, T. and J.P. Kuettner (Eds.), 1976: _Forecasters Manual for Soaring Flight._ Organisation Scientifique et Technique International du Vol a Voile (OSTIV), Geneva. 119pp.

Browning, K.A., 1971: "Structure of the atmosphere in the vicinity of large Kelvin-Helmholtz Billows." _Quarterly Journal of the Royal Meteorological Society, 97,_ 283-299.

Buck, R.N., 1988: _Weather Flying._ Third Edition. MacMillan, New York. 311pp.

Buckler, S.J., 1965: "An Analysis of Meteorological Conditions During a Case of Severe Turbulence." Department of Transport, Meteorological Branch, Canada. CIR 4211, TEC 563. 17pp.

Burnham, J., 1970: "Atmospheric Gusts — A Review of some recent R.A.E. Research." _C.P. No. 1091._ HMSO, London. 24pp + 33 figs.

Byers, H.R., and R.R. Braham, 1949: _The Thunderstorm._ U.S. Weather Bureau, Washington. 287pp.

Camp, D.W., and W. Frost (Eds.), 1987: _Atmospheric Turbulence Relative to Aviation, Missile, and Space Programs. NASA Conference Paper 2468._ 265pp.

Caracena, F., R.L. Holle, C.A. Doswell III, 1990: _Microbursts, A Handbook for Visual Identification,_ Second Edition NOAA, ERL, NSSL. 35pp.

Collins, R.L., 1982: _Thunderstorms and Airplanes._ Delacorte Press/Eleanor Friede. New York. 280pp.

Chambers, E. 1973: "BOAC Experience with Turbulence" in *Flight in Turbulence. AGAARD Conference Proceedings No. 140.* NATO. 6-1 to 6-13.

Chandler, C.L., 1986: "Turbulence Forecasting" in *Atmospheric Turbulence Relative to Aviation, Missile, and Space Programs. NASA Conference Publication 2468.* 137-154.

Colson, D.C., 1968: "Clear Air Turbulence and Upper Level Meteorological Patterns" in *Clear Air Turbulence and Its Detection.* Plenum Press, N.Y. 337-360.

Cooley, J.R.,1971: "Dust Devil Meteorology." *NOAA TM NWS CR-W2,* National Weather Service. 34pp.

Corby, G.A., 1957: "Preliminary Study of Gravity Waves Using Radiosonde Data." *Quarterly Journal of The Royal Meteorological Society, 83.* 49-60.

de Saint-Exupery, A., 1939: *Wind, Sand and Stars.* Harcourt, Brace, Jovanovich, Inc. 222pp.

Doswell, C.A., 1982: "The Operational Meteorology of Convective Weather Volume I." *NOAA TM NWS NSSFC-5.* U.S. Department of Commerce. 162pp.; 1985: "The Operational Meteorology of Convective Weather Volume II." *NOAA TM ERL ESG-15.* U.S. Department of Commerce. 240pp.

Dreyling, H., 1973: "An Airlines Experience on Turbulence" in *Flight in Turbulence, AGAARD Conference Proceedings No. 140.* 7-1 to 7-7.

Durran, D., 1990: "Mountain Waves and Downslope Winds" in *Atmospheric Processes over Complex Terrain Meteorological Monographs, 23, 45.* (W. Blumen, Ed.) American Meteorological Society. 59-81.

Dutton, J.A. and H.A. Panofsky, 1970: "Clear Air Turbulence: A Mystery may be Unfolding." *Science, 167,* 937-944.

Edgar, L., 1955: "Frightening Experience during Jet-Stream Project." *Soaring* (July-August). 20-23.

Ellrod, G., 1985: "Detection of high level turbulence using satellite imagery and upper air data." *NESDIS 10.* NOAA National Environmental Satellite, Data, and Information Service. 30pp.

Endlich, R.M., 1964: "The mesoscale structure of some regions of clear air turbulence." *Journal of Applied Meteorology, 3.* 261-276.

Endlich, R.M., 1991: "Clear air turbulence and the loss of the space shuttle, Challenger." *Report.* Atmospheric and Environment Research Associates. 186 Avalon, Los Altos, CA 94022. 27pp + figures.

Endlich, R.M., and R.L. Mancuso, 1968: "The Turbulence Climatology of the United States between 20,000 and 45,000 feet estimated from aircraft reports and meteorological data." *Stanford Research Institute Report AFCRL-68-0337* under Contract AF 19(628)-5173. 81pp.

FAA, 1975: *Aviation Weather. AC 00-6A.* U.S. Department of Transportation, Federal Aviation Administration, and National Oceanic and Atmospheric Administration, NWS, Washington, D.C. 219pp.

FAA, 1983: *Thunderstorms. AC 00-24B.* Federal Aviation Administration. 7pp.

FAA, 1985: *Aviation Weather Services. AC 00-45C.* U.S. Department of Transportation, Federal Aviation Administration, and National Oceanic and Atmospheric Administration, NWS, Washington, D.C. 122pp.

FAA, 1988: *Rules of thumb for avoiding or minimizing clear air turbulence. AC 00-30A.* Federal Aviation Administration. 4pp.

FAA, 1988: *Pilot Wind Shear Guide, AC 00-54.* Federal Aviation Administration. 56pp.

FAA, 1991: *Wake Turbulence. AC 90-23E.* Federal Aviation Administration, Washington, D.C. 15pp.

Foss F., and J. Hinkelman, 1991: "Operational Aviation Weather Service Requirements." *Preprints, Fourth International Conference on Aviation Weather Systems.* Paris. American Meteorological Society, Boston. 202-207.

Frost, W., J. McCarthy, K. H. Kuang, and P. Hildebrand, 1985: "Terrain-Induced Windshear: Potential Cause of Jetstar Accident." *Preprints of the Second International Conference on the Aviation Weather System.* Montreal. American Meteorological Society. 177-185.

Fujita, T., 1985: *The Downburst.* SMRP Research Paper 210. The University of Chicago. 154pp.

Fujita, T., 1986: *DFW Microburst.* SMRP Research Paper 217. The University of Chicago. 122pp.

Gary, B.L., 1992: "Predicting Clear Air Turbulence From Microwave Radiometry." *NASA Tech Briefs.* March.

Goff, R.C., and R.H. Gramzow, 1989: "The Federal Aviation Administration's Low-Level Wind Shear Alert System: A Project management Perspective." *Preprints, Third International Conference on Aviation Weather Systems.* Anaheim. American Meteorological Society, Boston. 408-413.

Guingnard, J.C., and M.E. McCauley, 1990: "The accelerative stimulus for motion sickness," Chapter 9 in *Motion and Space Sickness*, G.H. Crampton (Ed). CRC Press, Boca Raton, FL.

Hansen, A., 1991: "A New Age in Aviation Weather Forecasting." *Preprints, Fourth International Conference on Aviation Weather Systems*. Paris. American Meteorological Society, Boston. 100-101.

Harrison, H.T., and D.F. Sowa, 1966: "Mountain Wave Exposure on Jet Routes of Northwest Airlines and United Air Lines." *UAL Meteorology Circular No. 60*. 66pp + Appendix.

Hislop, G., 1951: "Clear Air Turbulence over Europe." *Journal of the Royal Aeronautical Society*, April. 185-225.

Holmboe, J. and H. Klieforth, 1957: "Investigation of Airflow Over the Sierra Nevada." *Final Report Contract AF 19(604)-728*. 290pp.

Hopkins, R.H., 1977: "Forecasting Techniques of Clear Air Turbulence including that associated with Lee Waves." *WMO TN No.155*. World Meteorological Organization. 34pp.

Huschke, R.E.(Ed.), 1959: *Glossary of Meteorology*. American Meteorological Society. Boston. 638pp.

Jaeckisch, H., 1968: "Waveflow above Convection Streets." *OSTIV Publication X*.

Jeppesen Sanderson, 1993: *Private Pilot Manual*. Jeppesen Sanderson, Inc., Englewood, CO. 462pp.

Jeppesen Sanderson, 1993: *Instrument Rating Manual*. Jeppesen Sanderson, Inc. Englewood, CO. 512pp.

Kaimal, J.C., and J.A. Businger, 1970: "Case Studies of a Convective Plume and a Dust Devil." *Journal of Applied Meteorology, 9*. 612-620.

Kraus, K.A., 1972: "Aspects of the Influence of Low Level Wind Shears on Aviation Operations." *Preprints, International Conference on Aerospace and Aeronautical Meteorology*. Washington, D.C. American Meteorological Society. 332-333.

Kessler, E. (Ed.), 1983: *Thunderstorm Morphology and Dynamics*. University of Oklahoma Press, Norman. 411pp.

Klein, P. 1989: "Data Link Processor (DLP), Pilot Access to Weather Data." *Preprints, Third International Conference on Aviation Weather Systems*. Anaheim. American Meteorological Society, Boston. 430-432.

Kuettner, J., P.A. Hildebrand, and T. Clark, 1987: "Convection Waves: Observations of Gravity Wave Systems over Convectively Active Boundary Layers." *Quarterly Journal of The Royal Meteorological Society, 113.* 445-467.

Kupcis, E.A., 1989: "The FAA Sponsored Windshear Training Aid." *Preprints, Third International Conference on the Aviation Weather System,* American Meteorological Society. 317-322.

Lester, P.F., and R.E. Bach, Jr., 1986: "An Extreme Clear Air Turbulence incident Associated with a Strong Downslope Windstorm." *Paper AIAA-86-0329.* AIAA 24th Aerospace Sciences Meeting. Reno. 7pp.

Lester P.F., and M. Burton, 1988: "Development of Low-Level Turbulence (LLT) Forecasting Methodologies." *Report CR-88-0001-4* prepared under Contract DAAL03-86-001, U.S. Army Atmospheric Sciences Laboratory. 67pp.

Lester, P.F., and W. A. Fingerhut, 1974: "Lower Turbulent Zones Associated with Mountain Lee Waves." *Journal of Applied Meteorology, 13.* 54-61.

Lieurance, N.A., 1969: "The Development of Aeronautical Meteorology." *Aeronautical Meteorology. WMO TN No. 95.* 1-8.

Lilly, D.K., 1978: "A Severe Downslope Windstorm and Aircraft Turbulence Event Induced by a Mountain Wave." *Journal of Atmospheric Sciences, 35.* 59-77.

Lindsay, C.V., 1978: "Flying the Invisible Roller Coaster." *FAA World, 8.* 2-5.

Lindsay, C.V., and S. Lacy, 1976: *Soaring Meteorology for Forecasters,* Second Edition. Soaring Society of America. 73pp.

Mathews, M.D., 1988: "National Weather Advisory Unit Operations and Recent Developments." *Paper AIAA-88-0681,* AIAA 26th Aerospace Sciences Meeting, Reno. 7pp.

McCarthy, J., 1991: "The Aviation Weather Products Generator." *Preprints, Fourth International Conference on Aviation Weather Systems.* Paris. American Meteorological Society, Boston. 106-111.

McLaurin, H., 1992: "Data Link for General Aviation." *FAA Aviation News.* July-August. FAA. 13-15.

McLean, J., 1986: "Determining the effect of weather in aircraft accident investigations." *Paper AIAA-86-0323.* AIAA 24th Aerospace Sciences Meeting. Reno. 7pp.

McLean Jr., J.C., 1986: "Comments on the Problem of Turbulence in Aviation," in *Atmospheric Turbulence Relative to Aviation, Missile, and Space Programs.* NASA Conference Publication 2468. 11-16.

McManus, R.M.P., 1973: "Experience with a Low Altitude Turbulence Model for Autoland Certification." *Flight in Turbulence, AGAARD Conference Proceedings No. 140.* 18-1 to 18-8.

Money, K.E., 1970: "Motion Sickness," in *Physiological Reviews, 50, 1.* 1-39.

Musaelyan, Sh. A., 1962: "Barrier Waves in the Atmosphere."*GIMIZ.* Leningrad. Translated from the Russian Israel Program for Scientific Translations. Jerusalem (1964). 112pp.

NASA, NTSB, 1992: Unless otherwise indicated, turbulence accident and incident descriptions were abstracted from *NTSB Accident Reports, Accident Briefs,* and the *NASA Aviation Safety Reporting System* (ASRS).

Nicholls, J.M., 1973: "The Airflow Over Mountains. Research 1958-1972." *WMO TN No.127.* World Meteorological Organization, Geneva. 73pp.

NOAA, 1968: *Climatic Atlas of the United States,* National Climatic Data Center (NCDC), Asheville, NC, 28801 ($12.00). 94pp.

NOAA, 1991: *Comparative Climatic Data.* USDC, NOAA, National Climatic Data Center (NCDC), Asheville, NC, 28801 ($3.00). 94pp.

NWS, 1992: *National Implementation Plan for Modernization and Associated Restructuring of the National Weather Service. Fiscal Year 1992 Update.* USDC, NOAA. 70p + Appendices.

Palmen, E., and C.W. Newton, 1969: *Atmospheric Circulation Systems.* Academic Press, New York. 603pp.

Pantley, K., and P.F. Lester, 1990: "Observations of Severe Turbulence near Thunderstorm Tops." *Journal of Applied Meteorology, 29.* 1171-1179.

Pao, Y-H., and A. Goldburg (Eds.), 1969: *Clear Air Turbulence and Its Detection.* Plenum Press, N.Y. 540pp.

Parks, E., K. Wingrove, R.E. Bach, Jr., and R.S. Mehta, 1985: "Identification of Vortex-Induced Clear Air Turbulence using Airline Flight Records." *AIAA Journal of Aircraft.* 124-129.

Purdom, J., J. Weaver, R. Green, 1983: "Analysis of Rapid Interval Goes Data for the 9 July 1982 New Orleans Airliner Crash." *Preprints, Ninth Conference on Aerospace and Aeronautical Meteorology.* American Meteorological Society. 331-334.

Ray, P.S.(Ed), 1986: *Mesoscale Meteorology and Forecasting*. American Meteorological Society, Boston. 793p.

Roach, W.T., 1969: "Some aircraft reports of high level turbulence." *The Meteorological Magazine, 98*. 65-78.

Rudich, R.D., 1986: "Weather-involved U.S. Air Carrier Accidents 1962-1984. A compendium and brief summary paper" *AIAA-86-0327*. AIAA 24th Aerospace Sciences Meeting. Reno. 8pp.

Scorer, R.S., 1972: *Clouds of the World*. Stackpole Press, Harrisburg. 176pp.

Scorer, R.S., 1978: *Environmental Aerodynamics*. Ellis Horwood, Ltd. Chichester. 488pp.

Scorer, R.S., and A. Verhaik, 1989: *Spacious Skies*. Sterling Publishing Company. 192pp.

Serebreny, S. M., E. J. Wiegman, and R. G. Hadfield, 1962: "Some characteristic fields of the jet stream complex during selected synoptic conditions. *Journal of Applied Meteorology*. 137-153.

Shaw, T.B., 1991: "Weather-Related Accidents in the Canadian Aviation Industry: An Analysis of the Chief Contributory Factors," in *Preprints of The Fourth International Conference on Aviation Weather Systems. Paris*. American Meteorological Society, Boston. 19-22.

Smith. M.J., 1983: "Adverse Weather Impact on Aviation Safety, Investigation, and Oversight." *Proceedings, 7th Annual Workshop on Meteorological and Environmental Inputs to Aviation Systems. NASA CP-2312*. 37-42.

Sorenson, J.E., 1976: "Mountains and Clear Air Turbulence." *United Air Lines Meteorological Circular No. 63*. 20pp.

Sparks, W.R., S.G. Cornford, and J.K. Gibson, 1977: "Bumpiness in Clear Air and its relation to some synoptic scale indices." *Meteorological Office, Geophysical Memoirs 17, No. 121*. HMSO, London. 53pp.

Stack, D. T., 1991: "Turbulence Avoidance." *Preprints, Fourth International Conference on Aviation Weather Systems*. Paris. American Meteorological Society, Boston. 283-286.

Stull, R.B., 1988: *An Introduction to Boundary Layer Meteorology*. Kluwer Academic Publishers. 666pp.

Sumwalt, R., 1991: "The importance of proper aviation weather dissemination to pilots: an airline captain's perspective." *Preprints, Fourth International Conference on Aviation Weather Systems*. Paris. American Meteorological Society, Boston. 60-65.

Taylor, D.L., R. Londot, and G. Ligler, 1991: "The Meteorological Data Collection System: Status and Future Directions." *Preprints, Fourth International Conference on Aviation Weather Systems.* Paris. American Meteorological Society, Boston. 144-145.

Turner, E. W., 1985: "Categorization of atmospheric turbulence in terms of aircraft response for use in turbulence reports and forecasts," in *Preprints of The Second International Conference on Aviation Weather Systems, Montreal.* American Meteorological Society, Boston. 265-268.

Uccellini, L.W., 1986: "A report on upper wind conditions preceding and during the Shuttle Challenger (STS 51L) explosion." *Bulletin of the American Meteorological Society, 10.* 1248-1265.

USAF, 1974: *Worldwide Airfield Summaries.* Available from National Climatic Data Center (NCDC), Asheville, NC, 28801. ($50.00) CD-ROM.

USAF, 1982. *Meteorological Techniques AWSP 105-56* (with changes through August 1988). 197pp.

Van Dyke, M., 1982: *An Album of Fluid Motion.* Parabolic Press, Stanford, CA. 174pp.

Vinnechenko, N., N. Pinus, S. Schmeter, and G. Shur, 1980: *Turbulence in the Free Atmosphere.* Consultants Bureau. New York. 310pp.

Wallington, C.E., 1966: *Meteorology for Glider Pilots.* (Second Edition) John Murray, Ltd., London. 284pp.

WMO, 1969: "Aeronautical Meteorology." *WMO TN No.95.* World Meteorological Organization, Geneva. 493pp.

Wolfson, M. M., 1988: "Characteristics of Downbursts in the Continental United States." *The Lincoln Laboratory Journal, Volume 1, No. 1.* MIT. 49-74.

Young, G.S., 1987: "The Structure and Prediction of Thermals," *Soaring.* August. 37-39.

INDEX

A

B

C